METHODS AND TECHNIQUES IN GEOPHYSICS

VOLUME I

METHODS AND TECHNIQUES
IN GEOPHYSICS

Edited by

S. K. RUNCORN

University of Durham
King's College
Newcastle-upon-Tyne

VOLUME I

1960

INTERSCIENCE PUBLISHERS INC., NEW YORK

INTERSCIENCE PUBLISHERS LTD., LONDON

First published 1960.   All rights reserved
Library of Congress Catalog Card Number 59-15395

INTERSCIENCE PUBLISHERS INC.,
250 Fifth Avenue, New York 1, N.Y.

INTERSCIENCE PUBLISHERS LTD.,
88–90 Chancery Lane, London, W.C.2

Made and Printed in Great Britain by Richard Clay and Company Ltd.
Bungay, Suffolk

AUTHORS

A. E. BECK, Assistant Professor in Geophysics, The University of Western Ontario, London, Ontario

E. C. BULLARD, Assistant Director of Research, Department of Geodesy and Geophysics, University of Cambridge

D. W. COLLINSON, University of Durham, Physics Department, King's College, Newcastle-upon-Tyne

K. M. CREER, University of Durham, Physics Department, King's College, Newcastle-upon-Tyne

G. D. GARLAND, Professor in Geophysics, University of Alberta, Edmonton, Alberta

T. F. GASKELL, British Petroleum Limited, Brittanic House, London, E.C.2

J. C. HARRISON, Institute of Geophysics, University of California, Los Angeles, California

D. S. HUGHES, Professor of Physics, University of Texas, Austin, Texas

W. MARKOWITZ, Director Time Service Division, U.S. Naval Observatory, Washington, D.C.

A. D. MISENER, Department of Physics, University of Western Ontario, London, Ontario

P. THREADGOLD, BP Research Centre Exploration Division, Sunbury-on-Thames, Middlesex

K. WHITHAM, Division of Geomagnetism, Dominion Observatory, Ottawa, Ontario

P. L. WILLMORE, Department of Mines and Technical Surveys, Dominion Observatory, Ottawa, Canada

PREFACE

In recent years a large number of books and review papers have been published which set out admirably the observational data in pure geophysics and the theories which have been developed from them about the interior of the earth. There seems to be no comparable literature concerning the modern advances in physical techniques in this subject, which have made possible much of the great development in pure geophysical research. In discussion with Dr. Paul Rosbaud, I decided to make the attempt to repair this deficiency and the present book is the result.

In accordance with a common convention, geophysics is taken to include only the physics of the solid state, and no mention is made of techniques designed mainly to throw light on the physical processes in the oceans, atmosphere and high atmosphere.

It is hoped that this book may be of value to those experimental geophysicists who wish to embark on research, the technique of which is unfamiliar to them, to the geologist, who having read about the conclusions the geophysicist arrives at, wishes to inform himself more fully about the methods used and their limitations, and to the mathematical geophysicist, who is often in dire need of being brought to a realization of the difficulties of the experiment and the inaccuracies of the data, on which he confidently bases his impressive theories.

S. K. RUNCORN

CONTENTS

MEASUREMENT OF TEMPERATURE GRADIENT IN THE EARTH

E. C. BULLARD, *Department of Geodesy and Geophysics, University of Cambridge*

CONTENTS

I. INTRODUCTION

The temperature in a mine or borehole increases with depth, the gradient normally lying in the range 10° to 50°C/km. The gradient is due to a flow of heat from within the earth which can be estimated if the temperature gradient and thermal conductivity are known. The heat flow frequently varies by a factor of two above and below its mean, and no useful purpose is served by attempting to make very accurate measurements of the gradient; the elimination of gross systematic errors is of much more importance.

II. MEASUREMENT OF TEMPERATURE GRADIENT ON LAND

1. In boreholes

Measurements can be made in boreholes with very simple equipment. Mercury maximum thermometers enclosed in sealed glass envelopes are very satisfactory. These thermometers have a constriction just above the bulb; on cooling the mercury thread breaks at the constriction, the thread remaining above the constriction till it is centrifuged back into the bulb after reading. The practice of whirling the thermometers on a string to get the mercury

1

back into the bulb is not to be recommended. A tube which can be swung round on a handle is less likely to break the thermometer.

To measure a temperature three or more thermometers are placed end to end in a perforated steel tube which is lowered by a piano wire. The wire passes over a measuring wheel of accurately known diameter which is provided with a revolution counter. The wire may be wound and unwound by hand or by an electric motor or gasoline engine. Care must be taken that the mercury thermometers are below the temperature to be measured before they go down the hole and that they are not heated above it between reaching the surface and being read. In summer the air temperature may be above the temperature in the upper part of the hole, and it may be necessary to measure this part of the hole at night or to use cold water to cool the thermometers. A correction should be applied for the contraction of the mercury thread between the temperature to be measured and the temperature, T_1, at which the thermometer is read; for this reason the thermometers are best read while in a water bath at a known temperature. The correction to the thermometer reading, T, is

$$\sigma(T - T_0)(T - T_1)$$

where $(T - T_0)$ is the length of the mercury thread measured in units of the scale of the thermometer, and σ is the coefficient of expansion of mercury in glass. T_0 is a constant of the thermometer which may be found by causing the thread to run away from the constriction into the calibrated part of the scale and noting its length; for most thermometers the value of σ may be taken as $0.00017°C^{-1}$. The correction rarely exceeds $0.2°C$.

Mercury thermometers enclosed in glass jackets take a considerable time to come to temperature equilibrium; the author has usually left them in the hole for 2 h, though 1 h would probably suffice. To make measurements at many points in a hole is thus a tedious matter, and if much work is to be done electrical thermometers are to be preferred. These have the disadvantage that they require an electric cable which is heavy and expensive and requires a power-driven winch. Platinum resistance thermometers have been used. The change of resistance of the cable with temperature is then not negligible and must be eliminated by using dummy leads. Thermistors give a larger change in resistance, but are somewhat unstable and need occasional checks of their resistance at 0°C.

Many other methods of measuring temperatures in boreholes have been suggested and some have been used. A device depending on the vapour pressure of pentane is available commercially. This plots temperature against pressure in a way analagous to the oceanographer's bathythermograph. It is quick and convenient to use but not comparable in accuracy to mercury or electrical thermometers.

The temperatures measured in a borehole do not necessarily represent the undisturbed temperature of the rocks. Rotary drilling dissipates heat which is carried up the hole by the circulating fluid; simultaneously cold fluid is introduced at the top and flows down the drill stem. The disturbance is therefore complex, but usually results in a cooling at the bottom of the hole and a warming in the upper part. The time for the disturbance to decay will depend on the diameter of the hole, the nature of the rocks and the time spent in drilling. The theory has been discussed by Bullard,[4] who concludes that the disturbance of temperature will fall to 1 per cent of its maximum value in 10 to 20 times the time interval between the drill reaching the point in question and the final cessation of the circulation of the drilling fluid. Equilibrium may be attained in a few days at the bottom of the hole, but may take many months in the upper part. Measurements in four holes in England [6] made up to five years after drilling agreed within 0·1°C with measurements made one year after drilling. A detailed set of measurements was made by Misener in a bore in Toronto; these agreed approximately with the theory.

The temperature gradient is often sufficient to render the fluid in a well unstable [12] and to start thermal convection. If this disturbed the temperature gradient it would be expected that there would be a discontinuity in gradient at points where the diameter of the bore changed and at the surface of the fluid. Such discontinuities are not found; also the gradient seems to be the same in holes filled with mud and with water. It thus seems likely that convection of the fluid in a borehole does not disturb the gradient to any important extent. On the other hand, if water, oil or gas flows or is pumped from a bore the temperature distribution will be completely upset and may take a very long time to settle if the flow is stopped. A similar disturbance may be produced by the natural circulation of ground water, and it is common to find that the gradient is low in the upper parts of holes penetrating permeable rocks, an example [3] is shown in Fig. 1.

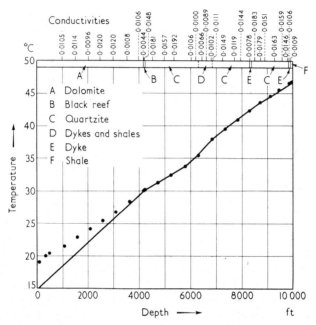

Fig. 1. Variation of temperature with depth in a bore in South Africa. The line represents the variation to be expected if the heat flow by conduction is the same at all depths. The lesser gradient in the first 4200 ft is believed to be due to the circulation of water in the dolomite through which this part of the hole is drilled [from E. C. Bullard, *Proc. Roy. Soc. A* **173**, 474 (1939)].

It is difficult to find holes that have been allowed to stand for a year or more and which are still available for measurement; there therefore exist relatively few holes in which the temperature gradient has been studied in the detail shown in Fig. 1. When a complete series cannot be obtained it is often possible to get a usable gradient by combining the temperature at the bottom of the bore, which can be measured a day or two after drilling, with the mean surface temperature of the ground. The latter is usually about a degree above the mean air temperature. The result is liable to be disturbed by low gradients in the upper part of the hole due to heat transport by moving water.

A disturbance in the temperature gradient is produced by topography. A correction may be applied for this,[2, 11] but some uncertainty is usually introduced by lack of quantitative knowlege of the history of the area around the borehole.[8, 14] This correction is important only in mountainous areas, where it may reach 30 per cent.

The temperature may also be disturbed by inclined beds or domes of rocks that are better or worse conductors than their neighbours; these disturbances may reach 20 per cent.[5, 9]

Past changes in climate may produce disturbances in underground temperatures which are propagated downwards as a strongly damped wave motion.[8] A rise in surface temperature, such as that which occurred at the end of the ice age, produces a decreased gradient near the surface. The effect is believed to be small and the resulting curvature of the depth/temperature relation cannot be separated from other effects. The effect of the daily variation of temperature is negligible at depths below 25 m.

Temperatures in permanently frozen ground are discussed by Brewer.[1]

2. Measurement in mines and tunnels

The temperature of the rock in a mine or tunnel is disturbed by ventilation. The distance to which the disturbance penetrates into the rock depends on the nature of the rock, on the time for which the rock face has been exposed and on the shape of the mine gallery. Misener [13] has made measurements in many holes up to 33 m long and finds no effect of ventilation beyond 23 m.

III. MEASUREMENTS OF TEMPERATURE GRADIENT AT SEA

The temperature gradient in the sediment beneath the ocean floor is usually in the range 30° to 100°C/km. It has been measured by forcing a probe 3 to 5 m long into the soft sediment and measuring the temperature gradient along the probe by thermocouples or thermistors.[5, 7, 18] The arrangement of the probe and recorder is shown in Fig. 2. The whole assembly is lowered by a steel cable and run into the bottom at a speed of 2 to 3 m/sec. The cable used for lowering must be capable of taking the strain of pulling out the probe; this does not usually exceed 700 kg. A cable with a breaking strain of about 12 tons is suitable, though it would probably be possible to use a lighter cable without much risk of losing the equipment.

The recorder is enclosed in a case capable of withstanding the water pressure at the ocean floor (560 kg/cm² at a depth of 3000 fm). It may consist of a galvanometer and a rotating drum carrying photographic film, or of an amplifier and pen recorder. If a galvanometer is used it is necessary to reverse the connections of the thermocouple about twice a minute in order to eliminate the effects of change of galvanometer zero caused by the shock of entering the bottom. A record may also be made of the tilt of the apparatus, though it is found that, if suitable fins are fitted to the top of the recorder, this is always within a few degrees of vertical immediately after entry. The drifting of the ship usually bends the probe near its top end after it has been in the bottom for half to three-quarters of an hour, and some care and skill is necessary to prevent the probe being dragged out of the bottom before sufficient record has been obtained. The depth of penetration can be judged from the sediment sticking to the outside of the probe, and by the point at which the sudden bend occurs. It is usually possible to get complete penetration up to the top of the probe. The probe shown in Fig. 2 is fitted with a trip device that releases it before it reaches the bottom and allows it to fall freely for a few metres. The trip is operated when a weight, hanging from the rope to the right of the probe, reaches the bottom. The probe is pulled out by the wire rope seen coiled beside the fins. The trip complicates the rigging of the equipment and imposes a severe jerk on the galvanometer if it releases prematurely, before reaching the bottom. It is usually not necessary to employ it.

When the probe enters the sediment it is heated by friction, the rise in temperature being larger the smaller the diameter of the probe. The lower end of a probe 2·5 cm in diameter, as used in the English experiments, is usually heated above the temperature of the surrounding sediment. The recorded temperature therefore rises rapidly for 2 or 3 min as the frictional heat is conducted inwards to the thermocouples or thermistors and then falls slowly

Fig. 2. Probe used for measuring temperature gradient in the ocean bottom.

B

as the probe comes to the temperature of the surrounding sediments. The final approach to equilibrium is only as the reciprocal of the time, and it is not possible to wait for equilibrium to be reached sufficiently closely for no correction to be necessary. The correction depends on comparing the observed change of temperature, T, with a theoretical expression for the cooling of a cylinder in the form

$$T = T_1 + T_0 F(a, \kappa t/a^2) \qquad (2)$$

Here T_1 is the final temperature when the initial disturbance has subsided, T_0 is the initial disturbance, t is the time, κ the thermometric conductivity of the sediment, a the radius of the probe and a the ratio of the heat required to raise the temperature of the probe by 1°C to that required to raise twice the volume of sediment through the same temperature interval. The function F is a complicated integral of Bessel functions which has been tabulated.[5, 10]

T_1 is obtained by fitting equation 2 to the observations, treating it and T_0 as unknowns. The observed and calculated curves usually agree closely. With a probe 2·5 cm in diameter the extrapolation to obtain T_1 commonly involves a correction of about −10 per cent to the last observed temperature. A probe 3·1 cm in diameter, as used in the U.S. experiments, is heated less by friction than a smaller probe. The initial temperature of the lower end is therefore below that of the sediment and the correction required is positive. The general agreement of the results with the two types of probe giving corrections of opposite sign is evidence that no very gross error has been committed in making the correction.

The principal limitation in the measurement of temperature gradient at sea is the restriction on the possible length of the probe. The longest so far used is 5 m, this might be increased somewhat, but it seems unlikely that a probe exceeding say 20 m could be used. There seems no hope of measuring the temperature over a great range of depth unless a hole can be drilled in the sea bed. The consequences of this limitation are less severe than they would be on land, since there is unlikely to be an appreciable transfer of heat by anything corresponding to the circulation of 'ground water'. The annual variation of temperature in the bottom water is unobservably small in deep water; in shallow seas it is several degrees and prevents useful measurements being taken. The possible effects of past climatic changes have been discussed by Bullard, Maxwell and Revelle [7] and seem unlikely to be serious. There is no reason to suppose that the measurements at sea do not give a gradient and a heat flow that can be compared with those on land, though it would be reassuring if an independent check could be obtained in a submarine borehole.

References

1. Brewer, M. C. *Trans. Amer., geophys. Un.*, **39**, 19 (1958).
2. Bullard, E. C. *Mon. Not. R. astr. Soc. (Geophys. Suppl.)*, **4**, 360 (1938).
3. Bullard, E. C. *Proc. Roy. Soc. A*, **173** 474 (1939).
4. Bullard, E. C. *Mon. Not. R. astr. Soc. (Geophys. Suppl.)*, **5**, 127–130 (1947).
5. Bullard, E. C. *Proc. Roy. Soc. A*, **222**, 408 (1954).
6. Bullard, E. C. and Niblett, E. R. *Mon. Not. R. astr. Soc. (Geophys. Suppl.)*, **6**, 222 (1951).
7. Bullard, E. C., Maxwell, A. E. and Revelle, R. *Advanc. Geophys.* **3**, 153 (1956).
8. Birch, F. *Bull. geol. Soc. Amer.* **61**, 567 (1950).
9. Coster, H. P. *Mon. Not. R. astr. Soc. (Geophys. Suppl.)*, **5**, 131–145 (1947).
10. Jaeger, J. C. *Austral. J. Phys.* **9**, 167 (1956).
11. Jeffreys, H. *Mon. Not. R. astr. Soc. (Geophys. Suppl.)*, **4**, 309 (1937).
12. Krige, L. J. *Proc. Roy. Soc. A*, **173**, 450 (1939).
13. Misener, A. D., Thompson, L. G. D. and Uffen, F. J. *Trans. Amer. geophys. Un.* **32**, 729 (1951).
14. Niblett, E. R. and Clark, S. P. *Mon. Not. R. astr. Soc. (Geophys. Supply.)*, **6**, 176 (1956).
15. Revelle, R. and Maxwell, A. E. *Nature, Lond.* **170**, 199 (1952).

THE MEASUREMENT OF HEAT FLOW OVER LAND

A. D. MISENER and A. E. BECK, *University of Western Ontario, London, Canada*

CONTENTS

I. INTRODUCTION

In recent years there has been a considerable rise of interest in the equilibrium heat flux across the crust of the earth, both over the continents and over the ocean floors. The equilibrium heat flux is of great importance to an understanding of many physical problems connected with the earth's interior and is the flux that would be observed if the earth had not changed its shape since its creation and if climatic conditions had remained constant. Since these ideal states have not existed, the measured flux is affected by a number of factors which may be grouped under the term 'geological history'. To find the flux occurring locally it is necessary to determine the temperature gradient and the thermal conductivity of the rocks in the area; if the dimensions of the area are small compared with the dimensions of the earth and if there is no horizontal variation of constituents, the flow of heat may be considered linear and the flux is given by the product of the temperature gradient and the thermal conductivity. To allow for the effects of the geological history of the area a correction, generally to the temperature gradient, can be applied to arrive at a value for the equilibrium heat flux. Unfortunately even the corrected values are only approximations, as in general the geological history of an area is not known with sufficient accuracy. It appears, therefore, that perhaps the greatest need in this sort of work is for a large number of results from all over the earth. By plotting these results on a world map and drawing isoflux lines it may be hoped that some general picture of the pattern of terrestrial heat flow will appear.

It is in the hope of stimulating further work and of saving many frustrating hours that we set out in detail some of the more important methods and discuss their physical limitations. For a discussion of the fundamental implications of the results so far obtained the reader is referred to the excellent review articles by Bullard [32] and Jacobs,[52] both of which have very comprehensive bibliographies.

II. MEASUREMENT OF TEMPERATURE GRADIENT

1. Regional Methods

Measurements of temperature gradients in the crust of the earth were made as long ago as 1744 by Gensane,[46, 62] but until the British Association for the Advancement of Science formed a committee in 1867 'for the purpose of investigating the rate of increase of underground temperature downwards in various localities of dry land and under water',[25] few attempts were made to interpret the results and improve the methods of measurement on an organized basis. Since then occasional efforts have been made [1, 3, 27, 37, 41, 73, 74] to collect and tabulate all geothermal data (including oceanographic measurements) available both in published and unpublished form; owing to the formidable volume of measurements now being made this practice appears to have ceased.

The majority of the published observations have been made with maximum thermometers, but lately numerous electrical methods have been tried with varying degrees of success; again most of the work has been carried out in boreholes, although some has been done in mines and tunnels. The chief advantage of recording the temperatures at various levels in mines is the ease of taking readings over a representative area of the crust. No great length of cable is required, so that electrical measurements, which are inherently the most accurate, can be made more easily than they could in boreholes. However, to ensure that the temperature-measuring element is in a region where the natural rock temperatures, usually referred to as virgin rock temperatures (v.r.t.), have not been disturbed by the changed temperature of the shaft, holes at times have to be drilled into the shaft walls to a distance of up to 100 ft.[63] This is a serious drawback, since most mining engineers are loath to drill a hole specially for temperature measurements.

When measuring the temperature gradients in boreholes it is desirable to use those which are filled with water or drilling mud. The relatively high thermal capacity of these liquids results in the thermometer, either liquid-in-glass or electrical, taking less time to reach equilibrium than it would in an air-filled hole; furthermore, a hole is more likely to be thermally stable when it is filled with liquid instead of gas. Some of the early workers thought that convection currents were causing instability and so affecting the readings. Later observations by Krige [57] showed that in theoretically stable boreholes convection currents, if they do exist, are so slow that they have no detectable effect on the temperature gradients.

Before measurements are made in a borehole time should be allowed for it to regain its equilibrium temperature distribution. Estimates of the time to reach equilibrium range from 10 to 100 times [31, 54] the drilling time. That is, if it takes a month to drill a hole it will take at least a year for the top to return to normal but the bottom will give a v.r.t. within a few hours. In many countries there are laws which require an exploratory hole to be blocked off as soon as it is finished with. This means either pouring in quick-setting cement or blocking off with lead every 100 ft or so. In either case it is impossible to allow the hole to return to equilibrium, since the hole has to be blocked while the drilling rig is still on the site. In these cases a useful technique, which has been successfully used in England,[36] is to follow the hole down, measuring bottom-hole temperatures whenever there is a lull in the drilling operations.

No matter what form of temperature-measuring device is used it is usual to measure temperatures going down the hole so as to avoid stirring up the fluid at the point of measurement.

Whether mines, tunnels or boreholes are used in a series of measurements, if sufficient readings are taken it is possible to construct isothermal planes for the area, and this method of presenting the results is discussed in the final section.

2. Equipment and Its Use

A. *Maximum thermometers*

A rider type of maximum thermometer is very unreliable, since unavoidable jerks when withdrawing the thermometer cause the rider to slide either up or down. The mercury-filled constriction type of thermometer is generally used, but even with these trouble is sometimes experienced due to an overlong column of mercury running back into the reservoir. However, for the sizes of constriction and capillary usually found in these thermometers, little trouble is experienced if the length of the mercury column does not exceed about one-third of the total length of the capillary.[57]

There are wide variations in the reliability of thermometers even when they are taken from the same batch. Before any field trip each thermometer is carefully calibrated and the constriction tested for its ability to support a column of mercury. If a sharp flicking of the thermometer with a finger causes any mercury to drop below the constriction when the mercury column is one-third of the length of the capillary the thermometer is discarded.

To prevent errors arising from pressure on the reservoir bulb, the thermometers have to be placed in a metallic water-tight container before being lowered into a fluid-filled hole. A simple type of container is shown in Fig. 1.

Errors which may arise from knocks when pulling the container up the hole are reduced by sending down two, four or even six thermometers in the one container, half of the thermometers being inverted. If the thermometers have been carefully selected and calibrated, one will usually be sufficient; in fact, it is frequently found that in narrow boreholes there is only room for a narrow container holding one thermometer.

If there is good thermal contact between the mercury bulb and the metallic container, for instance by partly filling the container with water, most thermometers will take about 30 min to reach equilibrium in a water-filled hole; in an air-filled hole the time required is nearer 5 to 10 h. With care an accuracy of 0·01°C can be obtained for individual readings.[57]

One great advantage in using maximum thermometers is that when using boreholes for a temperature gradient survey, the equipment used for lowering the thermometer can be made very

THE MEASUREMENT OF HEAT FLOW OVER LAND

light in weight. For instance, Beck [6] has described a winch for use in holes up to 500 ft deep, which weighs only 10 lb complete with $\frac{1}{16}$-in.-diameter wire rope and container. This winch was used for other purposes which required the heavy steel wire rope but for use only with maximum thermometers 30 s.w.g. piano wire is strong enough; thus about 5000 ft of piano wire can be used with no increase in the weight or size of the equipment.

It might be added here that there seems to be a general, but

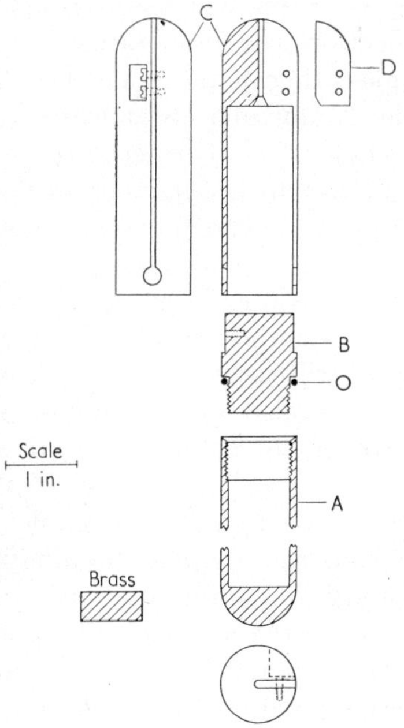

Fig. 1. Maximum thermometer container. The thermometers are held in A. Section B screws into A so that the O-ring O makes a pressure-tight seal. The lowering wire is slipped into the slotted cap C which is then secured to B by three or four countersunk screws. The section D is bolted into the upper part of the slot to prevent the lowering wire from fraying in the slot.

Scale
1 in.

Brass

erroneous, impression that only holes deeper than about 1500 ft give useful results. This is by no means true. The daily temperature fluctuations are damped out after a few feet and the annual fluctuations are damped out after a few tens of feet. Thus any hole over 200 ft deep will give, provided it is not too near hilly terrain, just as reliable a value of the heat flow at the surface as a deep hole. The main advantage of using a deep hole is that under ideal conditions it may be possible to detect variations of heat flow with depth.

B. *Electrical thermometers*

(i) *Thermocouples.* In any type of temperature measurement the thermocouple is an attractive idea because of its rapid response to changes in temperature, much more rapid than any of the other thermometers described. For this reason the first attempts to observe borehole temperatures with an electrical apparatus were made with thermocouples. In a 100-ft borehole, Thomson, in 1868,[25] used a copper–iron thermocouple with the reference junction in water which was heated until a galvanometer gave zero deflection; the temperature of the water was read with a mercury-in-glass thermometer and thus gave the temperature in the borehole. Unfortunately, for direct reading of temperatures in a long borehole the thermocouple is impracticable; the long leads required imply a high circuit resistance and hence a low output at the surface. The voltage cannot be amplified, since at the present time there is no d.c. amplifier available which is stable enough to give the required accuracy. Even if there was a suitable d.c. amplifier the method would be suspect because of appreciable errors which will arise over long lengths due to the Thomson effect. There is also much trouble providing a stable cold junction. However, these difficulties will be considerably reduced if the temperature gradient, instead of the temperature, is measured and current work on thermocouples for use in long boreholes includes the construction of a 100-junction thermopile,[8] 2 ft long, for continuously recording the temperature gradient.

(ii) *Platinum resistance thermometers.* The platinum resistance thermometer is the most accurate and most reliable of all the thermometers used in geothermal work. The first measurements were made in Australia by Jenkins [4] in 1902 using a 25-Ω resistance element, but the results were not very accurate. A great improvement was made by Johnston and Adam,[56] who used a three-cored cable and a 250-Ω resistance element; the temperatures could be read to an accuracy of 0·01°C, the time taken for the thermometer to reach equilibrium being about 30 min. In 1937 Schlumberger *et al.*[76] published an account of the use of a continuously recording platinum resistance thermometer in oil wells. The accuracy claimed was 0·1°C for a lowering rate of 2 000 ft/h. Weiss [80] produced another type of equipment which incorporated a Callender and Griffiths bridge giving an accuracy a little better than that of Johnston and Adam.

In borehole work the advantages of accuracy and reliability of a platinum resistance element are greatly offset by the bulkiness of the apparatus required. Three or four low-resistance copper leads are required, and the great weight and low breaking strain of these means that the cable and element have to be supported by a steel cable or sheath; this still further increases the weight, and a large winch has to be used. For instance, the equipment of Weiss weighed 2·5 tons and the armoured cable alone weighed 1·5 tons. This, of course, restricts the field of operations to easily accessible areas. However, for use in shotholes in mines and tunnels no great weight of cable is needed, and Misener [63] has described a simple and lightweight apparatus which can easily be carried by one man. Rather delicate galvanometers were required, and this equipment was later modified [65] for use with thermistors.

(iii) *Thermistor resistance thermometers*. Thermistors offer obvious advantages for determining temperatures, since they have a high temperature coefficient of resistance (negative and about 4 per cent) which makes it unnecessary to measure the resistance, for a given accuracy of temperature, with the accuracy needed in the other types of resistance thermometry. As with the maximum thermometers, great care has to be taken with the selection of suitable thermistors. Each is checked for stability for a few months before it is taken out on a field trip; even then the calibration is checked periodically. If actual temperatures are required, then no drift outside the limits of the required accuracy can be tolerated; however, if the temperature gradient only is required, then a certain amount of drift is tolerable,[5] Table 1.

Despite the attention required for thermistors, the simplicity of the design and operation of the associated equipment makes them more desirable than the platinum resistance thermometer, and two types of equipment will be described, one for use in holes up to 100 ft long and giving an accuracy of 0·1°C and the other for use in longer boreholes and giving an accuracy better than 0·01°C with a stable thermistor.

The apparatus for use in mines and tunnels was first described briefly by Misener and Thomson.[65] The d.c. measuring bridge is shown in Fig. 2 and is about the size of an ordinary multi-test

Table 1. Drift of a single thermistor

τ = 5 months			τ = 11 months			τ = 15 months			τ = 17 months		
t_0	t_c	$(t_0 - t_c)$	t_0	t_c	$(t_0 - t_c)$	t_0	t_c	$(t_0 - t_c)$	t_0	t_c	$(t_0 - t_c)$
5·27	4·60	0·67	14·09	12·59	1·54	14·22	12·42	1·80	11·71	9·29	2·42
6·60	5·93	0·67	16·62	15·07	1·55	16·16	14·35	1·81	13·95	11·52	2·43
7·88	7·21	0·67	18·46	16·91	1·55	18·44	16·62	1·82	16·18	13·74	2·44
9·32	8·64	0·68	20·46	18·90	1·56	20·55	18·73	1·82	18·50	16·05	2·45
10·73	10·05	0·68	22·38	20·82	1·56	22·44	20·62	1·82	20·76	18·30	2·46
12·02	11·34	0·68	24·28	22·72	1·56	24·63	22·81	1·82	23·05	20·58	2·47
13·29	12·61	0·68	30·89	29·32	1·57	26·68	24·85	1·83	25·37	22·89	2·48
14·59	13·90	0·69				28·68	26·85	1·83	27·63	25·14	2·49
15·87	15·18	0·69				30·84	29·00	1·84	29·90	27·40	2·50
17·21	16·52	0·69							32·24	29·73	2·51
18·31	17·62	0·69									

The thermistor was calibrated at times $\tau = 0$, 5, 11, 15 and 17 months. For each calibration the first column, marked t_0, gives the observed temperatures in °C, the second column, marked t_c, gives the temperatures calculated from the observed resistances using the constants obtained from the original calibration at $\tau = 0$; the third column, marked $t_0 - t_c$, shows how the error in the calculated temperature increases as the temperature increases. Thus over a range of approximately 10° C, relative temperatures may be measured to an accuracy of 0·02° C provided the change in constants is not so great as to give an error greater than 1·5° C in the absolute temperature.

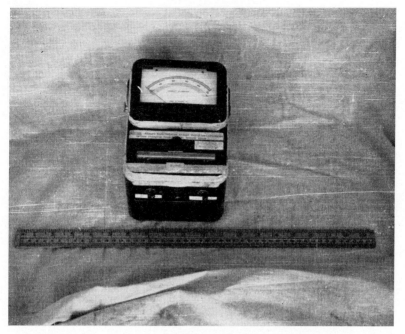

Fig. 2. The d.c. measuring bridge for use with probes in short holes in tunnel walls. Temperature is found from a calibration graph of temperature versus out-of-balance current.

meter; a circuit diagram is shown in Fig. 3. The resistance of the thermistor, a glass-enclosed bead type, is about $2\,000\ \Omega$ at room temperature. Since the equipment is used only in holes up to 100 ft long, the effect of a change in lead resistance due to a change in temperature is negligible; the method of calibrating the thermistor with all the wire in circuit eliminates the need for a correction for lead resistance. An added advantage for the $2\,000$-Ω thermistor is that no great precautions have to be taken to protect the leads from moisture.

The thermistor is protected from mechanical damage by a brass container and is sealed in with the use of O-rings; the container is sealed to protect the thermistor from the highly conducting water sometimes encountered underground. Many of the shotholes are dry, and to decrease the thermal time lag the mass of the container is reduced as much as possible by the use of flanges for the O-ring seals. A typical container is shown in Fig. 4. Since the holes are short, it is not necessary to streamline the container or to use special cable with stranded steel strengthening. Ordinary rubber-covered multiflex is used and an O-ring seals the rubber to the container, the arrangements being similar to those shown in Figs. 8 and 9. The lower section of a container, designed for use with a single centrally mounted thermistor, can be removed to replace the thermistor without disturbing the soldered joints or the O-ring seal around the rubber-covered leads. When two or more thermistors are mounted in the same container the cable seal has to be loosened before the lower section can be removed.

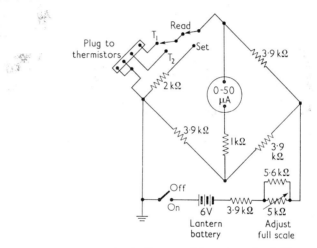

Fig. 3. Circuit diagram of d.c. measuring bridge.

In a typical operation the thermistor is pushed to the required distance and allowed to attain the temperature of its surroundings with the bridge current switched on. A reading of the temperature is then found from a calibration graph of temperature versus out-of-balance current.

There is no need to use the exponential relation between resistance and temperature, since the accuracy of the meter limits the accuracy of the temperature to only 0·1°C and this is easily attained with graphs.

Recently a slightly modified version of the bridge was built for the Snowy Mountains Hydro-Electric Authority, Australia. Two thermistors are mounted in the same container, Fig. 4, and readings can be made on either of them by means of an extra switch on the bridge. This arrangement was made to check the drift of the thermistors. If the same temperature is registered by the two thermistors, when the container is in either a borehole or an insulated compartment in the bottom of the box, Fig. 5, it can be assumed that the thermistors have not drifted. The possibility that the two have drifted by the same amount can be discarded as too remote. However, with suitable rearrangement a third thermistor can be used to check this if desired.

Howard [50] has added a transistor current amplifier, similar to

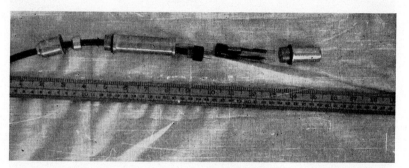

Fig. 4. Exploded view of low mass type of thermistor container for use in short holes. This container is used to check the drift of the thermistors by mounting two on a three-core cable.

that described by Anderson,[2] to the circuit and can measure to 0·01°C over the limited range of 0·5°C.

For more accurate measurements the use of a d.c. bridge over the range usually required is not feasible. Robust meters of the required sensitivity are not available. It is therefore necessary to amplify the out-of-balance voltage, and the easiest way to do this is to use an a.c. amplifier.

The a.c. bridge developed by Newstead,[70] for use with thermistors in deep boreholes is shown in Fig. 6; the circuit diagram is shown in Fig. 7. In its original form the shock-mounted bridge was the size of a medium-sized suitcase and weighed about 40 lb. This instrument has now been transistorized and weighs 7 lb complete with batteries.[69] Special coaxial cable with a stranded

Fig. 5. Type of d.c. bridge used when the drift of thermistors has to be checked. A well-insulated compartment at the bottom takes the whole length of the probe shown in Fig. 4.

steel and copper inner conductor is used; this gives it a good electrical conductivity and a high strength so that an extra supporting steel cable [70] is not necessary. The cable is made to the design of the British Atomic Energy Commission, weighs 25 lb per 1000 ft and has a breaking strain of 300 lb.

To protect the thermistors against the effects of pressure [66] and current leakage across the leads, pressure-tight containers have to be used. Two types of thermistor pressure-tight containers are shown in Fig. 8. Details of the construction of one of them are shown in Fig. 9 (a); the pressure-sealing details of the other are essentially the same. An O-ring seals the plastic covering against the brass top; this seal can hold the weight of the container and

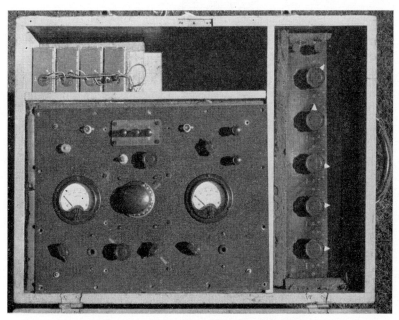

Fig. 6. The a.c. measuring bridge for use in deep boreholes. The bridge is balanced by alternately adjusting the capacity balance (large central knob for fine adjustments) and the resistance box until a null point is found for the bridge. The temperature is then found from the exponential relation for thermistors.

has withstood a pressure of 2 000 lb/in². The lower section of the container can be removed to facilitate replacing thermistors without disturbing the cable seal.

The thermistors are calibrated with all the coaxial cable, or an impedance representing a given length of the cable, in circuit; the method is thus one of substitution, and many sources of error, notably the cable impedance, are eliminated. Errors arising from

C

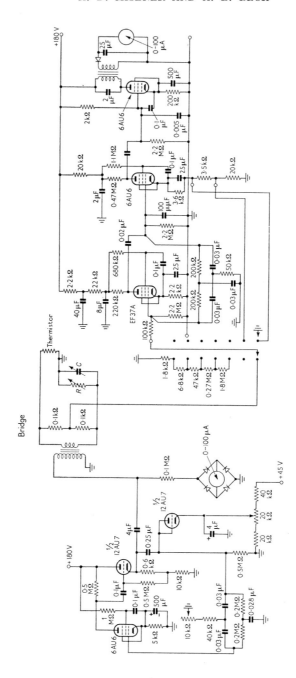

Fig. 7. Circuit diagram of a.c. bridge broken up into bridge circuit, oscillator circuit and amplifier circuit.

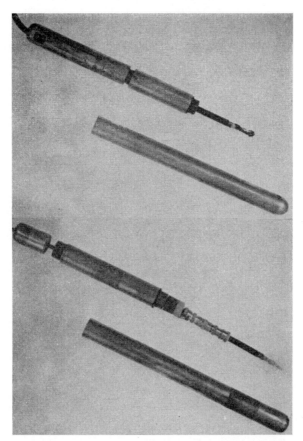

Fig. 8. Two types of thermistor container for use in deep boreholes. The upper container is used with low strength coaxial cable and an extra supporting steel cable is required to take the weight of the cable in the borehole; a slotted cap similar to that of the container shown in Fig. 1, but with an extra hole for the coaxial cable, is therefore used. The other container is used with high strength coaxial cable which does not need to be supported in the hole; the O-ring seal on the cable takes the weight of the container. All types of containers for use in deep holes are streamlined to prevent them catching on snags when they are being raised or lowered; the streamlining also reduces water disturbance and hence reduces the time required to reach the equilibrium temperature.

variations of cable impedance with temperature are reduced to negligible proportions by the use of thermistors with a nominal resistance of $10^5\ \Omega$ at 20°C. The accuracy of the apparatus is better than 0·01°C with a stable thermistor.[70] Since it is impracticable

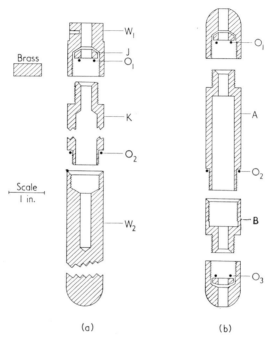

(a)   (b)

Fig. 9. (a) Details of construction of thermistor container. For low strength coaxial cable a slotted cap can be fitted on to W_1. W_1 is screwed on to K until J causes the O-ring O_1 to make a pressure-tight seal between the cable and K. For a high strength coaxial cable O_1 will take the weight of the container. W_2 is screwed on to K causing the O-ring O_2 to make a pressure-tight seal. As an aid to lowering the containers can be made heavier by lengthening W_2.

(b) Pressure-tight container for line connectors. O-rings O_1 and O_3 make seals on the cable and O-ring O_2 forms a seal between A and B.

to use a graph when measuring to 0·01°C over a range of about 20°C, the relation

$$R_T = a \exp\ (\beta/T) \qquad (1)$$

has to be used where a and β are the 'constants' of the thermistor, and R_T the resistance in ohms at the absolute temperature T.

Table 2. Temperature measurements in one borehole to check the drift of a thermistor

Depth (ft)	Temperatures measured by thermistor No. 1 (°C)										Temperatures measured by thermistor No. 2 (°C)					
	τ = 17		τ = 19		τ = 37		τ = 51		τ = 61		τ = 37		τ = 51		τ = 61	
	B	A	B	A	B	A	B	A	B	A	B	A	B	A	B	A
200	10·83	12·99	10·81	12·97	8·82	10·96	8·75	10·89	9·09	11·22	10·85	11·53	10·83	11·51	10·84	11·52
300	11·40	13·57	11·38	13·54	9·40	11·54	9·32	11·47	9·65	11·80	11·42	12·10	11·40	12·08	11·42	12·10
400	11·99	14·17	11·97	14·15	9·98	12·13	9·90	12·06	10·23	12·39	12·01	12·69	11·99	12·67	12·01	12·69
500	12·61	14·79	12·58	14·76	10·59	12·75	10·52	12·68	10·86	13·02	12·62	13·31	12·61	13·29	12·63	13·31
600	13·21	15·39	13·19	15·37	11·18	13·34	11·12	13·28	11·45	13·62	13·22	13·91	13·21	13·89	13·23	13·91
700	13·83	16·03	13·80	15·99	11·79	13·96	11·73	13·90	12·07	14·24	13·84	14·52	13·82	14·51	13·84	14·53
800	—	—	14·40	16·60	12·38	14·56	12·33	14·51	12·65	14·84	14·44	15·13	14·43	15·11	14·45	15·14

Temperatures were measured by two thermistors, Nos. 1 and 2, in the same borehole on various dates denoted by τ = 17, 19, 37, 51 and 61 days, the original calibration being made at τ = 0. For each date the values in the first column, marked B, are calculated from constants determined by the laboratory calibration at time τ = 0 and those in the second column, marked A, are derived from a calibration after returning to the laboratory two months later. The values in the B column of τ = 17 and in the B column of τ = 37, thermistor 2, agree with measurements made by maximum thermometers; the thermistors had therefore remained stable until these measurements were commenced.

To determine the 'constants', the thermistor is calibrated at intervals of approximately 2°C. The mean of all the values of β obtained from the calibration observations is used in conjunction with the resistance at the mean temperature to determine a value of α. Using these 'constants' the temperatures are then calculated from the observed resistances and compared with the observed temperatures. As noted by several workers [5, 11, 24, 68, 77] the 'constants' are, in fact, functions of the temperature. Therefore, if the extreme error is greater than the desired accuracy, say 0·01°C, the calibration is divided into two ranges and the process repeated. Occasionally over a 20°C interval three sets of 'constants' are required, since the range over which one pair of 'constants' can be used to give temperatures to within 0·01°C varies between 6° and 12°C according to the thermistor used and the portion of the R_T/T curve on which the range lies.

It is no longer possible to check the drift of the thermistors by the method used with the d.c. bridge equipment if special two-conductor coaxial cable is used. Instead, it is necessary to select some conveniently situated borehole and periodically measure the temperature gradient in it. Some typical results are shown in Table 2. To check the short-term stability the shallowest temperature measured on the way down can be remeasured on the way up. The winch used with this apparatus is shown in Fig. 10.

If necessary the equipment can be handled easily by one man by removing the cable drum and handling each part separately. If greater lengths of cable are required it is better to have separate reels; this makes the whole equipment easy to handle and keeps the winch a convenient size. Two cables can be joined by a coaxial line connector and sealed in a container as shown in Fig. 9 (b).

All the equipment, including two or three drums of coaxial cable, can be carried in a small four wheel drive pick-up truck. This clearly is a distinct advantage over bulky platinum resistance thermometer equipment.

(iv) *Discussion of fields of use for each type of equipment.* No one type of equipment is suitable, or even desirable, for all types of field conditions. If it is possible to make a large number of measurements at various depths over a wide area, say one or two miles square, then an accuracy of only 0·1°C is all that is required. Thus in a mining area the d.c. thermistor equipment is entirely adequate.

For most other purposes an accuracy of 0·03°C is sufficient and for boreholes less than about 500 ft deep the quickest and simplest method is to use maximum thermometers; these remarks also apply if bottom-hole temperatures are being measured as a hole is drilled, even if the hole eventually reaches a few thousand feet. However, a certain amount of caution must be exercised, since

Fig. 10. Winch for use with high strength coaxial cable. A revolution counter operated by the pulley reads the depths to 0·1 ft. All parts except the bearings are made of a light aluminium alloy and the total weight, complete with 1 500 ft of steel core coaxial cable, is less than 80 lb.

occasional inversions of the temperature gradient are encountered if the thermometers are lowered too soon after drilling has ceased. The a.c. bridge type of equipment is best used on all other boreholes, but if it is used in swamp or jungle conditions the instrument, including all exposed terminals, must be sealed against the humidity; failure to do this results in errors due to a leakage current across the terminals of the high-resistance thermistor and the variable-resistance box.

Only occasionally is an accuracy of 0·01°C or better really needed, such as when trying to detect a variation of heat flow with depth in a long borehole passing through very uniform rock.

The greatest advantage of any electrical thermometer over the maximum thermometer is that it can record the temperature continuously. Thus it is possible to be sure when the thermometer has reached equilibrium, to detect inversions of the temperature gradient and to determine the temperature and point of entry or

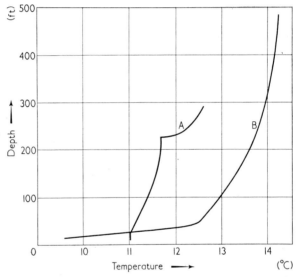

Fig. 11. Temperature depth curves for two holes with water flowing along them.

exit of a water flow in a borehole with great accuracy. Two particularly interesting examples of the usefulness of an electrical thermometer in detecting water flow are shown in Fig. 11.

In borehole A the water was clearly entering through a fissure at a depth of 226 ft at a temperature of 11·65°C. A second and much more rapid flow of water entered at a depth of 23 ft at a temperature of 11·03°C.

No water was flowing out of the collar of borehole B. However, the temperature/depth curve indicates that water was flowing into the hole at about 500 ft and flowed out again at about 40 ft.

Correlation with the rock types and driller's log showed that the water was probably entering through a layer of gravels, 24 ft thick commencing at 456 ft, and flowing out through a narrow highly vesicular horizon at 47 ft in a basalt flow. Later measurements with a heating probe [71] gave a good estimate of the rate of water flow.

3. General Sources of Error

A. *Stretching and twisting of the supporting wire*

Whether a single-strand or multi-strand supporting cable is used, allowance has to be made for the stretching and twisting which occurs. It is therefore good practice to put permanent marks on the cable every 50 ft. When a wire rope is remeasured after a field trip permanent extensions of 0·5 per cent are quite frequent, particularly when heavy equipment is being used. This occurs even with rope which is alleged to have been wound so as not to twist. Since readings are usually taken on the way down a hole the cable has several hours in which to stretch and untwist. However, when being rewound the rope does not have time to contract and twist up again and it is wound on to the cable drum in a stressed state. If a reliable revolution counter is used to measure depth and if there is no slipping, the extension is indicated by a negative reading when the cable has been rewound; the stressed state of the cable is shown by loosening a few turns of the cable on the reel and noting the tendency to kink. Over the course of a few hours the energy stored in the rewound cable is gradually dissipated, the result being an apparent permanent set.

To avoid this initial error the best procedure is to stretch a length of the cable equal to the length of the longest borehole to be encountered. Obviously the easiest way to do this is to stretch the cable in the borehole. If the equipment is lowered to the bottom of the hole and left for a day or so before being rewound, the cable will stretch to its maximum length. With sensitive electrical equipment this can be detected by measuring the temperature at given intervals of time. What is frequently thought to be a long thermal lag is actually an increase in temperature due to the gradual extension of the cable. If the cable is then rewound and stored for another day or two the apparent permanent set will appear. The cable can now be marked every 50 ft. Further slight extensions can be expected over a period of use, but they are negligible compared with the initial stretch.

The extensions to be expected can, of course, be estimated from the usual elastic equations.

B. Stability of temperature gradients in boreholes

(i) *Convection currents.* Consideration has to be given to the possible existence of convection currents in the medium with which the borehole is filled, since they may lead to an unstable temperature gradient and thus to a misleading value for the heat flux.

A borehole has a stable temperature gradient [57] if

$$\frac{dT}{dx} < \frac{gaT}{C_p} + \frac{B\kappa v}{gaa^4} \tag{2}$$

where dT/dx is the temperature gradient, g is the acceleration due to gravity, a is the radius of the borehole, T is the absolute temperature and B is a numerical constant equal to 216 for a tube the length of which is very much greater than its radius. The other symbols refer to the physical constants, at $T°K$, of the fluid with which the borehole is filled: a is the coefficient of volume expansion, v is the kinematic viscosity, C_p is the specific heat at constant pressure and κ is the diffusivity. When

$$\frac{dT}{dx} = \frac{gaT}{C_p} + \frac{B\kappa v}{gaa^4} \tag{3}$$

the temperature gradient is known as the critical gradient.

In Fig. 12 the critical gradient in °C/km has been plotted against temperature in °C for boreholes of radius 1·78, 2·54, 3·17 and 3·81 cm. Fig. 13 shows the curves obtained by plotting the critical gradient against borehole radius for fixed temperatures of 5, 10, 15 and 25°C. Both sets of curves refer to water-filled boreholes. It can be seen that for temperatures greater than 20°C and diameters greater than 5 cm the critical gradient decreases very slowly.

It is interesting to note that the temperature gradient in one borehole, 4500 ft deep, was measured [47] when the hole was dry; convection currents were assumed to be absent. The assumption was confirmed in a remarkable way [48] when two years later the hole was found to be full of water and new measurements showed no sensible difference over the previous ones.

(ii) *Underground water flows.* Unreliable temperature gradients

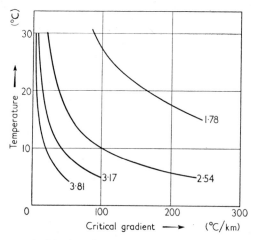

Fig. 12. Curves of critical gradient versus temperature for typical boreholes
of radii 1·78, 2·54, 3·17 and 3·81 cm.

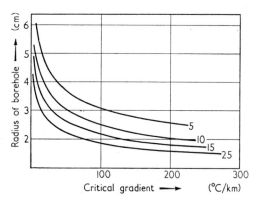

Fig. 13. Curves of critical gradient versus borehole radius for temperatures
of 5, 10, 15 and 25° C.

are also caused by the underground movement of water. If the flow is seasonal it is easy to discover this and to avoid those boreholes where this occurs. Again an inflow or outflow of water at a given depth can easily be found by looking at the temperature depth graph. However, very slow regional movements of water, such as may occur in Nottinghamshire,[33] are very difficult to discover and to determine. The only sure way of eliminating this effect is to cover a large region, as did Misener *et al.*[63, 67] and to plot isothermal planes. Any consistent dip of the isothermal planes, which cannot be correlated with rock type or geological history, will indicate a regional flow of water.

C. *Effect of a metal casing*

It is sometimes necessary to measure the temperature gradient in a borehole lined with a metal casing. This will not introduce errors into the temperature gradient unless measurements are taken at a distance less than 50 a from the top of the casing, [28, 64] where a is the radius of the hole.

III. MEASUREMENT OF THERMAL CONDUCTIVITY

1. Preamble

The first experiments to determine the thermal conductivity of rocks were not connected with an investigation into the flow of heat from the crust of the earth; they were conducted merely to collect physical and geological data.

Rock conductivities may be determined in two fundamentally different ways: by measurements *in situ* and by measurements in the laboratory. In both cases a troublesome contact resistance between the specimen and temperature-measuring device has to be eliminated. The first determinations were made using *in situ* methods [42, 44, 78] which were superseded, at least temporarily, by laboratory techniques introduced by Herschel and Lebour [26, 49] which at that time were less laborious. In more recent times it has been realized [9] that in certain cases the small rock specimens used in the laboratory are not representative of a large mass of the rock. For this reason, attention has again turned to *in situ* methods using boreholes or short holes in the sides of tunnel walls.

2. Laboratory Methods

A. *Transient methods*

In general, the transient methods used for disc and cylindrical specimens in the laboratory suffer from the great disadvantage that they only measure conductivity indirectly. The quantity usually measured is the diffusivity κ and additional measurements have to be made to find the conductivity. For this reason only one method will be discussed here, and this method is, in a sense, a steady-state method.

Little is known of the theory, but, in the time-honoured words, 'It works'. The apparatus is known as a thermal comparator [72] and consists of two phosphor-bronze ball bearings B embedded in a block of balsa wood A (Fig. 14).

One of the balls protrudes slightly below the surface of the balsa wood, while the other is just within the base. Thermocouples are connected differentially between the two balls and the block is

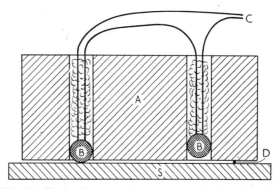

Fig. 14. Thermal comparator apparatus used by Powell.

heated to a constant temperature of 70°C. The specimen S to be investigated is allowed to come to equilibrium with its surroundings and the comparator is then placed on it with the protruding ball bearing touching the surface; two small legs D make the base of the balsa wood parallel to the specimen surface. The differential thermal e.m.f. across C increases with time owing to the more rapid cooling of the ball in contact with the material; for the first 10 or 20 sec this increase is linear and measurements are only taken over this range. The method is essentially a comparison one and the apparatus is calibrated for at least three values. Results can be obtained within a few seconds, but certain precautions have to be taken, since the cooling rate is found to vary with pressure, surface finish and thickness of the material. However, provided the size of the specimen under consideration is greater than about a 1 mm cube the latter effect will not cause an error in the results. This, of course, underlines the serious drawback of this method for terrestrial heat-flow work. The size of the volume affecting the apparatus is far too small to give the conductivity of a rock, but the method may prove extremely useful in determining the conductivity of small crystals of minerals; particularly is this important for minerals which only occur in small aggregates and which therefore have never been assigned a reliable value for conductivity.

B. *Absolute steady-state methods*

There are numerous methods which have been developed for the absolute measurement of the conductivity of bad conductors. They all consist essentially of measuring the heat flow and temperature gradient across a slab of the specimen. The variations in

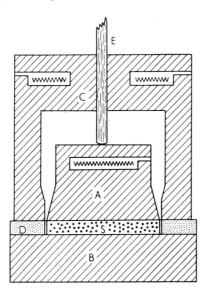

Fig. 15. Apparatus used by Birch and Clark for absolute determination of conductivity of rocks at temperatures up to 400° C.

technique lie mainly in the desire to improve the accuracy and the speed of measurement. Only one really reliable apparatus,[18] Fig. 15, has been designed specifically for accurate work on rocks, and this was also capable of being operated at high temperatures.

The apparatus consists of a heating block A, which is kept a few degrees hotter than a cooling block B, between which is placed the specimen S. Heat losses from the side are reduced to a minimum by the use of a guard ring D, the temperature of which is controlled by separate heaters in a block C; a certain amount of pressure can be applied via the Pyrex rod E. The whole apparatus is sealed inside a steel tube which can be immersed to a depth of about 12 in. in a thermostatic bath. Cooling of B is by natural heat loss to the fluid in the bath. Conductivities at elevated temperatures can thus be measured with only a few degrees temperature difference across the specimen.

Birch and Clark [18] overcame the problem of the contact resistance by using two gases of known conductivity, helium and nitrogen, and calculating the thermal resistance.

If the heat flow H and the temperature difference Θ across the two interface films and the specimen are known for each experiment involving a different gas, then for helium and nitrogen we have the two equations

$$H_h = \frac{\Theta_h}{(x/k_h + S/k)} \text{ and } H_n = \frac{\Theta_n}{(x/k_n + S/k)} \tag{4}$$

where the subscripts h and n refer to the experiments with hydrogen and helium respectively and S is the thickness of the specimen of conductivity k. If k_h and k_n are known, then by eliminating x, the combined thickness of the two air films, k is found from the expression

$$\frac{k_n}{k_h} = \frac{(\Theta_h/H_h - S/k)}{(\Theta_n/H_n - S/k)} \tag{5}$$

Using this apparatus, Birch and Clark carefully measured the conductivities of a variety of igneous rocks at a series of temperatures ranging up to 400°C. The general tendency was for the range of conductivities to converge [19] from 0·004–0·014 at 0°C to 0·004–0·009 at 400°C. Occasionally irreversible changes in conductivity were found above 300°C and these were attributed to the possibility of adsorbed films of water being driven off at this temperature.

Later, a modified apparatus was used by Clark [34] to test the effect of wetting and simple compression. In the light of later experiences [9] the experiments on the effect of wetting must be considered inconclusive, but application of pressure was found to increase the conductivity. Thus the effects of rising temperature and rising pressure as we go deeper into the crust tend to cancel each other out.

C. *Steady-state comparison methods; the divided bar*

(i) *Apparatus.* One of the simplest methods of determining the conductivity of a bad conductor is to compare its conductivity with that of another material of known conductivity. The method was first suggested by Lodge [61] in 1878 on purely theoretical grounds and first used by Lees [60] in 1892. In geophysical work the apparatus generally takes the form of a pair of cylindrical metal bars, usually brass, between which is sandwiched a disc-like specimen of the same diameter as the bars. Heat is supplied to the remote end of one bar and removed from the remote end of the other by thermostatically controlled water. By making temperature measurements in the bars after the steady state has been reached, the conductivity of the specimen is determined in terms of the conductivity of the bars. The effect of the thermal contact resistance between the bars and the specimen is eliminated by making observations on three or more discs of different thicknesses.

The bars are calibrated using a set of crystalline quartz discs cut parallel to the optic axis. The conductivity of the quartz may be taken as 0·0145 cal/cm.sec.°C at 30°C.[12] The value of the conductivity for brass is usually checked using fused silica, which has a conductivity of 0·00325 at 30°C. The uncertainty in the value for quartz is about 4 per cent, as may be judged by comparing the above value with data quoted by Gafner [45] which were obtained from recent unpublished work done at the National Physical Laboratory, Teddington, England. Until more details are available the above values are taken to be the best ones. If the two values of the conductivity of the brass agree to within 2 or 3 per cent then the instrument is useful over the range of conductivities likely to be encountered with rocks.

One great advantage of the divided-bar apparatus is that the temperature-measuring devices, usually thermocouples, do not have to be located with any great accuracy; if the nominal distance, used in the calculations, between two thermocouples is in error by

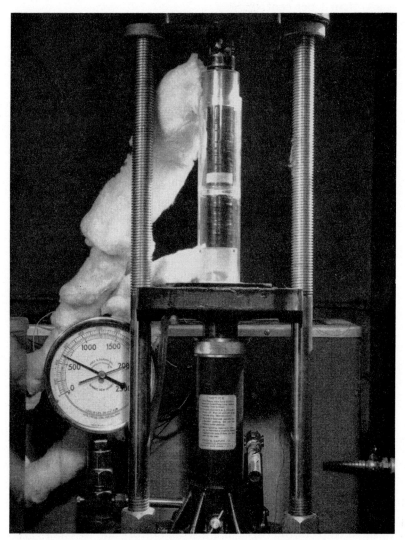

Fig. 16. Constant temperature difference divided bar apparatus and associated equipment.

D

10 per cent the error in the conductivity of a rock from this cause is less than 1 per cent.

The equation relating the conductivity of the specimen k_2, the temperature difference Θ between the two brass interfaces and the thickness D of the disc is

$$R = \Theta/(d\theta/dx) = B + (k_1/k_2)D \qquad (6)$$

where $d\theta/dx$ is the mean steady-state temperature gradient of the two bars, k_1 is the conductivity of brass and B is a constant which involves the sum of the contact resistances of the two interface films. With a carefully machined set of discs it is reasonable to assume that the surface finish is constant from disc to disc, and hence that the contact resistance will also be constant from disc to disc. Thus for one rock, measuring the total resistance R for three or more discs of different thicknesses and plotting R against D will give a straight line of slope k_1/k_2, from which k_2 can be determined. The standard deviation of k_2 will contain all the errors due to differences in the composition of each disc and the errors due to small differences in the contact resistance. By the use of liquid interfaces the contact resistance can be reduced to about one-tenth that found when dry interfaces are used.

There are, of course, many variations of divided-bar apparatus, but nearly all of them take a long time to reach the steady state. However, Beck [7] has described one with which the steady state is reached within ten minutes. In this apparatus, Figs. 16 and 17, the heat is supplied to the bars by spraying thermostatically controlled water through a shower on to the end surface of the upper bar and removing the heat from the lower end of the system by a similar method, the temperature difference between the two ends being about 20°C. This has many advantages over the more usual type of apparatus, which uses an electrical heater to supply heat, in that the bars, specimen and air films are always at a given mean temperature, and a guard ring can be incorporated which does not need separate controls. By the use of a thick guard ring, errors due to small chips in the edges of a disc and errors due to small variations in the diameter are reduced to negligible proportions; however, a standard diameter correction [55] has to be applied for the finite thickness of insulation between the bar and guard ring.

(ii) *Preparation of specimens.* Clays or sediments of the type recovered from the ocean beds have to be contained in a mould. The mould can be a Perspex or Lucite annulus with a wall thickness of $\frac{1}{32}$ in. and with an outside diameter equal to the outside diameter of the guard ring. Since the clays are usually plastic or viscous, the contact resistance can be taken as zero. However, it is

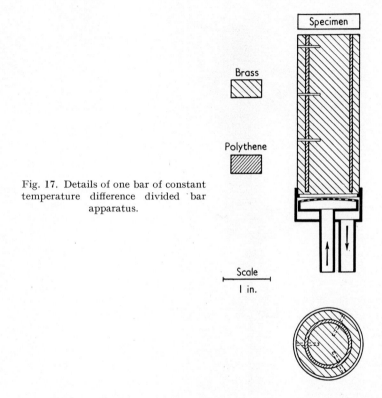

Fig. 17. Details of one bar of constant temperature difference divided bar apparatus.

a simple matter to check this by the use of moulds of different heights.

For rocks, whatever type of divided bar is used, discs have to be cut from cores, and sometimes ground as well, to within certain pre-determined limits of flatness. If hand specimens only are available, the simplest way to obtain a core is to use a thin-walled diamond coring drill; the use of brass or steel tubes and an abrasive is not only tedious but in the long run it is more expensive than a diamond drill. The drill is held in a special chuck, Fig. 18, which allows water to pass through a hollow spindle and which can be used on an ordinary drilling machine. A thin-walled drill, about 0·020 in. thick, allows the operator to drill rapidly without exerting too much pressure, and cores up to 3 in. long can readily be obtained

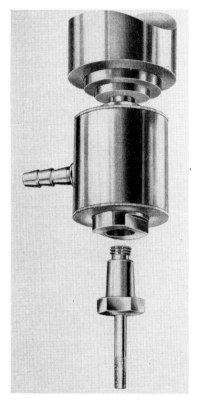

Fig. 18. Coring chuck. Photo by courtesy of Habit Diamond Products.

with diameters accurate to within ±0·002 in. over the length of the core. A copious flow of water is used to cool and lubricate the drill as well as to drive out all dislodged particles of rock. A drilling fluid is not used, since it may enter the interstices of the rock and thus affect its thermal conductivity, whereas if water enters the interstices of the rock it does not matter, since the chief interest is in the saturated or moist states of the rock.

For most purposes it is only necessary to get the surfaces flat to
within about 0·001 in. One method suitable for doing this is to grip
the cores in a chuck which can be rotated about an axis through its
centre, Fig. 19, and which is firmly bolted to the feed table of a
milling machine converted for use with a diamond saw, preferably
of 12 in. diameter; for the best results the diamond saw must have
a good square edge. The feed table of a milling machine can be
moved parallel to three mutually perpendicular axes, one of which
is arranged to be parallel to the length of the core and to the axis
of rotation of the diamond saw and chuck. If the rock core is
rotated about its axis at about one revolution every 20 sec and

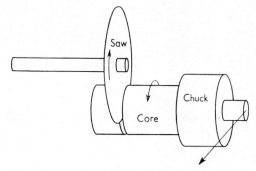

Fig. 19. Schematic diagram of 'rotating core' rock cutting method.

at the same time is slowly fed into the saw at a rate of $\frac{1}{8}$ to $\frac{1}{4}$ in./
min, specimens with edges parallel to within 0·001 in. can be cut
off in about 5 min. Occasionally, or frequently if the cutting edge
of the saw is in bad condition, a small 'pip' will be left at the
centre. This 'pip' is readily ground off on a diamond-impregnated
annular lap which is cooled and lubricated by water fed in at the
centre and thrown out over the diamond-impregnated surface by
centrifugal force. When the disc is held 'pip' downwards with the
thumb and middle finger and a light force exerted with the forefinger, the 'pip' is rapidly ground down. With only slight practice
there is very little danger of overgrinding and damaging the surface of the disc, for although the light force of the forefinger creates
sufficient pressure to push the 'pip' through the water film on the
diamond lap, it does not create enough pressure to force the whole
disc through the water film; this in fact needs considerable force.

The flatness of the disc is tested by taking six micrometer measurements around the edge and one at the centre. If the mean of the six measurements at the edge is within 0·001 in. of the measurement at the centre the disc is suitable for use without any further grinding; almost invariably it will be found that the disc is very slightly convex in shape.

Nearly everyone has his own idea of what the tolerances of flatness should be, but, within reasonable limits, it really does not

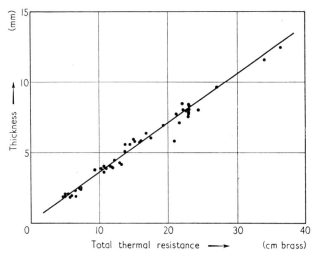

Fig. 20. Thermal resistances of 48 discs of a uniform coarse grained granite; disc thicknesses ranged from 2 to 12 mm.

matter what the tolerances are, provided the flatness and the surface finish are approximately the same from disc to disc.

(iii) *Use of single discs.* When sets of three or more discs are used it is frequently found that the points are well scattered and the standard deviation is large; Fig. 20 shows points plotted for 48 discs of coarse-grained granite. The scatter of points indicates a difference in thermal resistance per unit thickness and is due to (1) the high probability of finding, from disc to disc, a variation in the proportions of the constituent minerals; and (2) an increasing probability, as the disc thickness increases, of the disc having a 'series' arrangement of minerals. The question of 'series' and 'parallel' arrangements of minerals is discussed below.

It can be seen then that in any set of discs, particularly if the rock is coarse grained, it is possible to get significantly different values of the conductivity merely by omitting one of the discs from the calculations; this is illustrated in the first four columns of Table 3. In addition, the scattered points often give an apparent

Table 3.   Deviation of conductivity [cal. cm.$^{-2}$ sec^{-1}.($^\circ$C)$^{-1}$]

| Rock | Conductivity of sets of discs | | | Conductivity of individual discs obtained by subtracting a standard contact resistance |
	Disc omitted from set of four	Conductivity from least squares straight line	Standard deviation (%)	
1	1	0·0133	49·6	0·0085
	2	0·0097	12·3	0·0079
	3	0·0094	15·5	0·0097
	4	0·0106	32·7	0·0090
	None	0·0101	16·9	Mean 0·0088 ± 4·4%
2	1	0·0095	67·5	0·0072
	2	0·0093	35·4	0·0092
	3	0·0096	7·0	0·0066
	4	0·0064	30·6	0·0090
	None	0·0089	26·2	Mean 0·0080 ± 8·1%

negative contact resistance. A better estimate of the conductivity of each disc would be obtained if a contact resistance, valid for all discs, could be used.

With a little skill very uniform discs can be produced, and if one apparatus has been used to make many measurements on all types of rock it is possible [9] to obtain a standard contact resistance for the instrument and given tolerances of rock machining. This standard contact resistance may be applied to most rocks, for, with liquid contacts, the contact resistance is approximately one-tenth the resistance of a disc of average rock 2 mm thick. Thus an error of 20 per cent in the contact resistance will give only a 2 per cent error in the thermal resistance of the thinnest disc and will be less for the thicker ones.

With this method the conductivities have been found for individual discs of the rocks 1 and 2 and are shown, together with their mean value, in the last column of Table 3; the standard contact resistance of the apparatus was equivalent to 0·5 cm of brass.

D. *Comparison of single disc results with computed values*

Once the conductivity of an individual disc has been measured the value can be compared with a value calculated from a knowledge of the conductivities and proportions of the constituent minerals.[18, 19] For a fine-grained rock the mineral composition (mode) can be found accurately from examination of a thin section under a microscope. However, for coarse-grained rocks the observations have to be made on the individual discs, for the mode of a slide, although more accurately determined, bears little relation to the mode of a disc; the reasons for this have been set out briefly in the previous section.

Further errors are likely to arise because the minerals often form chains or aggregates which in certain circumstances cause the value of thermal conductivity determined in the laboratory to differ from the bulk conductivity.[9, 18, 19, 30]

For example, if a rock is composed of two minerals, one of high conductivity and one of low conductivity, the specimen gives the true value for the bulk conductivity provided the thickness of a laboratory specimen is greater than the length l of the longest chain or aggregate of grains. If the thickness of a disc is just less than l, then, assuming that the chains of minerals are perpendicular to the faces of the discs, at least one of the chains will run directly from one specimen face to the other; if this chain is composed of the high-conductivity mineral, heat will be transmitted across the disc more rapidly than it would if a few grains of the less-conducting mineral were interposed. This leads to an apparent increase in the thermal conductivity of the rock as a whole. As the thickness of the specimen is decreased, an increasing number of the chains will run from face to face of the specimen, thus increasing the apparent conductivity of the rock until the thickness is less than the size m of the smallest grain. Under these conditions the minerals are said to be in 'parallel', since the equivalent electrical circuit is several high and low resistances connected in parallel. When the specimen thickness is greater than l the minerals are said to be in 'series'. The apparent conductivity of the rock will therefore vary from a low conductivity equal to the bulk or 'series' conductivity (k_s) when the specimen thickness is greater than l to a comparatively high, or 'parallel', conductivity (k_p) when the specimen thickness is less than m.

If there are n minerals present in the disc, with α parts of a mineral of conductivity k_a, β parts of a mineral of conductivity $k_b \ldots \eta$ parts of a mineral of conductivity k_n, then the 'series' computed conductivity k_s is given by

$$\frac{n}{k_s} = \frac{\alpha}{k_a} + \frac{\beta}{k_b} + \ldots + \frac{\eta}{k_n} \tag{7}$$

while the 'parallel' computed conductivity k_p is given by

$$nk_p = \alpha k_a + \beta k_b + \ldots + \eta k_n \tag{8}$$

Approximate values for the conductivities of some of the more important minerals are given in Table 4. The data are for randomly oriented aggregates of crystals at 30°C and at pressures of only a few lb/in².

Table 4.   Approximate conductivity of typical minerals

Minerals	Feldspars Muscovite Sericite	Biotite Chlorite Epidote	Magnetite Calcite Topaz	Horne-blende Pyroxene	Quartz
Conductivity [cal.cm⁻².sec⁻¹.(°C)⁻¹]	0·0045	0·0060	0·0085	0·00100	0·0170

If the rock is formed of minerals of similar conductivities the 'series' computed conductivity and the 'parallel' computed conductivity will be indistinguishable. However, if the rock contains a significant quantity of a high conductivity mineral together with low conductivity minerals it is necessary to establish some working relationship between the average grain size, G, of the rock and the minimum thickness, D, of a specimen required to give the bulk conductivity. For instance, the quartz content of the rocks of Table 3 was 20 to 30 per cent, and it was found that for $D/G < 8$ the minerals were arranged in parallel. Therefore to be reasonably certain that the minerals are in series, D/G should be as high as 15 or 20.

In practice, the monomineral chains have a wide range of lengths and are usually at all angles to the faces of the specimens; further complications arise from other variations in rock texture, and to predict the exact thickness required in the general case of a rock containing more than one mineral would be a difficult if not impossible task. The best that can be done is to examine a thin section of the rock and to find the average grain size. If the rock contains a significant quantity of quartz the disc thickness should be made greater than 15 G. Quartz-bearing rocks are, of course, the worst cases, and for rocks containing other common fairly highly conducting minerals, but less conducting than quartz, the disc thickness can be less than 15 G. However, it is definitely a wise policy to examine a thin section of the rock before a decision is made as to the minimum thickness of disc to be cut.

E. *Effect of moisture content*

For crustal heat flow only the conductivity of the rock when saturated with water is required. If the rocks are porous or fractured, then the spaces will be filled with water; if the rocks are fresh and non-porous, then the question of saturation does not arise. In saturated or nearly saturated media it is practically impossible to make moisture move down a temperature gradient [51, 58, 59] so that the moisture migration problem will not arise in this work. However, there is some doubt as to when a rock is saturated [9] and this point is not yet cleared up.

In some fields of work, for example in the field of building materials or in mine-ventilation problems, the heat-transfer co-efficient of a damp porous substance is required. The term heat-transfer coefficient is used, since it is more correct than the use of thermal conductivity when reference is made to the flow of heat in porous media; heat is not only conducted but is also transferred by the movement of vapour and liquid down a temperature gradient.

The disadvantages of laboratory methods may be summed up as follows: they require additional apparatus and time for the preparation of the discs; they are selective in the sense that discs can only be prepared from fairly sound rock and that cores may not be recovered at all from highly altered or sheared zones; they use specimens that are frequently too small to be representative of even the sound rock; they do not take into account the effect of open veins or joints in the rock, which may well be important; they are generally used at pressures only a few lb/in² above atmospheric pressure instead of at the pressures prevailing *in situ*. All these disadvantages are considerably reduced by the measurement of the conductivity of the rock *in situ* in a borehole.

3. Field Methods

A. *Preamble*

The history of *in situ* measurements is surprisingly long, the first results having been produced by Forbes [44] in 1849 and by Thomson [78] and by Everett [42] in 1861. After this there was a long interval before the next serious work in a short borehole by Bullard [28] in 1938. Later, Blackwell [20] developed an approximate theory of radial heat flow which could be applied to a hollow heating probe in short holes in a tunnel wall. Concurrently, Jaeger [53] was developing an exact theory for use with a solid heating probe in long boreholes.

To simplify the theory and the experimental work it is necessary to have heat flowing radially at the point where the temperature is being measured. The length of the probe required to ensure this at the plane bisecting the probe axis perpendicularly depends on the radius of the probe and on the time of the experiment; for most purposes a probe length of 30 to 40 times the diameter of the borehole will produce less than a 1 per cent error due to axial heat losses.[21]

In geophysical work the probe has to be a loose fit in the hole, and this introduces a contact resistance between the probe and the walls of the hole; it is the theoretical treatment of this contact resistance that is the main difference between the methods proposed by Blackwell and by Jaeger.

B. *Short probes*

(i) *Hollow probe*. Blackwell suggested eliminating the contact resistance by the use of two approximate solutions for the heat-flow equation; an approximation valid for small times gives the contact resistance, which can then be used in an approximation valid for large times from which the conductivity is found.

Several types of probes were used, all of them designed for use in nearly horizontal short holes in tunnel walls. A typical probe,

Fig. 21, consists of a hollow brass tube of 1 in. internal diameter [40] and with a wall thickness of $\frac{1}{16}$ in.; the overall length was 3 ft. Shallow helical grooves were cut along the length of the probe; the brass surface was then insulated and two parallel coils of 20 B and S manganin wire wound into the grooves to give a total resistance of 26 Ω. The temperature at the mid-point of the tube was found by the use of the d.c. bridge described earlier and a bead-type

Fig. 21. Hollow heating probe of the type used by Blackwell and by Crowe.

thermistor pressed against the inner surface of the tube by a spring. The ends of the tube were sealed to protect the thermistor from moisture effects and to prevent convection losses from the inside of the tube.

A typical experiment lasts 3 or 4 h. In the laboratory the tube was used, with heat inputs between 0·01 and 0·02 cal/sec/in., to measure the conductivity of foamed polystyrene. The results from the transient method were within 6 per cent of the results found using a steady-state method. However, in short holes in the

Kemano, B.C., and Eucumbene–Tumut, Australia, tunnels the results were generally too high [22] when compared with the laboratory values. This is probably a real difference due to the troublesome effects of moisture in the rocks; since the d.c. bridge only reads to 0·1°C, it is necessary to have heat inputs to the probe which give a temperature rise of 50°C, and these high-temperature increases might be expected to accentuate the moisture migration.

In general, the use of a probe in short holes is a difficult undertaking. Once the holes are drilled they appear to do one of two things: the water drains away from them, leaving damp but unsaturated rocks which will then give a heat-transfer coefficient much higher than the conductivity or else, in a fresh rock, water drains into the hole from cracks and crevices and the hole becomes partly filled with water. In either case the modifications required to the cylindrical heat-flow theory are very complex and it is preferable to try to use water-filled holes or boreholes. However, the theory is being modified [23] to take account of the thermal mass of a cylindrical contact layer; this was neglected in the original theory, since the probe was primarily for use in dry materials.

(ii) *Solid probe.* Jaeger suggested the use of the exact theory for cylindrical heating to eliminate the contact resistance; families of theoretical curves are calculated for a range of likely values of the contact resistance and of the ratio of the thermal capacities of the rock and heating medium. An experimental curve is then fitted to one of the theoretical curves to give both the conductivity and the diffusivity [10] of the rocks. The thermal mass of the contact layer is taken into account by lumping it in with the thermal mass of the probe.

Since the method was developed primarily for use in water-filled boreholes, an efficient seal has to be used to prevent convection losses from the section of the hole being heated. The most efficient method is to use a pneumatic seal, and this has been done in Tasmania; one by-product of this technique was the development of a method for estimating small water flows along or across boreholes.[71] The depth at which a pneumatic seal can be used is limited by the pressure of compressed gas available to inflate the seals. A different type of seal, Fig. 22, was therefore developed for use at any depth and which can adjust itself to small irregularities in the walls of the hole. It consists of a series of rubber washers cut at close intervals around the perimeter and separated by thick ebonite washers; these were mounted on an ebonite former to make a sort of 'bottle brush'. This has been found very effective in preventing heat losses from a section of a vertical borehole.[6]

The probe is very similar to the temperature-measuring type shown in Fig. 8; it is, however, made longer and has helical grooves cut on it to take the heater wire; the whole assembly is then painted with an insulating varnish to prevent electrical losses in highly conducting underground water. A thermistor is located in the centre of the probe and the a.c. bridge described earlier is used to measure the resistance. Temperatures can therefore be measured to 0·01°C, and temperature rises of 10°C or less can be used to get

Fig. 22. Seal for preventing loss of heat from a heated portion of a borehole.

a good determination of conductivity. A typical experiment lasts between $\frac{1}{2}$ to $1\frac{1}{2}$ h, and the probe has been found to work very well in the laboratory and under ideal field conditions.

An alternative type of solid probe which, with development, may be of some use is a solid aluminium rod with a very fine wire thermocouple in its surface at the centre. If the rod is heated to a constant temperature and suddenly plunged into the hole the cooling curve may be compared with theoretical cooling curves.[53] At present the probe must be a close fit in the hole and can only be used in short holes; in addition, three parameters containing the contact resistance, the diffusivity and the thermal capacity per unit mass, have to be found from one curve. The method is only pointed out since in certain circumstances it may not be possible to use electrical heating methods; for instance the methane hazard in a coal mine will probably require use of a non-electrical method.

C. *Heating long lengths of a borehole*

Even the probe methods must be suspected of not giving the true value of the *in situ* conductivity because the act of drilling a hole may cause unknown changes in the rock immediately around the hole; this is particularly true of sedimentary rocks. It is well known, from continuous logging of the velocity of sound through rocks, that drilling causes a change in the velocity characteristics of the walls of the hole and it is reasonable to suppose that the conductivity will also change. The change may be insignificant, but this could be checked by the use of a method which takes in a large volume of the rock and reduces the effects of altered wall conductivity to negligible proportions; such a method would also take account of larger scale geological features.

The results obtained from short probes represent an average conductivity of the material over a region determined by the length of the probe and the depth of penetration of heat into the rock. The latter depends on the time of the experiment, and 1 h after switching a heater on in a 2in.-diameter hole through rock of diffusivity 0·01 the temperature rise a distance of 5 in. from the hole is only $\frac{1}{15}$ of that at the inner surface of the hole; [54] after 3 h it is still only $\frac{1}{5}$, and 100 h are required before the rise is half the rise at the surface. This order of temperature rise may be regarded as reasonable, but a long-time experiment requires a very long probe in order to retain radial heat flow conditions in the central plane.[21] Thus it seems that the best way out of these difficulties would be to heat a long length of borehole with a wire; corrections for convection currents can be applied, or else the convection can be limited by a series of baffles. Preliminary experiments of this nature have been carried out,[10] but, due to a lack of suitable holes at the time, the results did no more than indicate that the method is feasible.

It is perhaps worthwhile summing up the above views on determining the conductivity of a rock.

The plausible assumption is usually made that when a rock is brought to the surface any change in its thermal conductivity, or any other physical property, is due only to the change in pressure and temperature. However, apparently fresh and strong rocks have been known to burst on being drilled or cut, and this suggests that removal from their *in situ* position and the subsequent mal-treatment can set up or release strains which alter the physical properties of the rock sample. To a lesser extent these remarks are also true of the rocks in the immediate vicinity of a borehole. To determine whether the changes are significant very-long-time experiments, such as heating 100 or 200 ft of a borehole for a week, need to be performed in various rock formations and the results compared with the results from the short-probe methods and the divided-bar method. It is quite probable that the differences will be negligible for most rocks, but we emphasize that the point is by no means proved.

IV. CALCULATION OF FLUX

1. Methods of Combining Gradient and Conductivity

The temperature gradient and thermal conductivity having been determined, it is necessary to combine them to give a value for the heat flux across the crust.

If only a few boreholes have been used the first step is to divide each hole up into its respective lithological sections. The arithmetic mean conductivity and the temperature gradient derived from a least-squares calculation is then used to calculate a value of heat flux for each section. There is little point in the harmonic mean of the conductivity being used, since the difference between this and the arithmetic mean is usually far less than the standard deviation of the measurements. If there is no systematic trend or aberrant value in the heat flux down the hole, then the arithmetic mean of all the values may be taken.

It has been suggested [30] that the observations be combined according to the equation

$$T = T_0 + H.\Sigma\,(\Delta D/k) \qquad (9)$$

where T is the temperature at depth D, k is the thermal conductivity over the homogeneous sections and T_0 is a constant, whence H, the mean heat flux, may be found from the slope of the resultant straight line. In general, the accuracy of each temperature measurement is the same, and this equation is therefore true only if an equal weight can be placed on the conductivities; this is frequently not so, and this point should be borne in mind before the equation is used. In any case, this refinement is hardly justified at the present time, since again the difference between the value of H found by this method and that found from the arithmetic mean of the values over homogeneous sections is usually far less than the standard deviations.

The best way of presenting the results is to give a table showing the temperature gradient, thermal conductivity and heat flux for each homogeneous section in each hole. Some idea of the accuracy of measurement should be given for both the temperature gradient and the thermal conductivity. It is pointless to give a standard deviation, σ, unless the number of observations, n, is also given. The simplest way of combining σ and n is to use confidence limits. For example, if a 95 per cent confidence limit β is imposed on each quantity, and this limit is entirely adequate for heat-flow work, then a value of, say, the conductivity quoted as $k \pm \beta$ implies that there is only one chance in twenty of k lying outside the range $(k - \beta)$ to $(k + \beta)$. Tables are given by Fisher [43] showing how to combine σ and n for various confidence limits.

The usual elementary statistical methods are used for combining and testing for consistency values of H from several, say, boreholes to give a mean value of H for the area. If it is found that the results cannot be combined because of systematic variations it is helpful to plot heat flux as a function of depth and position; this will show up regional trends which will probably be explained by topographical variations or the geological history of the area.

When large numbers of measurements are taken in mine roadways at various depths the best method of presentation is to plot isoflux planes. Misener et al.[63, 67] did this for a region in Ontario; the rock was uniform throughout the area, so that a plot of temperature versus position and depth is equivalent to a similar plot for flux. It was found that below about 4000 ft the effects of topography were negligible and all the heat flow was normal to the earth's surface. In some later work an interesting heat flux anomaly was found to be due to a large open stope [65] which was below 0°C for most of the year.

E

2. Disturbance of the Equilibrium Heat Flow

A. *Ice ages*

So far only the local heat flux has been measured, but the quantity of great interest to the geophysicist is the equilibrium heat flux; this is necessary to form an estimate of the flux in the deep interior. The measured flux is the resultant of possibly several disturbing influences. One of the most interesting of these is the effect of ice ages.

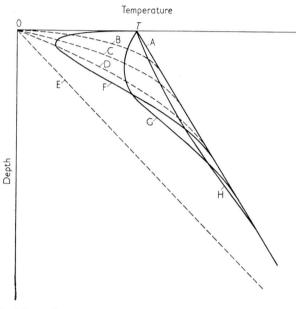

Fig. 23. Schematic representation of the effect of an ice age on the surface temperature gradient.

Line A in Fig. 23 is the temperature/depth curve of an earth which has had a surface temperature of $T°C$ and has been perfectly uniform in structure and climate for an infinite time. If now an ice age suddenly developed and the surface temperature dropped to 0°C while the temperature of a reference plane in the earth remained constant, then after an infinite time line E would be the temperature/depth curve. However, for a finite time the temperature/depth curve would progress from A to B to C to D. If, after curve D became established, the ice sheet suddenly retreated and the surface temperature returned to $T°C$, then the temperature/depth graph would progress from D to F to G to H. Thus the retreat of an ice sheet will reduce the temperature gradient and cause the measured heat flux to be less than the equilibrium heat flux. If the heat flux of the real earth could be measured accurately to great depths the maximum of the thermal wave could be detected and would give an estimate of the ice age. For example if the last ice age retreated 10 000 years ago the maximum disturbance would be at a depth of about 3 000 ft.[16] Alternatively if the date of the ice age is known a correction to the heat flux can be applied.[12]

B. *Uplift and erosion*

Fig. 24 represents a large block of land of thickness d, in a plane extending infinitely in all directions, which is suddenly uplifted a height h, causing a decrease in the surface temperature due to the increase in altitude. The original temperature/depth curve is A, and in the course of time the curve would change from A to B to C. If the temperature in the surrounding rock at depth $(d - h)$ remains constant, then the lower portion of the curve will change from A to B_1 to C_1, and finally curve D will be established. If the block is now suddenly eroded to the level of the original plane the curves will progress from D to E to F and finally the original curve will be re-established. Had the temperature at depth $(d - h)$ increased, due, say to a lava flow, then the lower portion of the temperature/depth curve would progress in the manner shown by B_2.

Thus the effect of uplift and of erosion is to increase the temperature gradient and hence the heat flow. However, in Persia the effects have been estimated at less than a 10 per cent disturbance of the gradient.[39] More refined calculations by Benfield [13, 14] indicate that uplift has a negligible effect under any conditions and that the effect of erosion will not be noticed unless there is a low heat flux combined with rapid erosion in the area.

C. *Topography*

Since the measurements of temperature gradient are made in the upper few thousand feet of the earth's crust, it is possible that topography will affect the results. Bullard [29] has described a method which allows for the effects assuming the topography is of infinite age. Birch [17] has taken into account, in one theory, the

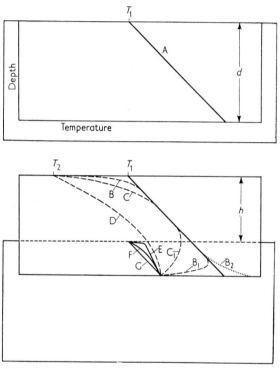

Fig. 24. Schematic representation of the effect of uplift and erosion on the surface temperature gradient.

finite age of the surface features and the effects of uplift and erosion. The disturbance to the temperature gradient can be either positive or negative but, except in extremely mountainous regions, it is not serious, the main contributions coming from an area within a radius of about 1 mile around the hole.[29]

D. *Local sources of heating*

It has frequently been suggested that possible local sources of heat occur due to the oxidation of oil, oxidation of ore bodies, tops of convection currents, absorption of neutrinos, local radioactive ore deposits, and increased radioactivity due to mountain roots. However, what work has been done tends to show that these sources contribute a negligible quantity to the heat flowing to the earth's surface.

Measurements in mines and oil wells [63, 79] do not show any noticeable effects, heat production due to absorption of neutrinos has been shown to be negligible,[38, 75] measurements in mountainous regions give conflicting results [15, 17, 35] and with the present state of the theories regarding the earth's interior convection currents could cause either low or high local heat flows according to which theory one prefers. Indeed, with the total lack of knowledge of the origin of the heat it seems a little foolish to try to force an explanation for differences in local heat flow, particularly as there are so few results.

References

1. *Prod. Bull. Amer. Petrol. Inst. No. 205*, 'Earth temperatures in oilfields' (1930).
2. Anderson, A. C. *Electronic and Radio Engineer*, **35**, 80 (1958).
3. Arago, D. F. J. *Œuvres Complètes*, Vol. 6 (Notices Scientifiques, Vol. 3), Baudry, Paris, 1854–59.
4. *Rep. Australas. Ass. Advanc. Sci.*, 309 (1902).
5. Beck, A. E. *J. sci. Instrum.* **33**, 16 (1956).
6. Beck, A. E. 'The measurement of the flow of heat through the crust of the earth and through rocks', *Ph.D. Thesis*, Australian National University, Canberra, 1956.
7. Beck, A. E. *J. sci. Instrum.* **34**, 186 (1957).
8. Beck, A. E. *Report N–47*, to Canadian National Research Council, Ottawa, 1958.
9. Beck, A. E., and Beck, J. M. *Trans. Amer. geophys. Un.*, **39**, 1111 (1958).
10. Beck, A. E., Jaeger, J. C., and Newstead, G. N. *Austral. J. Phys.* **9**, 286 (1956).
11. Becker, J. A., Green, C. B., and Pearson G. L. *Trans. Amer. Inst. elect. Engrs*, **65**, 711 (1946).
12. Benfield, A. E. *Proc. Roy. Soc. A*, **173**, 428 (1939).
13. Benfield, A. E. *J. appl. Phys.* **20**, 66 (1949).
14. Benfield, A. E. *Quart. J. appl. Math.* **6**, 439 (1949).
15. Birch, F. *Trans. Amer. geophys. Un.* **28**, 792 (1947).
16. Birch, F. *Amer. J. Sci.* **246**, 729 (1948).
17. Birch, F. *Bull. geol. Soc. Amer.* **61**, 567 (1950).
18. Birch, F., and Clark, H. *Amer. J. Sci.* **238**, 529 (1940).
19. Birch, F., and Clark, H. *Amer. J. Sci.* **238**, 613 (1940).
20. Blackwell, J. H. *J. appl. Phys.* **25**, 137 (1954).

21. Blackwell, J. H. *Canad. J. Phys.* **4**, 412 (1956).
22. Blackwell, J. H. *Internal Reports*, Australian National University, Canberra, 1956.
23. Blackwell, J. H. Private communication, 1958.
24. Bosson, G., Gutmann, F., and Simmons, L. M. *J. appl. Phys.* **21**, 1267 (1950).
25. *Rep. Brit. Ass. Advanc. Sci.* 510 (1868).
26. *Rep. Brit. Ass. Advanc. Sci.* 178 (1878).
27. *Rep. Brit. Ass. Advanc. Sci.* 74 (1882).
28. *Rep. Brit. Ass. Advanc. Sci.* 271 (1938).
29. Bullard, E. C. *Mon. Not. R. astr. Soc. Geophys. Suppl.* **4**, 360 (1938).
30. Bullard, E. C. *Proc. Roy. Soc. A,* **173**, 474 (1939).
31. Bullard, E. C. *Mon. Not. R. astr. Soc. Geophys. Suppl.* **5**, 127 (1947).
32. Bullard, E. C. 'The interior of the earth', in Kuiper, G. P., ed., *The Earth as a Planet* (The Solar System, Vol. II), University of Chicago Press, 1954.
33. Bullard, E. C., and Niblett, E. R. *Mon. Not. R. astr. Soc. Geophys. Suppl.,* **6**, 222 (1951).
34. Clark, H. *Trans. Amer. geophys. Un., Part II,* 543 (1941).
35. Clark, S. P. *Trans. Amer. geophys. Un.* **38**, 239 (1957).
36. Cooper, L. R., and Jones, C. *Geophys. J.,* **2**, 116 (1959).
37. Cordier, L. 'Essai sur la température de l'intérieur de la terre' in *Scientific Pamphlets* Vol. 3, A. Belin, Paris, 1827. Translation—John S. and Charles Adams, Amherst, 1828.
38. Cormack, A. M. *Phys. Rev.* **95**, 580 (1954).
39. Coster, H. P. *Mon. Not. R. astr. Soc. Geophys. Suppl.* **5**, 131 (1947).
40. Crowe, C. 'Transient heat flow methods for determining thermal constants', *Ph.D. Thesis*, University of Western Ontario, London, 1956.
41. Darton, N. H. *Bull. U.S. geol. Surv. No. 701* (1920).
42. Everett, J. D. *Trans. Roy. Soc. Edinb.* **22**, 429 (1861).
43. Fisher, R. A. *Statistical Methods for Research Workers*, 11th ed., Oliver and Boyd, Edinburgh (1950).
44. Forbes, J. D. *Trans. Roy. Soc. Edinb.* **16**, 189 (1849).
45. Gafner, G. *Brit. J. appl. Phys.* **8**, 393 (1957).
46. Gensane (1744). Not published at the time, but quoted by Mairan; see ref. 62.
47. Hallock, W. *Proc. Amer. Ass. Advanc. Sci.* **40**, 257 (1891).
48. Hallock, W. *Proc. Amer. Ass. Advanc. Sci.* **42**, 173 (1893).
49. Herschel, A. S., and Lebour, G. A. *Rep. Brit. Ass. Advanc. Sci., Transactions of the Sections*, p. 223 (1873).
50. Howard, L. Private communication, 1958.
51. Hutcheon, N. B., and Paxton, J. A. *Heat. Pip. Air Condit.* **24**, 113 (1952).
52. Jacobs, J. A. 'The interior of the earth' in Landsberg, H. E., ed., *Advances in Geophysics*, Vol. 3, Academic Press, New York, 1956.
53. Jaeger, J. C. *Austral. J. Phys.* **9**, 167 (1956).
54. Jaeger, J. C. *J. Math. Phys.* **34**, 316 (1956).

55. Jaeger, J. C., and Beck, A. E. *Brit. J. appl. Phys.* **6**, 15 (1955).
56. Johnston, J., and Adam, L. H. *Econ. Geol.* **11**, 741 (1916).
57. Krige, L. J. *Proc. Roy. Soc. A*, **173**, 450 (1939).
58. Kuzmak, J. M., and Sereda, P. J. *Soil Sci.* **84**, 291 (1957).
59. Kuzmak, J. M., and Sereda, P. J. *Soil Sci.* **84**, 419 (1957).
60. Lees, C. H. *Phil. Trans. A*, **183**, 481 (1892).
61. Lodge, O. J. *Phil. Mag.* **5** (Ser. V), 110 (1878); also in *Proc. phys. Soc. Lond.* **1**, 201 (1878).
62. Mairan, J. J. D. *Dissertation sur la glace ou explication physique ou la formation de la glace, et de ses divers phénomènes.* L'Imprimerie Royale, Paris, 1749, Ch. 11.
63. Misener, A. D. *Canad. Min. metall. Bull.* **42**, 280 (1949).
64. Misener, A. D. *Progress Report No. 110–91,* to Canadian National Research Council, 1956.
65. Misener, A. D., and Thompson, L. G. D. *Canad. Min. metall. Bull.* **43**, 542 (1950).
66. Misener, A. D., and Thompson, L. G. D. *Canad. J. Technol.* **30**, 89 (1952).
67. Misener, A. D., Thompson, L. G. D., and Uffen. R. J. *Trans. Amer. geophys. Un.* **32**, 729 (1951).
68. Müller, R. H., and Stolten, H. J. *Analyt. Chem.* **25**, 1103 (1953).
69. Newstead, G. N. Private communication, 1958.
70. Newstead, G. N., and Beck, A. E. *Austral. J. Phys.* **6**, 480 (1953).
71. Newstead, G. N., and Jaeger, J. C. *Engineer, Lond.* **202**, 76 (1956).
72. Powell, R. W. *J. sci. Instrum.* **34**, 485 (1957).
73. Prestwich, J. *Phil. Trans.* **165**, 587 (1875).
74. Prestwich, J. *Proc. Roy. Soc. A*, **41**, 1 (1886).
75. Saxon, D. *Phys. Rev.* **76**, 986 (1949).
76. Schlumberger, M., Doll, H. G., and Perebinossoff, A. A. *J. Instn Petrol. Tech.* **23**, 1 (1937).
77. Sillars, R. W. *J. sci. Instrum.* **19**, 81 (1942).
78. Thomson, W. *Trans. Roy. Soc. Edinb.* **22**, 405 (1861).
79. Van Orstrand, C. E. *Bull. Amer. Ass. Petrol. Geol.* **18**, 13 (1934).
80. Weiss, O. *J. chem. Soc. S. Afr.* **39**, 149 (1938).

BOREHOLE SURVEYING

T. F. GASKELL and P. THREADGOLD, *British Petroleum Company, London*

CONTENTS

I. HISTORICAL

Electrical well logging was introduced by the Schlumberger brothers in the late 1920s as an extension of the resistivity method of electrical prospecting (see Chapter 8). The resistivity values obtained with electrodes lowered into a borehole, when plotted against depth, gave a 'log' of the stratigraphical changes, and in particular provided an accurate depth of each rock layer below the surface.

The early success of the Schlumbergers was due in part to the insulated cable that enabled them to record, at the surface, observations made deep down boreholes. There are certain difficulties in the design of a cable which is strong enough to carry measuring instruments and yet can be lowered and raised in a borehole without damage to the insulation. The basic principle of transmitting a signal from instrument to surface, and vice versa, has found many useful applications.

The resistivity measured by an electrode system lowered into a borehole is due to several factors, because the medium surrounding the electrode system is far from homogeneous. It consists of the drilling fluid, the strata opposite the electrode system and the adjacent strata above and below. The recorded resistivity was therefore termed the apparent resistivity, R_a and the problem of determining the significance of R_a in terms of the different resistivities involved, occupied many early workers. Correction curves were plotted which allowed the true resistivity R_t of a given bed to be computed from the recorded resistivity R_a. Empirical formulas were established to relate the resistivity of porous strata to the resistivity of the saturating fluid, and to the saturation fraction of the conductive phase when two liquid phases (say hydrocarbons and water) were present.

Field work with the resistivity logging technique led to the discovery that if the potential of the borehole fluid with respect to earth (known as the Spontaneous Potential) was plotted against depth, deviations from a regular value were shown opposite porous and permeable beds. This was of great significance to the oil industry in that the logs immediately defined possible reservoir rocks.

The basis of quantitative interpretation of electric logs was established when the relationship between the Spontaneous Potential and the resistivity of the formation water was developed first by Doll [8] and later by Wyllie.[39] This step was followed by the introduction of devices to measure the additional parameters required for quantitative interpretation of the logs (porosity, etc.), and also to improve the formation resistivity values obtained from the logs. The latter led directly to the development of focused current devices.

Ancillary logging tools were also produced to obtain other necessary information. Among these the most important were calipers to measure the diameter of the borehole and thermometers to record the borehole temperature. Recent developments in instrumental techniques and in the application and measurement of radioactivity have produced corresponding advances in the field of logging. It has now become the work of a specialist not only to produce the logs required but also to interpret their significance.

A knowledge of some of the rock formation characteristics, and of the effects of the presence of the borehole, is required before the principles and application of the various devices can be understood.

II. CHARACTERISTICS OF EARTH STRATA

Most well-logging techniques have their counterparts in surface geophysical methods. However, the presence of the borehole filled with fluid produces a disturbing effect on most of the logging measurements taken, so that it is of primary importance to consider some of the characteristics of rocks from the particular aspects of logging. Electrical resistivity, natural and induced radioactivity, and acoustic wave velocity are the main physical properties that are of interest, because they can be used to make correlations of geological strata and to measure the type and relative fluid content of rocks. Density, magnetic properties and heat conductivity are of interest in particular problems concerned with the structure of the earth, but have not been found to be of great importance for universal well-logging application.

1. Formation Resistivity

With the exception of certain metallic ores, the solid matrix material comprising earth strata is not electrically conductive. Any flow of electric current takes place through conductive liquids filling the pores, that is, by virtue of saline interstitial water. It is clear therefore that non-porous rock and rock in which the pores are not interconnected will exhibit infinite resistivity.

Where connected porosity is present, the bulk resistivity of the rock is quoted in units of ohm.metres ^{2}/metre (the resistance across opposite faces of a metre cube). Denoting this by ρ, the resistance across a cube of side L is $\rho L/A$, where A is the cross sectional area, and here equal to L^2.

The various paths across the cube can be considered to be re-placed by a series of fluid-filled channels having a mean effective length L_e, greater than L, and having a total cross sectional area equal to ϕA where ϕ is the fractional porosity. If the fluid filling these channels has a resistivity R_w, then the total resistivity through the channels is given by $R_w L_e/\phi A$, so that

$$R_w L_e/\phi A = \rho L/A$$

and

$$\rho = R_w(L_e/L)(1/\phi)$$

$(L_e/L)^2$ is termed the electrical tortuosity, T.

For a given formation, ρ is proportional to R_w, and the constant of proportionality is defined as the formation resistivity factor F.

Where the pore space is filled with only one fluid phase (in general, saline water) the rock resistivity is given the symbol R_0. Thus for a completely water-saturated porous rock:

$$R_0 = F \times R_w = (L_e/L)(1/\phi)R_w = (T^{1/2}/\phi)R_w \qquad (1)$$

It has been found that the formation factor and porosity can be related by the empirical equation

$$F = a/\phi^m \qquad (2)$$

where, for unconsolidated material, $a = 0 \cdot 6$ to $0 \cdot 75$, $m = 1 \cdot 8$ to

2·0; and, for consolidated material, $a = 1·0$, $m = 2·0$ to 2·15, are good approximations.

If some of the saline water in the pore space is replaced by a non-conductive fluid, in particular oil or gas, the resistance of the rock will obviously rise from its value R_0 to a new value, R_t. If S_w is the fraction of the pore space still containing water, it has been found that the empirical equation

$$S_w = (R_0/R_t)^{1/n} = (FR_w/R_t)^{1/n} \qquad (3)$$

defines the new condition, where R_0 is the resistivity at $S_w = 1$ and R_t is the new resistivity at $S_w < 1$. n is called the resistivity index exponent. The resistivity index I is given by $I = R_t/R_0 = S_w^{-n}$. In most practical cases n has a value of approximately 2.

Shales, clays and mudstones need special mention, since they are composed of minute particles, so that the individual pores and capillaries between grains are extremely small, even though under normal compaction forces the total porosity may be of the order of 30 to 40 per cent of the rock volume. The capillary forces present in the small capillaries are very high and at normal subsurface pressure gradients very little fluid will flow through the pores. Electric current will flow, however, and hence such materials have a finite, normally quite low, resistivity. Furthermore, the small grain size gives individual grains a large ratio of surface area to volume, which makes the clay materials surface active. They have, as a result, an ion-adsorption capacity which disturbs the ionic concentration of the saline fluid in the vicinity of the surface. This acts in such a way as to give the effect of surface conduction over the grains, and must be considered in attempting to compute the resistivity of a material containing clays. Equations 1, 2 and 3 are then no longer valid.

If clay materials are not present it is clear that a knowledge of R_w, F and R_t will enable the total quantities of water and hydrocarbons present in a reservoir rock to be evaluated.

2. Radioactivity

A. *Natural radioactivity*

The radioactive materials commonly found in formations penetrated by boreholes are the uranium and thorium series, and potassium. Generally these are associated with the smaller grains present, as surface-adsorbed materials. It is therefore to be expected that the shales and clays should exhibit the highest radioactivity of the sedimentary rocks, while shale-free sands and limestones show the least.

Each radioactive element emits radioactivity having a distinctive energy level. In travelling through the surrounding material, however, the gamma rays are scattered by colliding with the electrons present. Energy is lost at each collision, and a detector placed in the formation will receive some radiation at or near the original emission energy, and a considerable amount at lower levels.

The radioactivity range of earth strata measured *in situ* is as follows:

High activity	Marine shales
↑	Marine deposits other than shale
	Clays
	Marls
	Silts
	Sand
↓	Limestone
Low activity	Dolomite

B. *Gamma-ray scattering—attenuation effects*

If I_0 is the incident intensity of gamma radiation, and I the emergent intensity after travelling a distance l in any material, then

$$I/I_0 = e^{-\mu l}$$

where μ is the gamma-ray absorption coefficient of the material and is given per unit length by

$$\mu = \ln I_0 - \ln I$$

The absorption coefficient μ is approximately proportional to the density ρ of the absorbing material for a given energy of radiation, μ/ρ being roughly equal to 0·66 for an incident energy of 1·3 MeV. The absorption coefficient for earth strata is generally between 0·06 and 0·15 cm⁻¹.

C. *Neutron bombardment of earth strata*

If a source emitting fast neutrons (i.e. those having energies well above the level of the thermal equilibrium condition, approximately 0·025 eV) is lowered into a borehole, a fairly complicated set of events takes place. For ease of understanding, the effects due to the presence of the borehole will be ignored.

The fast neutron emitted by the source first loses energy in one or more of three ways:

(1) By elastic collision with a rock nucleus; this process obeys the laws of conservation of energy and momentum. The maximum energy loss depends on the mass of the nucleus in question, and increases as the nuclear mass decreases. Hydrogen nuclei have a mass comparable with that of the neutron, and hence are the most important in this energy loss or slowing-down process.

(2) By inelastic collision, when the law of conservation of momentum does not hold, as some of the energy of the neutron is lost in raising the energy state of the nucleus with which it collides. The nucleus then generally returns to its ground-energy state by the emission of one or more gamma rays, which have various energy levels depending on the nucleus excited.

(3) In some cases the fast neutron can be captured by the nucleus with which it collides. The compound nucleus so formed then disintegrates with the emission of energy in the form of gamma radiation, or charged particles.

The probability that one of the above interactions takes place is determined by the nuclear cross sectional area for the process. The cross sectional area is dependent on the energy of the impinging neutron. In a mixture therefore the relative probability that one of the processes will take place will be determined by the product of the nuclear cross sections and the density n of the different nuclei present. For neutron energies in the range used for logging purposes, the cross sectional area to elastic collision is the most important, and most of the energy loss occurs by this process.

Where several types of nucleus are present, as they are in rocks, the overall slowing down power of each type is the deciding factor. This is a function of the concentration of the nuclei, their nuclear cross section to elastic collision and the average energy loss per collision. Hydrogen is by far the most important in the slowing-down phase in porous rocks. In low-porosity rocks, or with high-energy neutrons, the slowing-down power of the other nuclei present becomes comparable.

When the neutron has been slowed down to the thermal-energy level the second process can take place. This is the capture of the thermal neutrons by the nuclei with which they collide. The predominant nucleus for thermal capture in porous rocks is hydrogen, because normally it is in relatively high concentration, compared with, for example, chlorine, although chlorine has a thermal cross sectional area of capture some hundred times that of hydrogen. When the hydrogen nucleus captures a thermal neutron the energy balance is restored by the liberation of a gamma ray. With the chlorine nucleus one or more of several gamma rays can be emitted, having energy peaks in the range 5 to 8 MeV.

The directly emitted or 'prompt' gamma rays are then attenuated by the rock through which they pass. The number of prompt gamma rays produced at any distance from the source is proportional to the number of slow neutrons at that distance. Hence a measurement of the number of gamma rays is also a measure of the thermal neutron intensity at a particular location.

As hydrogen is in general the most important element, both in the slowing-down phase and the capture phase, the thermal neutron intensity at a fixed distance from the source is a reflection of the amount of hydrogen between the detector and the source. Since pore space normally contains hydrogen in water or hydrocarbons, the thermal neutron intensity in earth strata is a measure of porosity, unless hydrogen chemically bound to the rock is present. As the porosity is increased more neutrons are slowed to thermal energies near to the source, and hence less higher-energy neutrons remain to be slowed down at large distances from the source. A thermal neutron detector near to the source will therefore give a reading which increases with increase in porosity, while one at a greater distance will show a decrease with increase in porosity. In most logging tools the source–detector spacing is large enough for the intensity of slow neutrons (or prompt gamma rays) to decrease with increase in porosity, and vice versa. The recorded count rate is then approximately inversely proportional to the log of the porosity.

3. Acoustic Properties

The fact that different kinds of rocks have different velocities for compressional waves is used in seismic prospecting, and it is this same property of rocks that forms the basis of one of the newest well-logging tools.

It is clear from the following list that the compressional wave velocity does not provide an unambiguous label to a particular rock type, but the variations in velocity from one rock type to another are sufficient to be of great value in limiting the field of speculation. When combined with other evidence, the velocity measurements can be of definite diagnostic value.

Material	Velocity of compressional waves ft/sec	km/sec
Coal	3 000 to 5 800	0·9 to 1·8
Sand	650 to 6 500	0·2 to 2·0
Sandstone	4 500 to 14 000	1·4 to 4·3
Clay	3 240 to 9 000	1·0 to 2·8
Shale	7 400 to 15 000	2·3 to 4·7
Limestone	⎰ 5 500 to 13 700 ⎱ 9 000 to 21 000	1·7 to 4·2 soft 2·8 to 6·4 hard
Chalk	6 300 to 8 300	1·9 to 2·5
Granite	13 000 to 19 500	4·0 to 6·0
Vesicular volcanic	13 000 to 15 700	4·0 to 4·8
Basalt	18 000 to 22 000	5·7 to 7·2
Steel	16 300	5·0
Salt	14 200 to 21 000	4·4 to 6·5
Earth's mantle	24 500	8·1

Sedimentary rocks are of primary interest in well logging, and the range of compressional wave velocities is from a few thousand feet per second for poorly compacted sand to 21 000 ft/sec for a tight, massive limestone. Lithological changes are frequently well emphasized by the compressional wave velocity; for example, coal has a velocity of about 4 000 ft/sec, while for millstone grit the value is about 9 000 ft/sec. Although there is a considerable overlap in velocity range for various groups of rock, in one locality the velocity of a given facies will vary only a few per cent from a mean value. The acoustic properties of rocks lend themselves, therefore, to geological correlations between boreholes.

The compressional wave velocity is determined by the elasticity and density of the rock, and is therefore susceptible to the effects of temperature and pressure. Increase of pressure tends to increase the velocity, while increase of temperature produces a lower velocity. Generally the pressure effect predominates, to give an increase of velocity with depth, for example in granite of 1·14 ft/sec in 100 ft, but occasionally a decrease of velocity with depth is observed, for example in some limestones (Hughes and Cross [22]). The change in velocity is not of great importance in well logging except perhaps in places where recent unconsolidated sediment exists, when a very large increase in velocity may take place in a small depth of rock, due to compaction under the pressure of the overburden.

The fact that there is a change of compressional wave velocity with pressure suggests a possible method of measuring overburden pressure. Careful velocity measurements at different depths in a uniform rock formation could be compared with laboratory measurements made on samples of the rock subjected to a series of pressures. This type of experiment is made possible with the velocity log because sufficient accuracy can be obtained over a section of rock short enough to be uniform in composition. However, there are other properties of rocks which affect the compressional wave velocity. Laboratory measurements on rock samples have shown that the velocity depends on the porosity and on what fluids fill the pore space, as well as on the kind of rock. A decrease in porosity leads to an increase in velocity, and in a particular formation, if there is no change in the fluid filling the pore space, a velocity/porosity calibration curve can be produced. If the pore space of a rock is filled partly with water and partly with oil the velocity decreases as the proportion of oil is increased.

If various assumptions are made, for example (Hicks and Berry [21] and Wyllie et al.[41]), that the fluid content is constant and there is no change in pressure on the fluid and rock matrix, the relationship between velocity V and porosity ϕ is

$$1/V = \phi/V_1 + (1 - \phi)/V_s$$

where V_1 is the velocity in the liquid and V_s is the velocity in the solid.

The acoustic waves sent through rock are attenuated at a rate of about 0·05 to 0·5 db per wavelength, the lower value pertaining to uniform crystalline rocks, such as granite, and the higher value to sedimentary rocks, such as poorly compacted sandstones. This type of attenuation can be measured on small samples in the laboratory, and measurements at a wide range of frequencies (40 c/s to 1 Mc/s) have demonstrated that the attenuation per

F

wavelength is independent of frequency. Some early work by Ricker [28] suggested an attenuation which was frequency-dependent, but the measurements on which the theoretical reasoning was based were made in a shale in which there was an increase of velocity with depth and in which bedding planes may have had their effect on the compressional wave transmission. A resonant frequency of 8 kc/s, corresponding to a wavelength of a few inches, was found. This may have been due to the bedding planes in the shale, and it suggests that resonance effects should be present at frequencies which are high enough to give wavelengths of the order of magnitude of the pore size or the grain size in a rock.

Change in amplitude during transmission of compressional waves takes place due to scattering and back-reflection at inhomogeneities in rock. The reflection coefficient for normal incidence of a wave at an interface between two rock layers in which v_1, v_2 are the compressional wave velocities and ρ_1, ρ_2 are the rock densities is equal to $(\rho_1 v_1 - \rho_2 v_2)/(\rho_1 v_1 + \rho_2 v_2)$. In general, the velocity is the important parameter, because the range of values of rock density is comparatively small.

III. EFFECTS DUE TO PRESENCE OF BOREHOLE

Mud is circulated while a borehole is being drilled. The mud is a water- or oil-based fluid chemically weighted to increase its gravity and viscosity, and in general it is thixotropic and gels on standing. The drilling fluid has a multiple duty. It lubricates and cools the drilling bit; it carries the drilled cuttings to surface as it circulates; by virtue of its hydrostatic head it prevents the formation fluid from entering the borehole, and helps to support the walls of the borehole. In order to fulfil the latter requirement, the gravity is adjusted so that the hydrostatic pressure of the mud is somewhat in excess of the formation pressures at depth. Hence when a porous permeable formation is encountered the drilling fluid is forced into the pores of the rock. The solid particles in the mud are filtered out on the walls of the borehole, forming a mud sheath or cake, which in a short time seals off the fluid paths and prevents further invasion of the rock by the fluid. During the formation of the mud cake, however, the fluids in the strata immediately surrounding the borehole are pushed back by the mud filtrate, resulting in a filtrate-invaded zone. The relative distribution of filtrate and original formation fluids in the invaded zone varies considerably, but it generally takes the form of a zone of maximum flushing (not necessarily complete), followed by an exponential decrease radially outwards of mud filtrate. The presence of the invaded zone forms one of the major troubles in estimating true resistivity from logs. In resistivity work the invaded zone is considered to be replaced by an equivalent annulus, having a diameter D_i and a resistivity designated R_i.

The presence of aqueous drilling fluid in the borehole is necessary to conventional resistivity logging devices in order to conduct the current to the formations surrounding the hole, but it unfortunately gives rise to disturbing effects. Some of the current will flow in the borehole and in the filtrate-invaded zone. Any computation of true resistivity from logs must therefore take into account the mud resistivity R_m and borehole diameter d, the invaded-zone equivalent resistivity R_i and diameter D_i, as well as the required true resistivity R_t. These effects due to the borehole can often completely mask the properties of the virgin rock strata.

As previously discussed, hydrogenous materials strongly affect fast neutrons, and are also good absorbers for gamma radiation. The drilling fluid is mainly water or oil, and hence has a large influence on any radioactivity-measuring tool suspended in it. It is therefore important to know the position of the instrument in the borehole, the neutron–gamma-ray log in particular being greatly affected by whether the tool is central or lying against the wall of the borehole.

IV. THE SPONTANEOUS POTENTIAL (SP) CURVE

The spontaneous potential curve is a record of the potential of the drilling fluid in the borehole with respect to a constant potential, usually surface earth, and it enables the value of the formation water resistivity R_w to be computed.

The measured potential has its origin in the ion-adsorption capacity of the colloidal material which forms naturally occurring shale. Shale itself is compacted clay which preferentially adsorbs negative ions from any ionic solution with which it is in contact. The negative ions are immobilized at the clay surface and in turn attract positive ions from the solution, forming a contra-layer which is not immobilized. An equilibrium condition is set up between the attraction due to the negative ions and the thermal agitation of the positive ions. Any ionic solution in the immediate vicinity of the clay surface is hence richer in mobile positive ions than negative. This is the condition of the fluid in the small interconnecting pores formed when the clay particles are compacted into a shale. Any ionic solution remote from the shale surface has, however, equal concentrations of mobile positive and negative charges. There is therefore an electronic potential difference between the solution in the body of the shale and that external to it, due to the difference in concentration of mobile positive ions.

If a shale is in contact with two ionic solutions, for example, formation water and drilling mud, a different phase-boundary potential will exist between the shale and each of the solutions. In addition, a diffusion potential will be set up, due to diffusion through the shale from one solution to the other. These potentials are all functions of the ionic concentrations of the solutions in question, or to be more correct of their ionic activities. Fig. 1 is a diagram of a borehole filled with drilling mud of which the filtrate

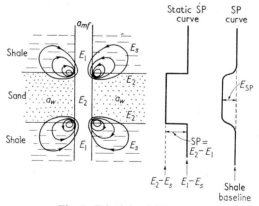

Fig. 1. Principle of SP curve.

has an ionic activity a_{mf}, penetrating a porous zone between two shales. The interstitial water in the pore space has an activity a_w.

If the potential of the fluid in the shale is E_s there will be a difference of potential $(E_1 - E_s)$ between the mud in contact with the shale and the fluid in the shale. Similarly, there will be a difference in potential between the fluid in the porous material and that in the shale $(E_2 - E_s)$. These potential differences give rise to current flow from the porous zone through the shale to the mud and back to the porous zone. The resistance of the path through the mud column is, in general, large compared with the paths through the shale and sand due to its relatively small cross sectional area. Hence in the limit the potential drop due to the current flow in the mud column approaches the value $E_2 - E_1$ which is the static value of the SP, that is, the value of potential difference which would exist in the absence of any current flow.

It must be noted that the current flow in the borehole is in the vicinity of the shale/mud/porous layer junctions only, and that there is no flow across the mud/porous layer boundary remote from the shales. Hence the potential of the mud column opposite the porous layer must also be equal to E_2. The static SP measured in the mud column is therefore equal to $E_2 - E_1$. In practice, the current flow rounds off the change of potential in the mud column at the shale/porous bed boundary, and unless the porous layer is fairly thick the measured potential difference will be lower than $E_2 - E_1$. The potential of the mud column opposite the shale is known as the shale baseline.

It can be shown that the equation relating the deflection of the SP curves opposite the porous layer from the shale baseline to a_w and a_{mf} is

$$E_{SP} = E_2 - E_1(\text{mV}) = - K \log (a_w/a_{mf}) \qquad (4)$$

where K is a temperature-dependent constant.

The recorded SP curve therefore enables permeable zones to be identified by the deflection away from the shale baseline. If a_w is greater than a_{mf} (interstitial fluid more saline than the mud filtrate), this deflection will be negative, and vice versa.

For dilute solutions of monovalent salts, in particular sodium chloride, the activity can be taken as inversely proportional to the resistivity, hence equation 2 can be written in the usual form

$$E_{SP} = -K \log (R_{mf}/R_w) \qquad (5)$$

The SP curve gives E_{SP}; K can be evaluated and is given in the interpretation charts issued by most field logging companies;

R_{mf} can be measured from a sample of filtered mud, and hence R_w the resistivity of the porous zone interstitial water can be computed. In general, most formation waters are sodium chloride solutions, and salt concentration can therefore be obtained from tables giving the relationship between R_w, temperature and concentration.

In practice, the porous zone may not be very thick and its resistivity may be high, when the assumption that all the potential drop due to the circulating currents occurs in the mud column is not true. Correction curves have, however, been computed to allow for the finite thickness and resistivity of the porous zone. The preceding discussion has also implicitly assumed that the porous layer is completely free from shale. If this is not true, local electrochemical cells are set up along the face of the porous zone, which reduce the amplitude of the observed SP deflection. To describe its condition the reduced deflection is termed the pseudo-static SP (PSP), whereas the theoretical value defined by equation 5 is the static SP (SSP). The static SP is so denoted because it is the value of potential difference existing in the absence of circulating current flow. The presence of shaly material in a porous layer can often be detected from the natural gamma-ray curve.

V. MEASUREMENT OF FORMATION RESISTIVITY FACTOR F

1. General Principle

The formation resistivity factor F is defined by relation 1 as the ratio of the resistivity of a fully fluid saturated porous rock to the resistivity of the saturating fluid. It is measured by considering that portion of the porous strata which has been invaded by the mud filtrate.

When the borehole penetrates a porous interval the mud filtrate invades the zone and forms a small annulus immediately round the borehole which is fully flushed by the mud filtrate. The resistivity of the zone completely saturated with mud filtrate is designated R_{xo}, and here the formation factor is, by definition,

$$F = R_{xo}/R_{mf}$$

where R_{mf} is the mud filtrate resistivity.

In porous strata originally containing hydrocarbons a fully flushed zone does not exist. Some residual oil saturation always remains in the pores. In this case by relation 3

$$S_{xo} = (FR_{mf}/R_{xo})^{1/n}$$

where S_{xo} is the fractional mud filtrate saturation of the zone. Putting $n = 2$

$$F = S_{xo}^2 R_{xo}/R_{mf}$$

Usually S_{xo} varies between 0·7 and 0·9 ($S_{xo} = 1$ for water-bearing strata). The mud filtrate resistivity can be measured from mud circulation samples, and hence F can be estimated from a knowledge of R_{xo}. R_{xo} is measured by means of micro-resistivity devices.

2. The Microlog or Contact Log

These are two names for similar devices which measure the resistivity of an annulus a few inches thick round the borehole.

The measuring instrument (see Fig. 2) has three small electrodes mounted vertically 1 in. apart on a rubber pad. The pad is on a spring which forces it against the borehole wall. Constant current

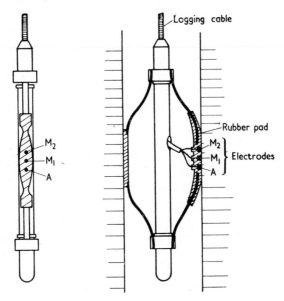

Fig. 2. The microlog sonde.

is sent from the lowest electrode A to earth, and the resulting potentials are measured between (1) M_1 and M_2 (sometimes known as the 1 in. $\times$ 1 in. lateral), (2) M_2 and earth (the 2 in. normal). In order to overcome the effects due to polarization of the electrodes, the current can be either sinusoidal or square-wave alternating current. The frequency varies in different commercial schemes from 30 to 400 c/s. Both of the spacings are affected only by a few inches of the formation, the depth of penetration of the larger spacing being greater than that of the smaller. The potentials measured, V, are related to the apparent resistivity R_a of the material affecting each spacing by the standard formula

$$V/I = R_a/K$$

where K is a geometrical constant and I is the current. I is maintained constant and hence R_a is proportional to V for each spacing, and can therefore be recorded directly against depth in the hole. The nature of the two curves obtained opposite the various types of strata is as follows.

A. *Permeable and porous strata*

This type will have a mud cake and an invaded zone because penetration of the drilling fluids can take place into a porous rock. Due to the different depths of investigation, the short spacing will 'see' mud cake plus a little invaded zone, whereas the larger spacing will see mud cake plus more invaded zone. The reading of both curves will be less than 20 to 30 times the mud resistivity. In general, the invaded zone will have a higher resistivity than the mud cake, and hence the longer spacing will indicate a higher resistivity than the shorter (known as a positive separation, or departure). The separation can tend to zero if the mud cake is very thin. Charts are available from the service companies which relate the readings of the two spacings, the borehole diameter (which is often measured simultaneously with the same sonde) and the mud cake and filtrate resistivities, to mud cake thickness and to R_{xo}, the required resistivity of the fully flushed zone.

B. *Shales*

Although the porosity of shales is of the order of 40 per cent their permeability is very small, and no mud cake is formed, so that the reading of both curves is very low and is usually slightly less than the shale resistivity; the curve departure is zero or even negative.

C. *Compact impermeable strata*

The curves derived from compact impermeable strata show great irregularity and tend to read resistivities greater than 20 to 30 times R_m, the mud resistivity.

3. The Microlaterolog

In low-porosity strata the value of R_{xo} is high compared with the resistance R_{mc} of the mud cake, and most of the current from the microlog electrodes tends to flow in the mud cake, and hence the resultant readings bear little relationship to R_{xo}. The micro-

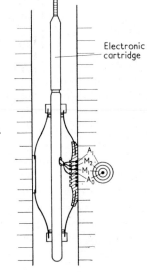

Fig. 3. The microlaterolog.

laterolog has been developed to overcome this difficulty. The device (Fig. 3) uses a rubber pad as in the microlog, but current is fed to the formation from a small central circular electrode A_0 surrounded by, and insulated from, three further circular electrodes M_1, M_2, and A_1. The potential difference between M_1 and M_2 is monitored and held at zero by controlling a separate current emitted from A_1, the outer electrode. This means that there is no current flow between M_1 and M_2, and hence all of the current from A_0 must be flowing radially outwards as a pencil beam, having an initial diameter roughly equal to the mean diameter of M_1 and M_2. Having entered the formation, the beam diverges so that all the material farther than approximately 3 in. from the borehole wall has little effect on the various electrode potentials. The potential of A_0, M_1 or M_2 (usually one of the latter) can then be related to the apparent resistivity of the material in this short distance. This for thin mud cakes (less than $\frac{3}{8}$ in.) is equal to R_{xo} without need for correction. Corrections can be applied for thicker mud cakes if additional curves are run (e.g. microlog or microlog–caliper, which is the combined microlog and caliper sonde).

4. Use of the Neutron–Gamma Log

The intensity of measured gamma radiation emitted as a result of neutron bombardment of formations is in general a function of their hydrogen content. For a given type of formation this measured intensity can be calibrated in terms of porosity. Suitable corrections have to be applied to allow for the disturbing effects due to the presence of the borehole. Correction charts are available from the logging companies supplying the service, and it is therefore possible to obtain formation porosity directly from the neutron–gamma-ray curve. The corresponding formation factor can then be deduced by the use of relation 2.

In some cases the pore space is filled with gas and, compared with oil or water, there is a large distance between the molecules. The moderating effect on fast neutrons and the attenuation of the prompt gammas is therefore somewhat modified. The result is that a gas-bearing porous zone will produce an anomalous high neutron–gamma intensity compared with that given by the same zone fully saturated with liquid.

VI. MEASUREMENT OF FORMATION RESISTIVITY

1. Conventional Devices

Conventional resistivity logs are obtained by measuring the potential set up between two electrodes due to current flow between two other electrodes. The device is a 4-electrode network,

and one of the electrodes is usually at the surface of the ground.
If current I is emitted from an electrode A [Fig. 4(a)] surrounded
by a homogeneous medium of resistivity R ohm. metres²/metre the

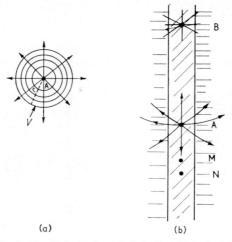

(a)   (b)

Fig. 4. The 4-electrode resistivity logging principle.

resulting equipotential surfaces are spheres concentric with the
electrode. The potential of a spherical surface at a distance r from
A is

$$V = RI/4\pi r$$

For the electrode configuration of Fig. 4(b) the potential of M
due to current I flowing between A and B is given by:

$$V_m = IR \left[\frac{1}{4\pi \text{AM}} - \frac{1}{4\pi \text{BM}} \right]$$

$$= \frac{IR}{4\pi} \left(\frac{\text{BM} - \text{AM}}{\text{AM} \times \text{BM}} \right) \qquad (6)$$

Similarly for electrode N

$$V_n = \frac{IR}{4\pi} \left(\frac{\text{BN} - \text{AN}}{\text{AN} \times \text{BN}} \right) \qquad (7)$$

Hence

$$V_m - V_n = \frac{IR}{4\pi} \left(\frac{1}{\text{AM}} - \frac{1}{\text{BM}} - \frac{1}{\text{AN}} - \frac{1}{\text{BN}} \right) \qquad (8)$$

If AM and AN are small compared with AB, then both $\dfrac{1}{BM}$ and $\dfrac{1}{BN}$ can be neglected and

$$V_m - V_n = \frac{IR}{4\pi} \frac{AN - AM}{AM \times AN} \tag{9}$$

The two potential measurements V_m and $V_m - V_n$ form the conventional resistivity survey. With equation 6 either the B or the N electrode is at surface, and the spacing AM is small compared with the overall length of the down-the-hole electrodes. This is often known as the 'normal' device, and usually two curves are taken having different AM spacings of 10 or 16 in. and 38 or 64 in. (the short and long normal).

If the B electrode is at surface and the length MN is small compared with AM the arrangement is known as the lateral device (equation 9). The spacing is then defined as the length from A to the mid-point of MN, and is usually of the order of 18 ft.

Most of the potential drop in the media surrounding an electrode emitting current occurs within a moderately short distance of the electrode. Hence only material within a given radius of the electrode will affect any potential measurements made. The depth of penetration of the electrode device used is often arbitrarily defined as the radius within which half of the total potential drop occurs. For normal devices this is approximately twice the spacing, and for lateral devices approximately one to one and a half times the spacing.

The resistivity of the filtrate invaded zone obviously varies with distance outwards from the borehole wall due to changes in mud filtrate saturation of the pore space. For ease of computation in the case of conventional electric logging the filtrate-invaded zone is considered to be replaced by an equivalent cylinder of homogeneous resistivity, R_i, and diameter, D_i. For simplicity the resistivity and length units are normalized in terms of the drilling mud resistivity R_m and the borehole diameter d, so that R_a/R_m is a function of $(R_i/R_m, R_t/R_m, D_i/d, e/d)$, where R_a is the apparent resistivity as recorded and R_t is the true formation resistivity. Where beds of interest are thinner than three or four times the electrode spacing, the effect of adjacent bed resistivities has also to be considered.

It is clear that at least three different spacings must be used to obtain a value for R_t. (R_m and d can be determined by alternative means.) In practice, R_t is determined by matching the R_a values given by various spacings to computed values of Resistivity Departure Curves, which are supplied by the various service companies. Unfortunately, for beds of finite thickness, several equivalent solutions for R_t are obtainable, irrespective of the number of different electrode spacings that are used. Often, however, the correct value for R_t can be chosen by making use of other supporting information obtained during drilling. This is largely a matter of experience and intelligent deduction from the facts that are available. For example, if a lengthy sand shale sequence is logged, and the various values assigned to the true resistivity do not give clear-cut evidence of hydrocarbons, one may use the evidence obtained from the oil content of drill cuttings. This may help to resolve the immediate doubt as to the presence or absence of hydrocarbons. The limits of error in the final detailed interpretation can therefore be considerably narrowed.

In addition to the difficulty due to the several different solutions for R_t that can fit the equations, conventional resistivity logs suffer from other disadvantages under certain conditions. The thin-bed effect is one of the most serious. Here it is obvious that a long electrode spacing will straddle the bed and hence be largely affected by the adjacent beds. On the other hand, the resistivity values with a short spacing will be mainly controlled by the mud column and the invaded zone, since there will be little penetration of the current paths into the non-invaded formation rock.

If R_t/R_m is very large, as it is when a very saline mud is used, the majority of the current flow will be confined to the relatively conductive mud column, and again the contribution from R_t will be small.

In drilling for oil a water-based mud is often undesirable, because the water that forms the invaded zone can form a barrier to the flow of oil. To avoid this, potential oil-producing formations are often drilled with an oil-based mud, which has a very high resistivity. Here once again, conventional resistivity logs are useless, because there is no medium to conduct the current from the electrodes out to the strata surrounding the borehole.

These inherent difficulties in the use of conventional logs have led to the development of focused-current devices and also the induction log.

2. Focused-current Devices

A. *The Laterolog 7*

The Laterolog 7 (Fig. 5) sends current to the formation from a centre electrode A_0. Two further current electrodes A_1 and A_2 symmetrically placed above and below A_0 also feed current to the formation, in phase with that from A_0. Two pairs of controlling electrodes M_1M_1' and M_2M_2' as shown are used as potential monitor electrodes. The potential difference developed between M_1M_2 and $M_1'M_2'$ is used to control the current emitted from A_1A_2 in

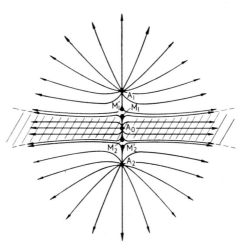

Fig. 5. The Laterolog.

such a way that the potential difference is held at zero. In this condition there can be no current flow from M_1 to M_1' or from M_2 to M_2'. Hence all the current from A_0 must flow into the rock formations confined between the horizontal planes through the mid-points of M_1M_1' and M_2M_2'. The current therefore enters the formation in the form of a sheet which is in practice 32 in. thick at the electrode assembly and increases in thickness with radial penetration from the borehole.

The apparent resistivity recorded, R_a, is given by $R_a = KV/I$

where I is the current sent out by A_0, V is the potential of A_0 or any of the 'M' electrodes and K is the geometrical factor of the device.

Qualitatively the laterolog will define thin bedding sequences in great detail, and quantitatively it has its greatest application for computing the true resistivity of thin beds, in particular those which have a lower resistivity than the adjacent ones. In addition, when very-low-resistivity drilling muds are used the potential drop across the mud and invaded zone is small, and hence the reading of the device is close to the true uncontaminated zone resistivity, R_t.

B. *The Guard Electrode or Laterolog 3*

The two names describe two forms of a device which has very similar characteristics to those of the Laterolog 7. The centre electrode (Fig. 6) is the middle 3 in. to 6 in. of the sonde, while above and below are two cylindrical guard electrodes each about

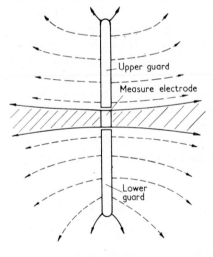

Fig. 6. The guard electrode.

Upper guard

Measure electrode

Lower guard

5 ft. long. In-phase currents are sent out from the centre measuring electrode and the two guards. In the Laterolog 3 the guard electrode current is controlled as in the Laterolog 7 to hold the potential difference between the guard and measuring electrodes at zero. Again the apparent resistivity is proportional to the

potential of the central electrode, and inversely proportional to the current emitted from it.

In the guard electrode method the guard and centre electrodes are held at substantially equal potentials by connecting the two together with a very low impedance, the potential drop across which is used to monitor the current emitted from the measuring electrode.

C. *The Induction Log*

Just as electrical induction methods are used at the surface for detecting underground ore bodies, so the induction log has its place in certain circumstances in working from a borehole.

Alternating current of constant amplitude and frequency is fed to the transmitting coil which is coaxial with the sonde body. This sets up an alternating magnetic field in the rock surrounding the instrument. The magnetic field is accompanied by induced currents in the rock, together with secondary magnetic fields which set up an e.m.f. in a receiver coil which is coaxial with the transmitter coil. This e.m.f. is proportional to the magnitude of the induced currents, which in turn are proportional to the formation conductivity. In addition to the main coils, focusing coils are arranged to minimize the effect of the mud column and the strata above and below the sonde.

The induced currents flow round the borehole, and the response of the device can be computed by considering the distribution in cylinders coaxial with the borehole and bounded by horizontal planes. The contribution of each cylinder is proportional to its conductivity and to its geometrical factor G. Thus for a sonde opposite an invaded bed

$$\frac{1}{R_a} = \frac{G_m}{R_m} + \frac{G_i}{R_i} + \frac{G_t}{R_t} + \frac{G_s}{R_s}$$

where $G_m + G_i + G_r + G_s = 1$. The values of G for the cylinders of various diameters have been computed and are available from the manufacturers of the device.

The induction log does not require any electrical contact with the rock and can therefore be run in non-conductive fluid such as oil-based mud. In addition, the higher the mud resistivity R_m, the less is the value of G_m/R_m, the effect of the mud column. This applies also to the invaded zone, since R_i is again large due to the high resistivity of the invading fluid.

The induction log gives good interpretable values of formation resistivity when $R_m > R_t$ that is, for low-resistivity formations.

VII. RADIOACTIVE MEASUREMENTS

Since measurements of radioactivity entail the counting of a number of impulses arriving at random, it is necessary to count for a certain time in order to achieve a desired accuracy. During logging, the detector passes stratigraphical changes at a fixed speed. Any change in mean radioactive level will take a finite time to register, in which time the detector will have moved. This gives rise to a slight discrepancy between the true and the logged depths of a formation change. The discrepancy is termed the depth constant of the equipment and is the product of the time constant of the counting device and the speed at which the log is run.

The relative variation in count rate observed in one time unit is inversely proportional to the square root of the average counts per unit time, and shows as 'jitter', or noise, on the log. For a fixed count rate the signal-to-noise ratio increases with increase in the counting-time unit. Furthermore, the detector must be opposite a given rock layer for at least one time unit if the effect of the individual layer is to be faithfully recorded on the log. The level of radioactivity therefore controls the unit of counting time or time constant requirements (to give as little jitter as practicable), and the time constant decides the maximum logging speed consistent with recording of the thinnest bed present.

The detectors used for measuring gamma activity can be Geiger–Müller tubes, proportional counters or scintillation crystals with associated photomultiplier tubes. The latter are becoming the most popular because the amplitude of output pulse is proportional to the energy of the activity producing it. The natural gamma-ray logging tool incorporates a detector with associated power supplies, together with pulse-shaping and amplifying circuits if required. The neutron–gamma tool is similar, but has a source of fast neutrons (radium–beryllium or polonium–beryllium) about 25 to 30 in. from the detector and shielded from it to cut

G

down the detector response to the direct gamma rays associated with the source. Considerable precautions are needed in the use of neutron–gamma tools because of the personal hazard caused by the strong radioactive source.

A further radioactive logging tool recently developed uses a source of gamma rays collimated by means of a lead shield having a window in it. This is separated from the detector, which is also shielded and collimated. The whole tool is forced against the bore-hole wall by a back spring so that the emitted gamma rays pass through the window to the formations. The gamma rays which are not absorbed by the formation are scattered, and some of them return from the formation to the detector. The intensity of these emergent gamma rays is almost an exponential function of the density of the scattering material. The record produced can thus be calibrated in terms of rock density.

One of the great advantages of radioactive measurements is that they can be used when steel casing lines the borehole. In these circumstances it is possible to carry out stratigraphic correlations and determinations of porosity, although for the latter measurements there is a greater degree of uncertainty than in the absence of casing.

VIII. PRODUCTION CHARACTERISTICS OF RESERVOIR ROCKS

The previous paragraphs have discussed the use of borehole logs to obtain estimates of porosity and relative fluid contents of reservoir rocks. It is also of great importance to the oil industry to assess the flow characteristics of the reservoir rock, that is, to obtain estimates of the amount of fluid which will flow through the strata under known pressure differentials. This quantity is proportional to the area perpendicular to the direction of flow, and to the pressure differential. The proportionality constant is the permeability and is measured in darcies (1 darcy permeability allows a rate of flow of 1 cm^3/sec of a fluid having a viscosity of 1 cP across 1 cm^2 under a pressure gradient of 1 atm/cm). Permeability is related to the cross sectional area and tortuosity of the flow paths for a given fluid. When oil migrates into a water-saturated porous rock the water is never completely flushed, but a residual irreducible water-saturation fraction, S_{wi}, of the pore space remains. In general, under comparable conditions the greater the permeability, the less will be S_{wi}. Several empirical equations have been postulated which relate permeability K with porosity ϕ (and/or formation resistivity factor) and S_{wi}. These are all of the form

$$K \propto (S_{wi})^{-2} \times f(\phi)$$

and can be used to estimate the order of magnitude of K.

It should be noted that in some cases the grains of a reservoir rock are preferentially oil-wetted rather than water-wetted; for these the above-mentioned relationships are not valid.

Logging tools are available to obtain permeability profiles of the porous strata with depth. The simplest of these is the spinner-type flowmeter, which has an impeller rotated by the fluid flowing in the well bore. The speed of rotation is taken at spot depths, say 1 ft intervals, down the borehole, and hence a profile can be plotted showing the relative intake or production capacity of the formation over the interval examined. Places where high permeability exists will be shown by a rapid change in flow rate. Somewhat more accurate but operationally more complicated are various uses of radioactive tracer techniques. In all cases a log of the natural radioactivity of the strata is taken as a control and then tracer material is injected either directly into the permeable strata or in such a form that it 'plates out' on the wall in proportion to the intake capacity, and a second radioactive log is taken. Comparison of this with the control log gives a measure of the relative production capacities at the various depths, because the permeability governs the rate of flow both into and out of the rock. The tracer technique lends itself to various operational methods which are described in the relevant service company literature.

Permeability profiles can also be obtained from temperature logs taken in boreholes under certain high flow-rate conditions, in particular when water is injected or when gas is being produced. The method equates the difference between the temperature obtained in the fluid at a given depth and the known formation temperature with the total heat transfer by the flowing fluid. The quantity of fluid flowing past a given depth can therefore be computed.

IX. ADDITIONAL BOREHOLE MEASUREMENTS

Electrical logging was first used as a method of correlating geo-logical formations from well to well and for giving accurate depths of lithological changes. With increase in understanding and know-ledge, it was developed into a means of estimating hydrocarbon potentialities of reservoir rock. New logging methods have been developed which are not at present directly used in hydrocarbon estimation. One of the most important of these is the continuous velocity logging tool.

1. Continuous Velocity Logging

Seismic reflection surveys form one of the most important geo-physical tools. A detailed interpretation of the results obtained can be made only if accurate vertical velocity values are available for the various rock layers. These values can be obtained by lowering a geophone into an exploration borehole and measuring travel times through the rock succession at different depths. Log-ging tools are now available which produce a continuous record, at the surface, of the rock velocities all the way down the hole.

The tool consists of two or more transducers separated by acoustic insulators. The transducers use either magnetostriction elements or piezoelectric crystals. The upper one acts as a trans-mitter and sends out sound pulses of about 10 to 20 kc/s at a rate of about 20 per second. Some units use two receivers in order to eliminate error due to the travel time through the mud between the transducers and the borehole wall. A geophone is normally in-corporated in the tool in order that overall travel times may be obtained by firing shots at the surface. The time taken for the pulse to travel a few feet between transmitter and receiver is con-verted to a voltage, and this voltage is recorded at the surface. In addition, the travel-time signal is integrated to produce a second record which, together with two or more overall travel times re-corded by the geophone, yields accurate averaged velocity data for the various layers of rock that are logged.

The logs produced not only give accurate velocity information, but are also extremely useful for geological correlation. Fig. 7 shows a continuous velocity log taken over the same rock section as an SP and a resistivity log. The top of the series marked Hunton was readily placed by geological examination of the rock chippings during drilling, but is not shown clearly on the electrical log. The velocity log, however, shows a well-marked rock interface.

The continuous velocity log has been instructive in showing that the vertical rock column is often much less homogeneous than most seismic calculations had previously assumed. Shale bands in limestone, for example, give a very irregular appearance to the velocity profile, and all the sharp changes in velocity are potential sources of reflections. It is possible to calculate the strength of the

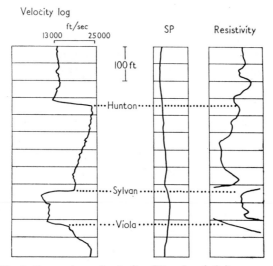

Fig. 7. Comparison of velocity, SP and resistivity curves.

various reflections, using coefficients of reflection obtained from the velocity values on the log combined with estimates of density and in some cases of attenuation in the rock. In this manner seismic reflection records may be synthesized. This will lead to a better understanding of how reflection processes take place in rock layers and will enable forecasts to be made of the effect of various possible underground structural changes on the appearance of the records. The synthetic record technique may also help to resolve multiple reflections and to disentangle overlapping reflections.

There is a linear correlation between compressional wave velocity and porosity in a given stratum (as discussed in Section

II–3) so that continuous velocity logs can give information about reservoir rocks. The velocity also depends on the fluid that occupies the pore spaces, and there is likely to be an ever-increasing application of the device.

2. Measurement of Strata Dip

A further measurement which is of primary geological importance is that of the angle and azimuth of strata dip. This can be obtained by means of a borehole dipmeter, of which there are several types.

All existing dipmeters depend on the assumption that a stratigraphical interface intersects the borehole in a plane. This plane can be completely located by any three non-collinear points in it. The three identifying points, in practice, are the three points at which three dipmeter probes running up the borehole wall cross the interface. The three probes are carried on three spring arms, and are usually some form of microresistivity measuring device. The probes are located 120° apart round the body of the tool. The three records produced at surface can be cross correlated and the height differences between each record at an interface locate the plane of the interface with respect to the plane of the probes (see Fig. 8).

An orientation device is also run as an integral part of the tool. This records the position of the probes with respect to horizontal and magnetic north. For example, photographs can be taken of a compass needle, a pendulum device (a ball rolling on an engraved spherical surface) and the location of one probe. More recently an instrument has been made available which continuously records the position of the reference probe and the angle and direction of the inclination of the tool.

3. Temperature Logs

One of the standard uses of temperature logs is in the location of the top of the cement column, between the casing and the surrounding strata. In cementing casing the cement slurry is pumped down the inside of the casing and forced up into the annulus between the casing and the walls of the borehole. The cement slurry is followed by mud, with a drillable plug separating the two fluids.

When the plug reaches bottom all of the slurry is obviously in the annulus and the inside of the casing is full of mud. The hole is then

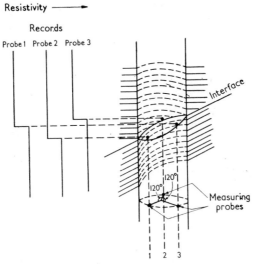

Fig. 8. Principle of borehole dipmeter.

left standing for the cement to set. Cement gives out heat on setting, and hence the temperature of the mud in the casing opposite the cement rises. A temperature log run in the casing some 12 to 36 h after cementing will show the presence of cement by this rise in temperature.

4. Pressure Measurements

Instruments also exist for measuring the high pressures that are found in deep boreholes. For example, a continuous record of pressure over about 36 h can be obtained to an accuracy of a few lb/in² at 5 to 10 000 lb/in². Similar high-pressure apparatus exists to collect samples of reservoir fluids, such as oil and gas, from deep down in boreholes.

X. FUTURE DEVELOPMENTS

The theoretical background to quantitative estimates of formation parameters from borehole logs is still in its early stages. A large proportion of the research and development effort has so far been spent on the interpretation of resistivity measurements, but many problems still remain to be solved. Analysis of the fluid distribution in the filtrate-invaded zone by means of focusing devices which have a controlled radius of investigation (depth of penetration into the rock) appears to be a promising line of attack for the future.

Since about 1950 an increasing effort has been put into radioactivity logging. The use of crystal scintillation detectors enables spectra to be obtained, since the number of pulses impinging on the detector can be plotted against pulse height. The pulse height is proportional to the energy of the gamma rays producing the pulses, and hence the plot can be calibrated in terms of energy. These measurements can be applied to both natural and neutron-induced radioactivity to identify various elements by their resulting gamma-ray spectra. The technique applied to natural radioactivity suffers by virtue of the low intensity of the activity. Neutron-induced radioactivity can be increased by using a greater source strength, but this has its disadvantages. The major one is the danger in handling the more powerful source, but in addition the associated gamma radiation, together with a wide neutron energy range from the source produces poor discrimination on the spectrum plotted. Development is proceeding on ion-accelerator type sources for use in boreholes. These will solve many problems, as they give mono-energetic neutrons which can be safely controlled by switching off when handling is necessary. One of the most promising possibilities is that of measuring the gamma radiation emitted by the chlorine nucleus when it captures a slow neutron. The chlorine is present as sodium chloride in reservoir water, and hence the method should allow the location of a formation oil/water contact behind steel casing.

Acoustic logging tools are still in their experimental stages, but the ability to correlate the records they give with seismic observations is already showing promise of improvement in the interpretation of reflection measurements. The attenuation as well as the velocity of the rock can now be determined as a routine procedure, and it is possible that measurements made at frequencies of the order of megacycles per second may give rise to methods of estimating grain size distribution in reservoir rock. The attenuation caused by fissure systems in rocks may possibly give a measure of the size of the fissures.

All logging instruments have limitations to their use, and only give accurate results when the logging conditions approach the ideal ones for the particular tool. In some cases corrections are possible for various effects, but the error in the final result will obviously increase with the number and magnitude of corrections required. For example, very accurate formation resistivities can be obtained with standard logging equipment only if: (a) the borehole diameter is uniform and small compared with the electrode spacing used; (b) the mud resistivity is less than ten times that of the rock; (c) the bed thickness is greater than four times the electrode spacing; and (d) the depth of invasion is small.

Improvements in instrumental techniques, however, are continually reducing the errors involved. This sometimes results in the production of a new type of instrument, as occurred with the laterolog or guard electrode devices. In other cases the improvement is obtained by making it possible to take simultaneous measurements, and using one to correct the other, as is done with the combined microlog–caliper instrument. Each improvement made removes some of the uncertainties from electric log interpretation, and so helps to add to the science of logging practice.

Electrical logging in twenty years has developed from a novelty to a regular routine process in all exploration boreholes. At the moment a considerable amount of analysis work still has to be carried out in order to obtain a correct physical picture of underground conditions. It does not, however, appear to be a tremendous step forward to complete analysis of underground strata by some form of well logging.

It is possible that well-logging methods may be of great value in future studies of the inside of the earth. There seems little doubt that boreholes could be drilled through the sediments of the deep ocean floor and probably down to the earth's mantle. The various tools that are already available, especially the continuous velocity logger, will have great value in finding out the properties of the rocks in place, even though samples may be brought to the surface. The logging methods might even be essential, since the drilling technique used to reach the mantle might prohibit taking cores, so that the only rock samples will be in the form of small fragments. Continuous coring always slows up drilling; this is undesirable, and the well-logging techniques will be invaluable to show where the rock properties change. Samples can then be obtained with specialized tools that have been constructed to take small cores from the side of the borehole at selected places.

The project for drilling to the earth's mantle [43] envisages a boring of about 10 miles, a depth which is a little more than twice the present deepest borehole. It will probably be necessary to use some form of drill that does not depend on the rotation of the drill pipe, but is driven by a motor at the bottom of the hole instead of, as at present, by rotation at the well head. Modern developments in pulling the drill-pipe from the borehole, and improvements in the life of rock-cutting bits, will also be needed, and these will be one of the benefits that will come to the drilling industry from such a research project.

Drilling through the sea-bed sediments appears to be feasible with present-day offshore drilling techniques from floating barges. It should be possible to drill in the deep ocean for at least the life of one drilling bit, and this will enable a sample to be obtained from whatever hard rock layer lies below the sediments. Cores can be cut and pulled up inside the drill-pipe on a wire line, so that there will be no complication of having to remove the drill and then re-locate the borehole. The special types of borehole log that have been designed to operate through casing will then be of use if this drilling method is adopted.

References and Useful Articles

1. Archie, G. E. 'The electrical resistivity log as an aid in determining some reservoir characteristics'. *Trans. Amer. Inst. min (metall.) Engrs*, **146**, 54 (1942).
2. Archie, G. E. 'Electrical resistivity as aid in core analysis determination.' *Bull. Amer. Ass. Petrol. Geol.* **31**, 350 (1947).
3. Baker, P. E. 'Density logging with gamma rays.' *Trans. Amer. Inst. min. (metall.) Engrs*, **210**, 289 (1957).
4. Bird, J. M. 'Interpretation of temperature logs in water and gas injection wells and gas producing wells.' *Prod. Mon.* (August 1954).
5. Breck, H. R., Schoellhorn, S. W., and Baum, R. B. 'Velocity logging and its geological and geophysical applications.' *Bull. Amer. Ass. Petrol. Geol.* **41**, 1667 (1957).
6. Caldwell, R. L., and Sippel, R. F. 'New developments in radioactive well logging research.' *Bull. Amer. Ass. Petrol. Geol.* **42**, 159 (1958).

7. de Chambrier, P. 'The microlog continuous dipmeter.' *Geophysics*, **18**, 929 (1953).

8. Doll, H. G. 'The S.P. log—theoretical analysis and principles of interpretation.' *Petrol. Tech., N.Y.* **11**, *TP–2463* (1948).

9. Doll, H. G. 'Introduction to induction logging and application to logging of wells drilled with oil base mud.' *Trans. Amer. Inst. min. (metall.) Engrs*, **186**, 148 (1949).

10. Doll, H. G. 'The Microlog—a new electric logging method for detailed determination of permeable beds.' *Trans. Amer. Inst. min (metall.) Engrs*, **189**, 155 (1950).

11. Doll, H. G. 'The Laterolog—a new resistivity method with electrodes using an automatic focusing system.' *Trans. Amer. Inst. min. (metall.) Engrs*, **192**, 305 (1951).

12. Doll, H. G. 'The Microlaterolog.' *Trans. Amer. Inst. min (metall.) Engrs*, **198**, 17 (1953).

13. Faul, M., and Tittle, C. W. 'Logging of drill holes by the neutron gamma method and gamma ray scattering.' *Geophysics*, **16**, 260 (1951).

14. Fearon, R. E. 'Gamma-ray well logging.' *Nucleonics*, **4**, April, 67 (1949).

15. Fearon, R. E. 'Neutron well logging.' *Nucleonics*, **4**, June, 30 (1949).

16. Ferguson, C. K., and Klotz, J. A. 'Filtration from mud during drilling.' *Trans. Amer. Inst. min. (metall.) Engrs*, **201**; *J. Petrol. Tech.* **6**, February, 30 (1954).

17. Flagg, A. H., Myers, J. P., Campbell, J. L. P., Terry, J. M., and Mardock, E. S. 'Radioactive tracers in oil production problems.' *Trans. Amer. Inst. min. (metall) Engrs*, **204**; *J. Petrol. Tech.* **7**, January, 1 (1955).

18. Green, W. G., and Fearon, R. E. 'Well logging by radioactivity.' *Geophysics*, **5**, 272 (1940).

19. Grynberg, J., and Ettinger, M. I. 'The continuous dipmeter.' *Oil Gas J.* **55**, 13 (166) and **55**, 16 (129) (1957).

20. Guyod, H. 'Electrical logging developments in the U.S.S.R. (Part 3).' *World Oil*, **127**, February (84) (1948).

21. Hicks, W. G., and Berry, J. E. 'Application of continuous velocity logs to determination of fluid saturation of reservoir rocks.' *Geophysics*, **21**, 739 (1956).

22. Hughes, D. S., and Cross, J. M. 'Elastic wave velocities in rocks at high pressures and temperatures.' *Geophysics*, **16**, 577 (1951).

23. Martin, M. 'The Microlog.' *Oil Gas J.* **54**, 19 September, 108 and 24 October, 106 (1955).

24. McCardell, W. M., Winsauer, W. A., and Williams, M. 'Origin of electric potential observed in wells.' *Petrol. Trans. Amer. Inst. min. (metall.) Engrs*, **198**; *J. Petrol. Tech.*, **5**, February, 41 (1953); *Tech. Publ. No. 3500*.

25. Owen, J. E., and Greer, W. J. 'The guard electrode logging system.' *Petrol. Trans. Amer. Inst. min. (metall.) Engrs*, **192**, 347 (1951); *Tech. Publ. No. 3222*.

26. Petroleum Engineer. 'New logging tool—world's smallest atom smasher.' *Petrol. Engr*, **28**, No.3, B–86 (1956).
27. Pirson, S. J. 'Formation evaluation by log interpretation.' *World Oil*, **144**, 5 (159); **144**, 6 (170) and **144**, 7 (193, 195) (1957).
28. Ricker, N. *Proc. 3rd World Petrol. Congr.*, p. 514 (1951).
29. Schlumberger Well Surveying Corporation. 'Interpretation Handbook for Resistivity Logs.' Schlumberger Well Surveying Corporation, *Document No. 4.*
30. Summers, G. C., and Broding, R. A. 'Continuous velocity logging.' *Geophysics*, **17**, 598 (1952).
31. Swift, G. 'Simultaneous gamma-ray and neutron logging.' *Geophysics*, **17**, 387 (1952).
32. Tittle, C. W., Faul, H., and Goodman, C. 'Neutron logging of drill holes —the neutron–neutron method.' *Geophysics*, **16**, 626 (1951).
33. Tixier, M. P. 'Evaluation of permeability from electric-log resistivity gradients.' *Oil Gas J.* **48**, 16 June, 113 (1949).
34. Winn, R. H. 'A report on the displacement log.' *J. Petrol. Tech.* **10**, February, 57 (1958).
35. Winsauer, W. O., and McCardell, W. M. 'Ionic double-layer conductivity in reservoir rock.' *Trans. Amer. Inst. min. (metall.) Engrs*, **198**, 129 (1953).
36. de Witte, L. 'A study of electric log interpretation methods in shaly formations.' *Trans. Amer. Inst. min. (metall.) Engrs*, **204**, *Tech. Publ. No. 4076* in *J. Petrol. Tech.* **7**, No. 7, 103 (1955).
37. de Witte, L. 'Resistivity and saturation distribution in infiltrated zones of porous formations around drill holes.' *Oil Gas J.* **49**, 17 July, 246 (1950).
38. 'New logging technique measures density and porosity.' *World Oil*, **139**, No. 7, (142) (1954).
39. Wyllie, M. R. J. 'A quantitative analysis of the electrochemical component of the S.P. curve.' *J. Petrol. Tech.* **1**, Part 2, January, 17 (1949).
40. Wyllie, M. R. J., and Rose, W. D. 'Some theoretical considerations related to the quantitative evaluation of the physical characteristics of reservoir rock from electrical log data.' *Petrol. Trans. Amer. Inst. min. (metall.) Engrs* **189**, 105; *J. Petrol. Tech.* **2** (1950); *Tech. Publ. No. 2852.*
41. Wyllie, M. R. J., Gregory, A. R., and Gardner, L. W. 'Elastic wave velocities in heterogeneous and porous media.' *Geophysics*, **21**, 41 (1956).
42. Wyllie, M. R. J., Gregory, A. R., and Gardner, G. H. F. 'An experimental investigation of factors affecting elastic wave velocities in porous media.' *Geophysics*, **23**, 459 (1958).
43. Gaskell, T. F. 'A borehole to the Earth's mantle?' *Nature* **182**, 692 (1958).

APPENDIX

The Mohole Project

The ability of well-logging methods to cope with the increased difficulties that will arise with borings ten miles deep into the Earth's crust is not doubted, but there are many problems associated with deep drilling itself. The Mohole project that is being actively pursued in various parts of the world aims at drilling a hole deep enough to go through the Earth's crust so that a sample of the underlying mantle rock can be obtained.

There is little need to stress the interest and importance to geologists, especially those who have a leaning towards volcanology, of discovering the nature of the mantle. This layer, stretching from below the crustal skin of the Earth almost halfway to the Earth's centre, is the main constituent of the Earth, but its chemical nature is not known. Some reasonable guesses have been made by examining the composition of material erupted by volcanoes and rocks that have been intruded into the heart of large mountain masses, but there is no certainty that processes of differentiation and mixing have not occurred to alter the original mantle rock during melting and subsequent movement upwards.

Some limits to the properties of the mantle have been provided by the results of seismic measurements, combined with the density distribution inside the Earth, and another line of attack on the problem has been given by the study of the abundance of the various elements in the Solar system and by examination of the composition of meteorites. While all the evidence points to the mantle being made of some basic rock typified by dunite or harzburgite, the exact composition is unknown, and the lack of knowledge is holding up theoretical investigations into the history of the formation of the Earth. For example, calculations of the heat balance inside the Earth can be made to demonstrate the two extremes of a cooling and of a heating-up regime; the controlling factor is the amount of radioactivity in the mantle and the internal heating that it supplies.

The recent researches that have been made into the geology of the floors of the deep oceans have provided a fresh interest in the Earth's crust, but the interpretation of the gravity and seismic

measurements remains ambiguous, especially in respect of the
Layer 2 stratum of rock that has been shown to lie between the
soft sea bed sediments which can be sampled by grab and corer,
and the 6·7 km/sec primaeval crustal layer. The submarine
geologists have reached a stage where borehole evidence for the
rock sequence that they have discovered is a necessary check on
the results, and in particular a knowledge of the composition of
Layer 2 and of the 6·7 km/sec layer is desirable.

It is the sea seismic experiments that have changed the idea of
direct sampling of the mantle from being a worth-while project to
one that has every appearance of being possible. Instead of the
mantle being covered by 30 km or so of rock as is the case on the
continents, the Moho (the accepted term today for the boundary
between the crust and the mantle) is only about 10–13 km below
the surface of the deep oceans. The shallowest Moho depth beneath
dry land occurs beneath isolated islands or atolls in the deep
oceans, where the mantle is depressed somewhat by the crustal
rocks so that it is about 15 km below sea-level. The deepest borehole, drilled by the oil industry, exceeds 8 km so that the sampling
of the mantle entails an extension of present techniques by less
than a factor of two, if a hole is drilled where the crust is thin, that
is somewhere in the oceans. The seismic results suggest that a hole
drilled from an island would pass through 10 000–20 000 ft of
vesicular volcanic rock, interpersed with dense solidified lava
before reaching the 6·7 km/sec material, which should be uniform
basic rock, and which should continue to a depth of 50 000 ft to the
mantle. If the hole could be drilled in deep water the sequence of
layers would be about 18 000 ft of water, a few thousand feet of
sediment in which the hard 'Layer 2' will be encountered, and
perhaps 10 000 ft of the hard basic 6·7 km/sec layer.

In the early days of the oil industry boreholes were made by
repeated dropping of a chisel, weighing about ten tons, onto the
rock. This 'cable tool' method has been largely superseded by the
rotary drill, in which the rock is ground to small chippings by a
drill bit which consists of a series of toothed wheels. The bit is
rotated from the surface by the drill pipe which extends to within
a few hundred feet of the bottom of the hole; mud or water is
circulated down the drill pipe in order to keep the bit cool and to
carry the chippings from the bottom of the hole up the annular

space between the drill pipe and the walls of the borehole to the surface. The thrust needed to drive the drill bit into the rock is provided by some extra heavy thick-walled, sections of drill pipe which are placed directly above the bit; the remainder of the drill pipe is in tension.

Although holes of 25000 ft depth have been drilled using the rotary method, it is probable that some modifications would be needed in order to drill 50000 ft to the Moho. One of the more obvious improvements would be to put the motive power of the cutting bit at the bottom of the hole rather than relying on the long, tenuous thread of pipe to rotate from the surface. Electrically powered drills may provide one solution, but a turbine drill shows the greatest promise, and the turbo-drill is already beginning to rival the rotary in oilfield practice. The main reason for this is that the bit can be rotated much more rapidly because of the absence of friction between rotating drill pipe and the walls of the borehole; with the turbo-drill the pipe merely acts as a channel through which the mud is circulated to power the turbine, and the pipe is not rotated. Higher bit speeds mean greater rates of rock penetration, and the fact that a turbine can be stalled without being damaged, provides another advantage, for with the rotary a stalled drill-bit often means a broken drill pipe and a long fishing job to recover the bit.

In order to take full advantage of faster rates of penetration, bits with a long life are required, otherwise more time will be spent in pulling out the pipe and running it back into the hole after replacing the worn bit. Promising research with diamond bits may give both long life and high rates of penetration. Another possible development that has been considered is a retractable bit that can be lowered down inside the drill pipe on a wire, since it is much quicker to lower a wire than it is to screw together many lengths of drill pipe. There are proposals for automatic pipe extracting machines, which unscrew and stack the pipe continuously, and therefore cut the pulling out and running in times to a third. However, with the best bits and lifting mechanisms that can be envisaged at present, the 50000 ft hole will be a long job. A good speed of penetration in the hard basalt will be 10 ft/h, so that 200 d drilling will be needed, and the pulling out time will probably be equally long.

It is possible, of course, that a modern version of the old cable tool type of percussion drilling with its rapid method of pulling the tools out on a wire rope may be more suited to the hard basalt rock; for example, pneumatic chippers, operating in dry holes, and using a stream of air to bring the rock chipping to the surface, have been very effective in the Sahara recently in drilling tough siliceous limestone.

It is not unreasonable to consider even more fanciful means of cutting rock when our standard methods are only capable of penetrating a few feet an hour. One such method is that of burning a hole by means of a flame torch. This is used for the 50 ft type of hole that is used for shot-firing in mining. Suggestions have also been made that hard tough rock might be successfully broken up by letting off explosive charges at the bottom of the hole. The loosened debris could be removed subsequently by conventional drilling methods. A small charge of an ounce or so should shatter about six inches of rock and if a technique could be devised to fire a shot every few minutes a drilling rate of ten feet or so an hour could be achieved.

It is quite clear that considerable research work is needed to produce a workable method of drilling the 50 000 ft hole down to the Moho; but the type of research work required is in fact already proceeding as part of the normal progress of oil-well drilling and rock mining. For example, the correct operation of the diamond cutter has been shown to depend on careful control of mud circulation and weight, and a factor of ten in distance of rock penetrated before the bit wears out, may soon be possible. After all, diamond is tougher than the rock it cuts and theoretically need not wear at all. In the opinion of most of those engaged in the industry, the problem of drilling to the mantle could be successfully tackled now if the money for the project is forthcoming—it will be in the millions of pounds class, but this is a lot cheaper than shooting at the moon. The most promising way to drill our hole would be a combination of diamond bit with turbo-drill and fully automatic lifting mechanism, using sea-water circulation. The research effort to make the necessary improvements in the various components of this scheme would undoubtedly be repaid by speeding up normal oil-well drilling—just as motor racing has helped to produce better vehicles for everyday use.

Although the mantle could no doubt be reached by drilling 50 000 ft from an oceanic island, it may be more economical and quicker to drill from a floating platform in a place where the water is 3 miles or so deep. Floating platforms have been used for drilling in shallow water, up to 600 ft in depth, and techniques have been worked out for guiding the drill pipe back into the hole after it has been withdrawn for a worn bit to be replaced. On the other hand, methods are available for collecting cores in cylinders that can be lowered down the inside of the drill pipe on wires so that it is conceivable that the problem of locating the hole after replacing a worn bit could be by-passed by combining this technique with the use of a retractable bit. The great advantage of attempting to reach the Moho from a floating platform is that the deep sea sediments will be effectively sampled, and the check on the seismic results will be achieved.

MEASUREMENT OF THE GEOMAGNETIC ELEMENTS

K. WHITHAM, *Dominion Observatory, Ottawa, Canada*

CONTENTS

I. INTRODUCTION

1. Description of Field

The geomagnetic field, $\mathbf{F}$, is a vector quantity which varies in space and in time. At any point the horizontal component, H, makes an angle with the geographic meridian known as the declination or variation, D, which is reckoned positive to the east. The inclination or angle of dip, I, is the angle made by $\mathbf{F}$ with the horizontal plane. This angle is reckoned positive when the north-seeking end of a freely suspended magnet dips downward, and is reckoned negative south of the magnetic equator. The components of **F** at any point resolved along three orthogonal axes through the point to the north, east and vertically downwards are by definition X, Y and Z respectively. Fig. 1 shows the relationships between

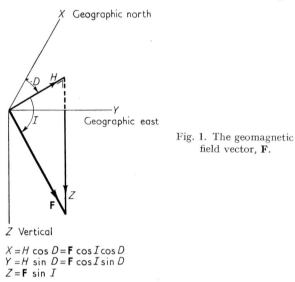

Fig. 1. The geomagnetic field vector, **F**.

$X = H \cos D = \mathbf{F} \cos I \cos D$
$Y = H \sin D = \mathbf{F} \cos I \sin D$
$Z = \mathbf{F} \sin I$

the seven components. It is necessary and sufficient to measure as a function of space and time three of the seven quantities to specify completely the spatial and time variations of **F**. The selection of the components to be measured in any given problem is usually determined by the nature of the problem. For example, in the study of time variations, many calculations in some analyses can be avoided if the three orthogonal components X, Y, Z or D, H, Z are recorded. Occasionally, however, instrumental limitations determine the selection: for example, in certain aeromagnetic surveys only the total intensity can be measured with sufficient accuracy at present.

2. Absolute and Relative Magnetic Measurements

An absolute measurement of a field component at a point connects the average value of the component over the time of measurement to the basic standards of length, mass and time. The factor μ_0, or the magnetic permeability of free space, is defined equal to the ratio of magnetic induction, B, to the magnetic field intensity, H, in free space. In electromagnetism the dimensions of field intensity are somewhat arbitrary, and depend on the definition of μ_0, but in the electromagnetic system of units which is commonly used in geomagnetism, μ_0 is defined equal to unity, and is considered dimensionless. Then the dimensions of the magnetic flux density or induction, B, and the field intensity, H, are the same, namely $M^{1/2}L^{-1/2}T^{-1}$. By international agreement, the gauss is used as the unit of induction, and the oersted as the unit of field intensity. Since in air at sea level $\mu - 1 = 3 \times 10^{-7}$ only, the oersted and gauss are indistinguishable in geomagnetic measurements, and for historical reasons many geophysicists incorrectly use the unit gauss for both induction and field intensity. The connection of an absolute measurement to the primary standards of length, mass and time is usually made in one of two ways. In the first, described in Section II–3–B, the connection is indirect and is made by the comparison of the field component with an absolute field produced by passing a known current through accurately constructed coils of known dimensions. In the second, described in Section VIII–2, the field intensity can be determined directly in terms of a standard of time, and a fundamental constant, which in turn can be determined in absolute terms by means of a current and accurately constructed coils.

Although it is technically incorrect, it is customary to refer to angle measurements (e.g. of D, I) as absolute measurements. They, however, give no information relating the field intensity to the primary standards, but merely specify its orientation with respect to the gravitational field and the geographical meridian.

Relative measurements are usually simpler to make, and are adequate for certain investigations. In the study of time variations, it is possible to convert variation measurements into absolute measurements by determining, with suitable instruments, the absolute value of one or more reference levels (baselines) on the record obtained. In investigating spatial variations, the simplicity of the sensitive methods employed explains the historical precedence of magnetic over other geophysical prospecting methods.

Many of the methods of measurement to be described below can be adapted for both relative and absolute observations, and for the study of spatial and time variations. However, the degree of versatility and the limitations of the different methods vary considerably, as will be seen later.

3. Magnitude of Spatial and Time Variations

In engineering and physical research, magnetic fields up to 10^6 oersteds are developed for small time intervals in small volumes; these fields are enormous compared to the main geomagnetic field and the methods used are quite different. Geophysicists wish to investigate, for academic and economic reasons, the spatial properties of the geomagnetic field at the surface of the earth some of which are shown in gammas (1 gamma = 10^{-5} oersted) in Table 1.

Table 1. Spatial properties of geomagnetic field

Type of measurement	Description	Magnitude
Absolute measurements	(1) Geomagnetic field of deep internal origin, F	3 to 6 × 10^4 gammas
Relative measurements	(1) Crustal anomalies, ΔF	
	(a) maximum	4 × 10^5 gammas
	(b) polarization anomalies	~50 to 4 × 10^5 gammas
	(c) structural anomalies	~10 to ~250 gammas
	(2) Horizontal gradients	
	(a) maximum $\partial(\Delta F)/\partial x$	6 × 10^3 gammas/km
	(b) of geophysical interest, $\partial(\Delta F)\partial x$	20 to 6 × 10^3 gammas/km
	(c) of field of deep internal origin, $\partial F/\partial x$	0 to 10 gammas/km

It is clear that an accuracy of 1 gamma, or 1 part in 5×10^4 of the mean value of the main field, is usually more than adequate, and in general other limitations prevent the use of results to such a high accuracy. It seems fair to say that in regional magnetic surveys, where the density of stations is low and the published charts are on a large scale (typically 100 miles to the inch), an accuracy of ± 100 gammas is sufficient; even in more detailed magnetic surveys, where the information is compiled at a scale of 1 mile to the inch, an accuracy of ± 5 gammas in mining work and ± 1 gamma in oil work is usually sufficient. Occasionally, however, in investigation of the vertical change in field at depths in mines or in the sea, or in rocket experiments in the ionosphere, spatial variations are required to be known to at least one gamma.

The time variations of the geomagnetic field are largely studied at a hundred or so magnetic observatories distributed about the surface of the earth. A complete observatory, in principle, furnishes complete values of all the time variations in the vector field, $\mathbf{F}$; these range from secular change phenomena with a time scale of 1 to 100 yr to sub-audio fluctuations in the earth's field in the frequency range 1 to 100 c/s. Events with a time scale much greater than 100 yr cannot be studied from observatory data because magnetic observatories are of comparatively recent origin; instead the methods of rock magnetism described in Chapter 5 are used. At the opposite end of the spectrum higher frequency fluctuations than 100 c/s are usually associated with meteorological phenomena. In addition to the study of time variations at magnetic observatories and upper atmosphere research stations, secular change data are usually supplemented by observations repeated in time at certain field stations. Fig. 2 shows some of the time variations of interest in geophysics in this large range of frequencies, and some typical magnitudes of the phenomena observed. In general, a change in method is necessary at about 30-sec periods: for much longer period phenomena an accuracy of $\pm 0\cdot 5$ gamma is generally sufficient, whereas for shorter period transient phenomena, a sensitivity of $0\cdot 01$ gamma/sec or better is required. The present international recommendations concerning magnetic recordings have been summarized by Bartels [5] and are shown in Fig. 2. It should be clear that investigations of some phenomena (e.g. secular variation) require absolute control whereas those of other events (e.g. sudden commencements) do not.

4. Limitations in Magnetic Measurements

The fundamental limitations of the practical instruments used in the different methods of measurement will be discussed in the appropriate places below. However, it should be emphasized that, in practice, instrumental limitations are often unimportant compared with limitations in the general method used for making measurements. This is often not clearly realized, particularly by the designers of instruments, but the three examples which follow should show its importance.

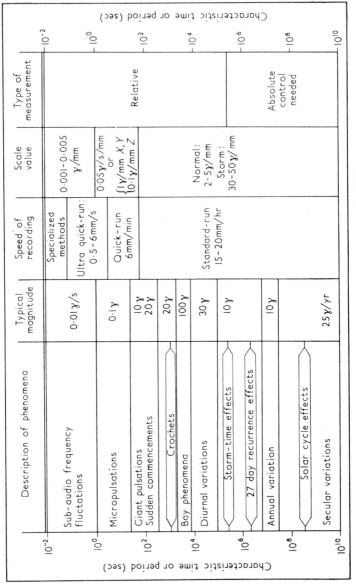

Fig. 2. Time variations in the geomagnetic field.

At moderate to high magnetic latitudes, the uncertainties in reducing observations to epoch at secular change repeat stations, even those near observatories, usually considerably exceed one gamma. Great accuracy in measurement is therefore pointless, and instruments should be chosen for convenience rather than high precision. A second example is that in conducting regional three-component magnetic surveys from the air, the largest uncertainties are of an operational, rather than instrumental, nature (Serson and Whitham.[50]) The increase in cost and complexity to reduce these operational uncertainties has not so far been judged worthwhile in terms of the present uses of regional magnetic charts. As a final example it is worth recalling that in total intensity aeromagnetic work there is inherently a lack of resolution from flying at a safe altitude with reasonable flight-line separations, and the most sensitive drift-free magnetometer cannot overcome this and other limitations in the method.

To summarize, it is essential in any programme of measurements to consider the geophysical problem as a whole and, in particular, the interactions of time variations with space variations. The limitations produced by factors external to the instruments used are probably the most important in the present state of development of geomagnetism, and very often, if they are clearly realized, it is possible to use adequately a simpler instrument, or a cheaper and quicker technique.

In the sections which follow, the different principles used in magnetic measurements will be outlined, and the geophysical uses of each method with its advantages and disadvantages mentioned. The account is confined to methods whereby practical magnetometers can be designed to operate in fields of a few oersteds or less, although a few of these methods have, of course, been more successfully used in very high magnetic fields. The many different techniques used in recording time variations can only be briefly mentioned. However, it will be clear that some of the methods of measurement are more easily adaptable to modern recording methods, suitable for automatic analysis, than are others.

II. TORQUE METHODS

1. General Principle

A magnet of moment **M** c.g.s.u. in a magnetic field **H** oersteds experiences a torque $\mathbf{T} = \mathbf{M} \times \mathbf{H}$ and a force $\mathbf{F} = (\mathbf{M} \cdot \mathrm{grad})\,\mathbf{H}$. Since the gradients of the geomagnetic field are so small, the force on a practical magnet can be shown to be less than 10^{-6} times the weight of the magnet, and so cannot easily be measured. However, the torque is appreciable, and can be measured or recorded in a variety of ways.

Torque methods are the oldest employed in geomagnetic studies, and have been very successfully used for many types of relative and absolute measurements. The stability of the instruments, using modern techniques, and their simplicity are such that they are still widely used for relative measurements in time variation studies and in ground magnetometer surveys. They have also formed the basis for the presently accepted world standards of magnetic field intensity. Certain portable absolute magnetometers based on this principle and used as secondary standards will remain in widespread use many years hence. The principle limitations in the use of torque methods are that, in general, they cannot easily be used to investigate very short period phenomena (less than 1 sec), and that only relatively crude measurements can be made from a moving support.

The improvements in practical instruments in recent years have been largely in the stability of magnet moments, the ease of adjustment, reduction in size, etc. Adequate accounts of many of the instruments have been given by Chapman and Bartels,[12] Heiland,[23] Thellier[52] and others. The account given below is confined entirely to those instruments which are still widely used, and are thought likely to remain so for some years to come, for one reason or another. Even so, the treatment in the space available must be very brief; for example, in the discussion of magnet variometers it is necessary to omit all mention of quick-run recording techniques and their relative merits.

2. Relative Measurements

A. *Magnet variometers with photographic recording*

These are used for recording time changes in the geomagnetic field. A schematic diagram of a magnet variometer is shown in Fig. 3. The optical system used for magnifying the movements of the magnet should be self-explanatory. Fig. 4 shows schematically a three-component (D, H, Z) magnet variometer and the basic theory for determining the static sensitivities s_D, s_H, s_Z in radians/oersted. The sensitivities at the drum are $2 \times 10^{-4} f s_D$, etc., in mm/gamma. The D system employs an essentially torsionless

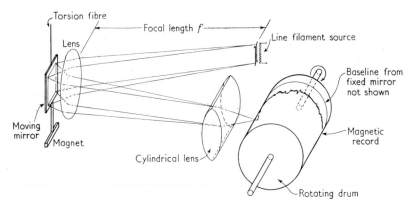

Fig. 3. Schematic diagram of a magnet variometer.

fibre ($c = 0$), and by the adjustment of the field H_0 of an auxiliary magnet in sense and in magnitude, it is possible suitably to adjust the sensitivity. It is, of course, not possible to increase the sensitivity without limit in this way because ($H - H_0$) must be many times the variation ΔH in H to avoid large variations in sensitivity. However, the recommended scale values shown in Fig. 2 can easily be achieved with a moderate focal length $\sim$1 m. The H system is suspended from a fibre with an appreciable torsion constant. The fibre is twisted, or the magnet otherwise deflected so that the axis of the magnet is perpendicular to the mean magnetic meridian, and its variations measured optically. Standard sensitivities are easily obtained with a fibre sufficiently strong to support the magnet, and higher sensitivities are obtained by decreasing the diameter of

Declination variometer

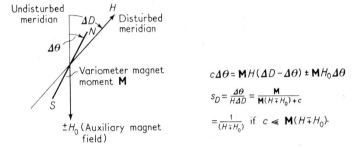

$$c\Delta\theta = \mathbf{M}H(\Delta D - \Delta\theta) \pm \mathbf{M}H_0\Delta\theta$$

$$s_D = \frac{\Delta\theta}{H\Delta D} = \frac{\mathbf{M}}{\mathbf{M}(H \mp H_0) + c}$$

$$= \frac{1}{(H \mp H_0)} \quad \text{if} \quad c \ll \mathbf{M}(H \mp H_0).$$

Horizontal field variometer

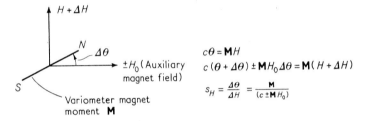

$$c\theta = \mathbf{M}H$$

$$c(\theta + \Delta\theta) \pm \mathbf{M}H_0\Delta\theta = \mathbf{M}(H + \Delta H)$$

$$s_H = \frac{\Delta\theta}{\Delta H} = \frac{\mathbf{M}}{(c \pm \mathbf{M}H_0)}$$

Vertical field variometer   (Balanced magnet type)

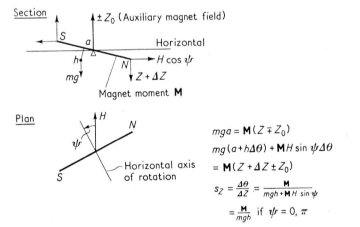

$$mga = \mathbf{M}(Z \mp Z_0)$$

$$mg(a + h\Delta\theta) + \mathbf{M}H \sin \psi \Delta\theta$$

$$= \mathbf{M}(Z + \Delta Z \pm Z_0)$$

$$s_Z = \frac{\Delta\theta}{\Delta Z} = \frac{\mathbf{M}}{mgh + \mathbf{M}H \sin \psi}$$

$$= \frac{\mathbf{M}}{mgh} \quad \text{if} \quad \psi = 0, \pi$$

Fig. 4. Illustration of orientation and theory of three-component magnet variometers.

the torsion fibre, or by the use of a suitable auxiliary field, H_0 (see Fig. 4). The Z variometer usually consists of a magnet assembly with quartz knife edges sitting on quartz plates, and with its centre of gravity displaced from the horizontal axis of rotation so that a gravitational couple provides the restoring torque. The axis of rotation is generally in the magnetic meridian to avoid interaction with changes in H. Again it is comparatively easy to obtain the maximum sensitivities usually recommended by a decrease in h. Alternatively, aged horizontal torsion fibres can be used, and twisted so that the magnet system is horizontal.

For the recording of a short-period magnetic disturbance, the dynamic sensitivities of magnet variometers are required. It can be shown [52] simply that the dynamic sensitivity to a field variation of angular frequency ω is obtained by multiplying the static sensitivity s by a factor $A = \{(1 - n^2)^2 + 4\xi^2 n^2\}^{-1/2}$ where $n = \omega/\omega_0 = T_0/T$, with ω_0 the natural undamped angular frequency of the variometer and $\xi = k/2\omega_0 I$, with I the moment of inertia of the magnet system about its axis of rotation, and k the damping constant of the variometer. The system response lags by an angle given by $\tan \beta = 2\xi n/(1 - n^2)$.

The variation of A and β with n for different ξ is illustrated in Fig. 5. Thellier [52] recommends that a value of $\xi = 0 \cdot 5$ (half critical damping) should be adopted. The factor A is then constant to within ± 16 per cent from $T = \infty$ to $T = 0 \cdot 9 T_0$. If it is desired to measure events with periods as short as a few seconds by this means, it is clear that T_0 should not exceed a few seconds. This requires small magnets, and correspondingly small magnetic moments, but the methods described above can be used to obtain adequate sensitivity. The period of Z variometers employing two horizontal fibres can be more easily reduced to a few seconds than the period of balance magnets.

Many of the different makes of variometers in common use are underdamped and resonance amplification occurs near the natural period. Modern variometers are such that the eddy current damping can be easily adjusted by moving copper discs under the magnet.

The moments of the suspended magnets, those of the auxiliary field magnets, if any, the torsion of the fibres and the mechanical properties of Z balances all change with ambient temperature. In general, the effects on the sensitivities are unimportant, but the change in position of the record with respect to the baseline is important. Four methods of temperature compensation are in general use for Z variometers. In one which is common in modern Z balances the changes in magnetic moment are compensated by the change in the mechanical moment arm. This is done by using an Invar latitude spindle, and an opposite compensating aluminium spindle (see Section II–2–C). A second method uses an auxiliary field magnet producing a field of suitable magnitude opposite to the component being measured. With increasing temperature the

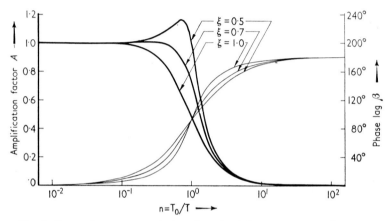

Fig. 5. Dynamic response and phase lag of quick-run magnet variometers.

decrease in magnetic moment, and hence in couple, is counteracted by the decrease in the opposing auxiliary field. A third method used with horizontal torsion fibres is to use two fibres with different constants and adjust suitably the amount of torsion in each. This method is also discussed later in Section II–2–C on field balances. Finally for Z systems as for H systems, optical compensation has been used, and for D systems, if no auxiliary magnets are used, temperature effects are generally negligible. Normally to take advantage of the great stability (baseline changes of 1 gamma per month are typical) of magnet variometers, it is best to control the ambient temperature of the operating enclosure to a few degrees, and to record the temperature of the variometers on the magnetogram, at a scale value of about 1°C/mm, by means of a bimetallic strip.

In general, in setting up variometers, care should be taken to obtain correct magnet orientations and to avoid interactions between the different magnets used. Recent photographic vario-meters can be more easily set up and adjusted, and some of their parts more easily interchanged than in older designs. Modern magnet materials have improved moment stability, and decreased variation with ambient temperature. Mobile variometers have been produced by putting three small magnet variometers in one thermostatted box and obtaining the great optical path lengths by multiple reflections. Experimental units have been built which are so small and rugged they can be transported without clamping the magnet systems.

The effective range on the recording drum in standard-run operation is usually increased by means of mirrors with three reflecting surfaces, producing a main trace and two reserve traces; formerly optical means were employed to obtain two traces of different sensitivity on the same drum. The modern quick-run optical systems are also much easier to set up.

B. *Magnet variometers with photocell recording*

At least two commercial systems have been produced using either a split photocell or diagonally separated selenium photo-cells connected in series as differential photocells, so that the polarity and amplitude of the output depends on the relative amount of light on each cell. The output is usually recorded with-out amplification on a suitable (usually 10 μA or 10 mV) pen recording meter. The record is immediately visible, and the speed of the chart easily varied. However, the range of linear measure-ment is very restricted even using very short projection distances and the stability depends directly on the constancy of the lamp filament brightness, whether or not scattered light enters the system, and the photocell characteristics, and is often quite poor.

These defects can be eliminated by the use of negative feedback. The output of a differential photocell is amplified and recorded. A portion of the output current is fed back to Helmholtz coils sur-rounding the variometer in order to restore the magnet system and keep the light beam in the centre of the photocell system. With sufficient gain and a high feedback ratio, great stability can be achieved and range problems can be overcome by electronic means (e.g. a servomotor–potentiometer arrangement) rather than by optical means. This principle has been successfully used by Chapman and Nelson [13] to construct a differential magnetograph for measuring the spatial gradients of the disturbance field produced by ionospheric currents. A variometer at one station records the difference between the disturbance at that station and the disturbance at a satellite station a few kilometres away. This is done by passing the current, which is fed back to the Helmholtz coils at the satellite station from the photocell and amplifier device, through identical Helmholtz coils around the variometer at the main station. It is important to note that very careful magnet orientation to within a few minutes of arc, and accurate temperature control, are essential to measure the field differences to 1 gamma reliably. However, some such automatic subtraction is certainly the only practical way to obtain the correct differences, particularly during times of great disturbance. It is possible to envisage a radio link to avoid the use of much wire.

C. *Field balances*

In mining geophysics, a number of simple and relatively crude devices, such as the dip circle, the Hotchkiss super-dip, and the Swedish mining compass, have been and are widely used for rapid measurement of large magnetic anomalies. These all depend essentially on the torque experienced by a magnet in the earth's field, and have been fully described, with their variations, by Heiland.[23] In general, the smaller magnetic anomalies, which often correspond to variations in the topography or composition of igneous or metamorphic basement rocks, or to variations in the structural arrangement of sedimentary rocks, are usually investigated by means of vertical or horizontal force magnetic balances. These were first developed by Schmidt in 1914.

The basic principle of a Z balance is that outlined above for magnetic variometers. The Z balance is usually arranged with copper dampers in an aluminium, temperature-insulated case which is fitted with levels and an arresting mechanism. Nowadays temperature-compensated magnet systems as described above are used with Alnico magnet blades, and a vertical brass screw for scale value adjustment. The systems are gold plated to prevent corrosion and scale value changes, and sapphire knife edges working on cylindrically faced quartz bearings are sometimes used. A detachable or non-detachable compass is used to orient the blades of the magnet perpendicular to the magnetic meridian and two stops, 180° apart, are provided for reading the instrument in the magnetic east and west positions respectively. The difference in the vertical field intensity between two points is measured on a scale in an autocollimating telescope viewing a mirror mounted on the centre block of the magnet system optically parallel to the knife edges. If, between two stations, the difference in scale reading of an appropriate index line, which is projected on to the mirror by the lens system, is Δs, then $\Delta s = 2f\Delta\theta$, where f is the focal length and $\Delta\theta$ is the angle of deflection of the magnet system between the two stations. With the magnet system oriented magnetic east–west, $\Delta\theta = \mathbf{M}\Delta Z/mgh$, and the scale value is $\Delta Z/\Delta s = mgh/2f\mathbf{M}$. The scale value changes with azimuth (see Fig. 4), but the mean of the two readings cancels out any error if the alignment is within 10° of magnetic east–west. Scale constants are usually adjusted to be in the range 10 to 30 gammas/division, corresponding to an effective range, using 3 index lines, of 1 200 to 3 600 gammas. Usually auxiliary magnets placed below the field balance with their axes vertical (in the first Gauss position) can be changed and adjusted so that the balances operate in any field up to 0·65 oersteds. It is, however, preferable to adjust the latitude weight to obtain on-scale readings in a given region rather than depend on the use of the calibrated auxiliary magnets.

Changes of 0·01 per cent in the scale constant can be caused by local anomalies in the gravitational field, but these are unimportant, since the method of determining the scale constant rarely has an accuracy better than 1 per cent. Larger errors are caused by tilting.[23, 8] The mean of two readings separated by 180° in azimuth eliminates small errors of misorientation and small errors of inclination of the knife edge, but effects such as a magnetic north–south inclination of the axis of rotation and a magnetic east–west inclination of the knife edges are not cancelled. Consequently the tripod axis should be carefully levelled in the magnetic north–south direction, and the instrument case in the orthogonal direction, for best results.

I

Many older balances are in use without the aluminium and Invar spindles. The large temperature variation in these balances can be considerably reduced by attaching one blade of the magnet system to the aluminium block by the screw nearest the north pole of the magnet only. In modern field balances the first method described above for a Z magnet variometer is used. It is possible to make the temperature coefficient of the magnet moment exactly equal to the total temperature coefficient in a horizontal direction of the system, in the field Z_0 for which the balance is horizontal. The compensation is then very close to zero for all values of Z within the range of the instrument, without the use of auxiliary magnets. Practical systems have residual effects of ~ 0.5 gamma/°C compared to ~ 7 gamma/°C without compensation.

In the practical use of Z balances it is clear that the time taken in setting up, levelling and orienting far exceeds the time spent in reading the instrument. The balances must be equipped with suitable mechanical devices for freeing the magnet system in exactly the same position at each use so that the axis is pre-determined. This requirement has led to the development of torsion field magnetometers, which sometimes do not require clamping during transportation. Haalck [22] has described a torsion magnetometer using a null method, in which the angle of twist measures Z but in which the reading is independent of orientation, so avoiding one operation. Using two fibres with torsion constants τ_1, τ_2 respectively, the scale value becomes $(\tau_1 + \tau_2)/2f\mathbf{M}$ and by changing the torsion in the two fibres it is possible to make the temperature coefficient less than 1 gamma/°C over a wide range. The tilt difficulties remain, and there are very small elastic after-effects. A self-levelling portable Z balance has been built which requires no orientation and no auxiliary magnets: a compensating field equal and opposite to the earth's vertical field is produced by Helmholtz coils. As in the torsion magnetometer the use of a null method eliminates the need for orientation, but the magnet system is floated and self-levelling by the action of gravity. The sensitivity, however, does depend on the azimuth in which the instrument is used. The range is controlled by switching resistances and the d.c. voltage is obtained from mercury standard cells.

In H field balances somewhat similar arrangements are used, but the magnet system is vertical and swings in the magnetic meridian and any auxiliary magnets are placed below the balance with their axes horizontal (second Gauss position). The scale constant is $(MZ - mga)/2fM$ where a is the vertical distance between the horizontal axis and the centre of gravity. Orientation and levelling errors are greater than in the vertical force balances, so requiring greater care in the one operating position used. The discussion above concerning temperature compensation and recent design improvements applies generally to these balances too. In Haalck's universal balance [23] a magnetic cross is used with two deflector magnets, one of which can be reversed. It is possible to determine ΔH and ΔZ by taking measurements in the magnetic north and south positions with the oblique deflecting magnet reversed in the two positions.

Many commercially made balances can be converted into base-station recording magnetometers by replacing the telescope by a reflecting head and a recording attachment tube. A typical system has a range of 500 gammas with a scale value of 10 gammas/mm on the photographic paper, and can operate for 12 to 24 h without attention.

3. Absolute Measurements

A. *Regional survey instruments and secondary standards*

The compass and dip-circle have been widely described, but it is worth recalling that the principal errors come from friction at the pivots. With the dip-circle, reversal procedures eliminate many errors, but large effects can be produced by small departures of the axis from a truly cylindrical form. The double-compass and its defects have been described elsewhere.[12]

Until quite recently deflection magnetometers have been widely used as regional survey instruments for the determination of H and as observatory standards.[12] These depend on the determination of the quantity MH by measurement of the period of oscillation of a freely suspended magnet on a torsionless fibre. Then by a suitable deflection experiment, the quotient M/H is determined and consequently M, H are determined independently. Usually the Lamont deflection position is used where the deflecting magnet of moment M is perpendicular to the second deflected magnet. Many practical difficulties arise, and one important fundamental limitation is that in weak fields the time of determination of the period of oscillation becomes excessively long. Normally the total time of determination of H is quite long and this is a severe disadvantage in standardizing observatory baselines at latitudes where magnetic disturbance is appreciable. Furthermore, it is necessary to correct for declination changes during the course of the experiment. In spite of corrections for the effect of temperature on the magnet moments, lengths and moments of inertia, the effect of induction on the moments and the distribution of magnetization in the magnet, comparisons of deflection magnetometers show discrepancies as large as 10 to 20 gammas. In a few observatory instruments where the distribution of magnetization has been carefully measured and allowed for in the deflection constants used, the discrepancies are reduced to a few gammas. The constants of portable deflection magnetometers are determined by periodic comparisons with standard observatory instruments, rather than by direct measurement of their dimensions. Nowadays, the quartz horizontal magnetometer (QHM) has largely replaced the deflection magnetometer.

Declination can be determined by using a telescope and horizontal circle to measure the angles between the axis of a magnet, which can swing in a horizontal plane and hangs from a practically torsionless fibre, and a distant mark of known true azimuth. The torsionless state of the fibre can be found by suspending a nonmagnetic bar, and residual torsion and misalignment between the normal to the mirror and the magnet axis can be determined by a technique using two magnets of different moments and suspending each magnet in two positions. The declinometer, as this instrument is called, is still commonly used as a D standard in observatories, and an accuracy of ± 3 seconds of arc is obtained with care.

A universal type of field theodolite magnetometer inductor is still made for regional field surveys. The theodolite is used for sunshots to determine the azimuth of the mark, one attachment is used to determine D and H by the methods described above, and in addition, an earth inductor can be attached to measure the inclination, I (see Section III–2).

In the QHM, designed by La Cour,[26] a magnet of moment $\mathbf{M}$ is suspended by a quartz fibre with torsion constant τ. Using an autocollimating telescope, a horizontal circle reading, corresponding to a meridian error α, is obtained when the residual angle of twist in the quartz fibre is δ. Readings $\alpha + \phi_1$, $\alpha - \phi_2$, when torsions of $+2\pi$, -2π respectively are introduced, are obtained. These angles are measured when, after rotating the head, the magnet is again in the same position relative to the case. Then $\mathbf{M}H \sin \alpha = \tau\delta$, $\mathbf{M}H \sin (\alpha + \phi_1) = \tau(\delta + 2\pi)$ and $\mathbf{M}H \sin (\alpha - \phi_2) = \tau(\delta - 2\pi)$. The difference in readings for the torqued positions is $2\theta = \phi_1 + \phi_2$ and we define $\phi_1 - \phi_2 = 2\beta$. Then for small values of α and β, $H = 2\pi\tau/\mathbf{M} \sin \theta[1 - \beta^2/\{2(1 - \cos \theta)^2\}]$ and $\alpha = \beta \cos \theta/(1 - \cos \theta)$. Thus, if $\tau/\mathbf{M}$ is known, H can be determined from a measurement of θ, with a second order correction for β, and α can be determined from the determination of β and θ. This means that D can be determined, since the residual torque (which can change with time) can be accurately determined and allowed for.

The ratio $\tau/\mathbf{M}$ is temperature dependent, and so the temperature must be carefully measured. A small induction correction must also be made to $\mathbf{M}$. However, the excellent elastic properties of the quartz fibres used and the stability of the magnet moments are such that QHMs are invaluable for field observations and for the convenient intercomparison of primary observatory standards. A stability of 1 in 10^4 or better over a few years seems common. Also the speed of operation of the QHM is a decided advantage in the determination of H baseline values at high latitudes. A typical result is that the scatter in six baseline determinations does not exceed 2 gammas even though the field may change by ten times this amount during the total time of observations (20 min). It should be noted that the same instrument can be used to give reasonable deflections ($\phi \simeq 60^\circ$) in higher fields by the introduction of a torsion of $\pm 4\pi$ and appropriate modification of the above formula. By suitably modifying the optical system, odd multiples of π can be used.

The BMZ, or magnetometer zero balance, developed by La Cour [27] is a modification of the Schmidt Z balance in which the centre of gravity of a very small magnet system is vertically below the knife edge, and the system is kept with its magnetic axis horizontal (determined by the telescope neutral division) by means of a fixed tubular field magnet, which cancels out most of the Z field, and an auxiliary turn magnet, which is rotated about a horizontal axis to cancel the remainder of the Z field. Very careful initial adjustments of the system are required, and the null reading in any azimuth is theoretically independent of the azimuth but readings are usually taken with the north end of the magnet system to the south where the sensitivity is greatest (see Fig. 4). La Cour [27] has described procedures for checking the stability of the neutral position and the initial adjustments. Induction effects must be allowed for and the temperature coefficient of the field and turn magnets and of the mechanical system separating the field and balance magnets must be known. In practice temperatures must be known to 0·05°C and rates of change to 0·03°C/min for an accuracy of 1 gamma.

It is clear that the use of the BMZ as an absolute instrument requires absolute calibration of the moments and positions of the field and turn magnets. In general, even the best magnetic materials suitably aged are such that drifts of ~5 gammas/month can be expected.

Although such a method would not, in general, appear satisfactory for measurements from a moving support subject to accelerations, apparatus of this type, suspended in gimbals, has been used in aeromagnetic Z surveys [29] and in experiments in the depths of the sea.[16]

B. *Observatory primary standards of geomagnetic field intensity*

Because of the many difficulties regarding temperature, induction and the uncertainties in the deflection constant in the absolute determination of H by the oscillation–deflection method described above, alternative methods have been developed in which the torque on a magnet in some component of the earth's field is balanced by the torque on the same magnet produced by a so-called absolute field, i.e. a field produced by a system of accurately constructed coils, and a known d.c. current. These methods have necessitated large and precise coils, and the measurement against a standard of voltage of the potential drop across a standard resistance carrying the coil current. Three types of instruments have provided the internationally accepted primary magnetic field standards, although it seems possible they will soon be replaced by the methods described in Section VIII.

In the sine galvanometer of Barnett [4] the applied field of the coils is perpendicular to the deflected position of the suspended magnet (Lamont method). In the Schuster–Smith method [51] a fixed field is applied and its direction adjusted so that the deflected position of the suspended magnet is perpendicular to the meridian and small errors become unimportant. Fig. 6 illustrates the methods. Using the Schuster–Smith method, a field survey instrument with a robust needle on a pivot and with fluid flotation has been built, but is not in use.

The Dye system [15] is somewhat different in that the field of the

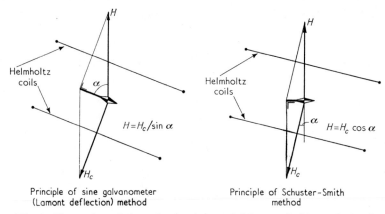

Principle of sine galvanometer
(Lamont deflection) method

Principle of Schuster–Smith
method

Fig. 6. Illustration of sine-galvanometer and Schuster–Smith methods of determining H absolutely.

coils is used to cancel the earth's field. A small galvanometer with its coil plane vertical, and sometimes with a high permeability core,[6] is set vibrating at the centre of the coil by an a.c. current at the mechanical resonance frequency. Vibrations occur except when $Z = 0$.

Since the absolute accuracy of the ampere is known to 5 parts in 10^6, in principle the problems of precise coil construction limit the absolute accuracy of these magnetic field standards. Coils have been constructed so that a precision of 1 part in 25 000 or better is possible. However, in practice, the standard resistance and standard cells used must be checked regularly against precise national standards to maintain the field standards to 1 gamma or better.

4. Modern Magnet Materials

With the exception of the instruments described in Section II–3–B above, all torque methods have gained substantially from the development of better permanent-magnet materials. This should be clear from the discussions above. One convenient measure of the suitability of magnet material for use in permanent magnets is the product of the coercivity in oersteds and the remanence in gauss. The coercivity is defined as the reverse field intensity, H_c, for which the induction becomes zero and the remanence is defined as the induction, B_r, in zero magnetizing field. These terms are illustrated in Fig. 7, which shows the demagnetization curves of

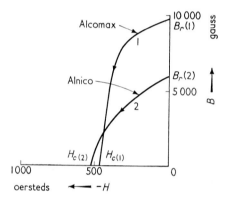

Fig. 7. Demagnetization curves of two typical modern magnet materials.

two typical modern magnet materials. Prior to 1930, a product $H_c B_r \sim 6 \times 10^4$ was obtained for the materials commonly used such as carbon steels, often with tungsten added, but nowadays the newer magnet steels such as Alnico, Alnico V and Alcomax with varying amounts of aluminium, nickel, copper and cobalt added have a product ~ 2 to 4×10^6.

Changes in the heat treatment, which nowadays often involves tempering in a large field, have been used to improve the stability of the newer magnet steels. These also have temperature coefficients of moment $\simeq -14 \times 10^{-5}/°C$ compared to $\simeq -48 \times 10^{-5}/°C$ for older materials. Irreversible changes in magnetization with temperature for short length/diameter ratio magnets can be largely eliminated by a partial demagnetization of a few per cent in an a.c. field. Without such treatment, a loss of 2 per cent in moment for a 70°C change is possible.

III. INDUCTION METHODS

1. General Principle

If the total magnetic flux Φ linked with a circuit changes, an e.m.f. is induced of magnitude $10^{-8}\dot{\Phi}$ V. This law of electro-magnetic induction has been used for many years in magnetic measurements in two general ways. In the first, used for absolute measurements and spatial investigations, a coil, which is usually circular and with many turns, is rapidly rotated at an angular speed of ω radians/sec about an axis lying along a diameter of the coil. If the coil has N turns of area A cm², and the component of induction perpendicular to the axis is B, an alternating e.m.f. of $10^{-8} BAN \cos (\omega t)$V is induced, and this can either be measured, or the null position found, when the axis of the coil is parallel to the induction B and no flux is linked with the circuit. In the second class fixed coils in various orientations are used and the e.m.f.s measured that are produced by the appropriate time rates of change of the geomagnetic field.

2. Absolute Measurements

The earth-inductor method of measuring the inclination, I, is commonly used in magnetic observatories for absolute control and has been adopted for use in regional survey instruments. The axis of the coil is carried in a frame whose direction can be varied and measured by a vertical circle. The induction coil is placed with its axis in the magnetic meridian by means of a compass attachment and the axis of the vertical circle is levelled. The coil is rotated by means of a non-magnetic linkage. The output is rectified by a commutator keyed to one end of the coil spindle and the d.c. current indicated by either a moving-coil galvanometer, or more often, to avoid external magnetic effects, an astatic galvanometer. The vertical circle reading, when the output is zero and the coil axis lies along the direction of **F**, determines the angle of dip. In the best observatory inductors the coil is supported in its gimbal by sapphire bearings, the mechanical design is such as to reduce the distortion or deflection of all the structural members and the brushes can be aligned and individually adjusted. An accuracy of 0·1′ is possible, and in a good instrument this corresponds to the determination of the galvanometer zero deflection to about 1 mm. The rectification of the current by means of commutators introduces thermocurrents and other parasitic contact voltages, which can be kept to the equivalent of about 0·1′ with good design. At sea in marine inductors the unrectified output from slip rings has been used to operate more rugged string galvanometers.

Alternatively the e.m.f. can be taken off by slip rings and fed to a suitable tuned amplifier. One such instrument has been designed as a portable three-component magnetometer.[54] By successive adjustments of the azimuth and inclination of the coil axis to obtain zero output, the declination, D, and inclination, I, are obtained from the horizontal and vertical circle readings. An accuracy of 0·1′ is claimed. The direction is then determined of the resultant of **F** and a field produced by Helmholtz coils with their axis perpendicular to that of the induction coil. **F** can then be computed as illustrated in Fig. 8. An accuracy of ± 1 gamma is claimed, but this depends on the stability of the dimensions of the Helmholtz coils and the standard resistance and cell used in determining **F**. It would appear more likely that the sensitivity is ± 1 gamma and the accuracy depends considerably on the stability of these three parameters and the frequency of their standardization.

3. Methods for Investigating the Spatial Variations of the Geomagnetic Field

A vibrating-coil system has been developed to avoid slip rings and use flexible leads.[17] Two elements are used to orient a third by servo means parallel to the total field, **F**. The output of the third element is rectified, and fed back to coils around it so that the induction is always near zero; the fed back current provides a record of **F**. Such a system mounted on a boom forward of a ship has been successfully used for recording small structural anomalies over the continental shelf.

Similar a.c. methods have been developed for airborne surveys,[28] and it is claimed they can be used for measurement of the vertical field intensity by alignment of the inductor-coil axis along the magnetic meridian. Thus at the latitude of Ottawa, an alignment error of one degree causes an error of less than one gamma in Z. However, level errors are much more important, and a one degree error can cause effects of 300 gammas. The errors must therefore be large unless complicated stabilization systems are used to compensate for aircraft accelerations. In some airborne devices high-speed air turbines have been used to increase the signal, the

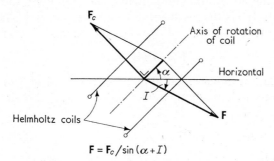

$$F = F_c / \sin (\alpha + I)$$

Fig. 8. Illustration of earth inductor method of determining **F** absolutely.

coil tuned to the frequency of rotation and an air transformer used to avoid contact noise. The theoretical limitation is then thermal noise in the system.

A ground-prospecting gradiometer using the principle of induction has been described by Roman and Sermon.[39] The instruments described above all use an air core, but ferromagnetic cores have been used in certain field instruments.

4. Methods for Investigating the Time Variations of the Geomagnetic Field

The e.m.f.s produced in fixed coils by the time variations in the induction produced by the geomagnetic field have been recorded in many ways, galvanometers or fluxmeters with photographic registration, or a.c. amplifiers with pen recorders or magnetic tape being the most common. The coils may be used with or without highly permeable cores. Thellier [52] and Selzer [46] have recently discussed many of the merits and the disadvantages of different combinations. The discussion below is given as an illustration of how the design should be related to the sensitivity and pass-band desired.

A. *Air-cored coils*

(i) *With moving-coil meters.* This method is often used at magnetic observatories because of its simplicity and cheapness. For stability it is desirable that the coils should be buried, or mounted on a sufficiently rigid stand to avoid wind sway. In any practical design therefore for the measurement of the rates of change of the horizontal components, the maximum radius of the coil is fixed. If σ is the resistivity of the wire material, ρ its density, W the weight of the coil, A its total surface area and r its resistance,

$$A = a(rW/4\sigma\rho)^{1/2}$$

The dynamic response in mm/gauss per second of a moving-coil galvanometer to a magnetic induction $B = B_0 + \Delta B \sin \omega t$ can be shown to equal

$\Delta s \sin (\omega t - \tfrac{1}{2}\pi - \beta)$ with

$$\Delta s/\omega\Delta B = s_g A 10^{-2}(r + r_g)^{-1}\{(1 - n^2)^2 + 4\xi^2 n^2\}^{-1/2}$$
$$= s_g a 10^{-2}(r + r_g)^{-1}(W_r/4\sigma\rho)^{1/2}\{(1 - n^2)^2 + 4\xi^2 n^2\}^{-1/2}$$

and $$\tan \beta = 2\xi n/(1 - n^2)$$

where ω_0 is the natural angular frequency of the galvanometer ($\omega_0^2 = c/I$), n is the ratio ω/ω_0, k is the damping constant of the galvanometer produced by air friction and fibre viscosity, a is the galvanometer coil constant, r_g is the resistance of the galvanometer coil, I is its moment of inertia, s_g is the sensitivity of the galvanometer in mm/μA, and

$$2\xi\omega_0 = k + a^2/(r + r_g).$$

If viscous damping is neglected, $\xi = (r_c + r_g)/(r + r_g)$ where r_c is the critical damping resistance and, by differentiation, it can be shown that the dynamic sensitivity at a frequency ω is a maximum when

$$r^2 = \{(1 - n^2)^2 r_g^2 + 4(r_c + r_g)^2\} /(1 - n^2)^2$$

Practical systems are required to operate in the range $n = 1$ to 10^{-2}, and r_c is usually much greater than r_g. The condition therefore becomes $r = 2r_c$ and $\xi = 0\cdot5$, and the frequency-dependent term is analogous to that discussed above in Section II–2–A, and the sensitivity is constant within 16 per cent for a range of periods from $T = \infty$ to $T = 0.9T_0$. This constant sensitivity in units of mm/10^{-5} gauss per second is $s_g 10^{-7}a(W/8\sigma\rho r_c)^{1/2}$ when the resistance r of the coil windings is made equal to $2r_c$, and so a galvanometer with a maximum value of $s_g r_c^{-1/2}$ should be chosen, subject to its natural period being sufficiently short for the experiment under consideration, and subject to r_c being not too large, which would involve too many turns for an easily constructed coil.

For a practical coil with $a = 1$ m, $W = 20$ kg, coupled to a typical good 1-sec galvanometer with $r_g = 450$ Ω, $r_c = 12\,000$ Ω,

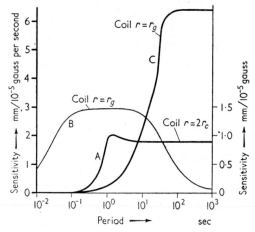

Fig. 9. Theoretical curves of dynamic response of a 20 kg, 1 m radius coil coupled to a moving galvanometer with $s_g = 1.5 \times 10^3$ mm/μA, $T_0 = 1$ sec, $r_c = 12 \times 10^3$ Ω and $r_g = 450$ Ω. Curve A corresponds to half critical damping and curves B and C correspond to the condition of power matching.

$s_g = 1.5 \times 10^3$ mm/μA, this involves 9×10^3 turns of No. 31 gauge magnet wire for r approximately equal to $2r_c$. Then the sensitivity in the pass band from $T = \infty$ to $T = 0.9$ sec is 1.75 mm/10^{-5} gauss per second and is illustrated in curve A of Fig. 9. One international recommendation is that the sensitivity to be used in observatory recording should be more than ten times greater, and equal to 20 mm/10^{-5} gauss per second. If it is desired to extend the pass band down to ~1 to 3 sec, the best galvanometers available are such that to achieve this sensitivity, the weight of the coil must be increased to ~300 to 1000 kg, which is absurd for a coil with its axis horizontal. There is no particular difficulty with $\dot{Z}$, since it is clear that in practice a radius of about 10 m can easily be adopted, corresponding to 10 times fewer turns of the same wire for the same weight (20 kg). The sensitivity would then approximately equal that internationally recommended.

Another design criterion which is sometimes used, if it is required to have the sensitivity in mm/gauss approximately constant over the spectral region of interest, is that of a power match at long periods, when r is made equal to r_g, and the maximum long-period sensitivity is obtained by choosing a galvanometer with the largest value of $s_g r_g^{-1/2}$. Usually then in the pass band of interest the damping is so great that the effective sensitivity in mm/10^{-5} gauss becomes $s_g a 10^{-7} \omega_0 (W/\sigma \rho r_g)^{1/2}(8\xi)^{-1}$ and since in this overdamped case $\xi = r_c/2r_g$, the sensitivity in mm/10^{-5} gauss becomes $s_g a 10^{-7} \omega_0 (W r_g/\sigma \rho)^{1/2}(4r_c)^{-1}$.

At high frequencies the response falls away as n^{-1}, and at low frequencies as n. In Fig. 9 curves B and C illustrate the response of a coil with $a = 1$ m, $W = 20$ kg, consisting of 1200 turns of No. 22 gauge copper wire with r approximately equal to r_g or 450 Ω and coupled to the typical galvanometer described above. Curve B shows the partial fluxmeter action and Curve C the response in terms of mm/10^{-5} gauss per second. These examples should make it clear that the optimum choice of galvanometer, and its method of loading by the induction coil, depends upon the pass band required, and the desirability of equalizing either the amplitude or the rate of change response. Kalashnikov [25] has described a typical overdamped system, and Thellier [52] has discussed critically damped systems in operation at various observatories.

It was shown above that the maximum sensitivity of a practical horizontal field rate of change system which gives approximately constant response down to ~1 sec is less than that required in some applications, even with the optimum design. It is, however, possible to use a long-period galvanometer with the requisite greater sensitivity and increase its short period response by the use of negative feedback. The damping is then effectively reduced, and it is possible to use a matched power system with the higher sensitivity illustrated by the long period part of curve C in Fig. 9. The light beam from the galvanometer falls on a differential photocell whose output is amplified and used to drive an insensitive short-period galvanometer, or a pen recording meter. The output is also mixed with the induction-coil output at the input to the sensitive galvanometer. Using well-balanced long-period galvanometers, it is possible to reduce the natural period up to ten times by this means. When the feedback ratio is large the ratio of natural frequencies with and without feedback, $\omega_0^1/\omega_0 = gs_g/R$ where g is the gain of the photocell and amplifier in $\mu V/mm$, s_g is the sensitivity of the galvanometer in $mm/\mu A$ and R is the feedback resistance in ohms. The amplifier output is R/r times that of the coil. Scale values of 5×10^{-7} gauss/sec per mm can be achieved, and by means of capacities in the feedback loop, the damping can be adjusted. The signal-to-noise ratio of the system is increased by choosing a galvanometer for which $s_g r_g^{-1/2}$ is large, and making $r = r_g$.

In the discussion so far self-inductance of the coils has been neglected. This is reasonable for large-diameter air-cored systems, and periods longer than ~ 1 sec. For the two coil designs discussed above the inductive impedance becomes equal to the coil resistance at frequencies of about 50 c/s only.

(ii) *With amplifiers.* The induced e.m.f. can be modulated by a vibrating reed at a suitable frequency (60 or 400 c/s), and the output amplified by a high-gain narrow-band amplifier. Thermal noise in the coil and pickup by the chopping reed limit the useful gain. With good design, a coil of 20 kg, radius 1 m and resistance a few thousand ohms, can be arranged with such circuits to give an equivalent noise level less than 2×10^{-6} gauss/sec. The amplifier output after demodulating can be integrated and displayed on a moving-chart recording meter at a suitable speed. Alternatively magnetic-tape recording can be used, which has great advantages for automatic spectral analysis of magnetic disturbances. Integration of the signal may or may not be used. One method which has been used in the period band $\frac{1}{4}$ to 60 sec is to feed the amplifier output to a multi-vibrator, the frequency of which linearly depends on the input, and record this frequency-modulated signal at slow speed ($\frac{1}{4}$ in./sec) on magnetic tape.

In investigations at sub-audio frequencies air-cored coils are usually used to avoid the magnetic noise associated with the ferromagnetic core systems described below. Wider band amplifiers are generally required.

B. *Coils with ferromagnetic cores*

These have been discussed by Thellier [52] and by Selzer.[46] Demagnetization effects which reduce the effective core permeability are shape-dependent and are minimized by making the length/diameter ratio large. Self-inductance effects are also important. The core material should be very stable, and for linearity should not become saturated in the ambient field in the central parts of the core where the demagnetizing field is weakest. Using a core with a diameter of a few centimetres, a length of 1 or 2 m and a weight of wire about equal to that of the core (about 10 kg), it is possible to wind the core so that in the centre of the pass band of interest ωL is approximately equal to r.[46] Such a system coupled to a partial fluxmeter ($T_0 = 20$ sec, $\xi = 15$), with $r = r_g$ gives a sensitivity of about 2×10^6 mm/gauss ± 10 per cent from 2 to 235 sec, and the peaking produced by the self-inductance occurs at periods less than 1 sec.

Again amplification has been used, and the output recorded on magnetic tape.

C. *Induction-coil variometers*

In these the ferromagnetic core is replaced by a large magnet variometer. The theory and operation of such instruments has been described by Grenet.[21] Sensitivities of about 10 mm/gamma in the pass band 4 to 40 sec can easily be obtained, using large magnets and a medium-quality galvanometer, but the sensitivity and phase depend strongly on the period, and the method appears to have few advantages over those described above.

IV. SATURABLE CORE METHODS

1. General Principle

Saturable-core magnetometers consist basically of a rod or strip of ferromagnetic material with suitable non-linear magnetization properties acting as a core for one or more windings which are connected to a.c. exciting and indicating circuits. The magnetic field under investigation produces magnetization in the core which is measured by means of the changes in the flux produced by the periodic excitation current. Sinusoidal waves, pulses and special waveforms have been used for excitation, and the induced voltages produced by the changes in flux have been measured in many different ways in order to detect the changes of amplitude, phase, harmonic content or some combination of these which results from changes in the ambient field. In principle, therefore, saturable-core methods are specialized induction methods, but their development has been so widespread and their advantages are so marked in many ways that it is convenient to describe them in this separate section.

The first saturable-core magnetometer was described in 1936 by Aschenbrenner and Goubau.[1] Saturable-core methods require no moving parts, and so their action is independent of the accelerations of their support. Consequently they can be successfully used for airborne and seaborne instruments provided suitable techniques of orientation are used. Wartime developments in airborne submarine detectors, and post-war developments in aeromagnetic surveys [3] have rapidly led to a variety of sensitive instruments using this method, and saturable-core magnetometers can now be used successfully for recording time variations, for the measurement of spatial gradients, for ground regional surveys and for rocket researches in the upper atmosphere. The principle is also used in such a well-known navigational device as the fluxgate compass. Electronic magnetometers based on the saturable-core principle have many advantages over most of the instruments described above in speed, flexibility, ease of recording, the smallness of the sensitive detecting head and so on. However, their stability and the complexity of some units make them less than ideal in certain applications, notably when very precise absolute values are required.

2. Suitable Core Materials

High-permeability alloys which saturate, and hence show pronounced non-linearity in moderate fields, are most suitable, although ordinary ferromagnetic materials give in principle the same, but much smaller, effects. Suitable alloys are the class of nickel–iron alloys, or Permalloys, which were originally developed as transformer materials and have narrow hysteresis loops. These alloys must be suitably heat-treated to release strains so that after cooling the initial permeability is high. For example, for a 79 per cent nickel Permalloy, rapid quenching followed by a slow anneal

K

in a magnetic field increases the initial permeability and reduces the hysteresis loop, crystal anisotropy and magnetostriction.[7] Mumetal, or Permalloy C, contains 75 to 80 per cent nickel, has an initial permeability of about 10000, a maximum permeability of about 60000 for a field of 0·03 oersted and saturates in a field of approximately 3 oersteds. It is especially suitable for use in saturable-core magnetometers, but other alloys, such as Mo-Permalloy, can be successfully used. The Barkhausen noise per cycle of the hysteresis loop depends somewhat on the heat treatment,[19] but in general this does not determine the best heat-treatment for this application of these alloys.

Even in long and thin rods there is a reduction in the effective permeability because of demagnetization. This reduction is difficult to estimate, for thin strips are often used in saturable-core magnetometers (typically 10 cm × 0·2 cm × 0·04 cm), but on occasion thin rods with a length/diameter ratio of only 100 have been used. The effective maximum permeability is then reduced some 25 times, and in making estimates of sensitivity, or in tuning saturable-core magnetometers, this reduction must be remembered.

3. Peak Voltage Method

The sensitive element consists of a bridge of two strips of Mumetal with oppositely wound primary exciting coils. The excitation fields at an audio frequency f are thus in opposite directions in the two cores. In one core a small ambient field, H, parallel to the common axis aids the exciting field and in the other opposes it. The usual explanation of the method is that, when the cores are driven by the a.c. field past saturation, there exists a time lag in the magnetic cycle of one compared to the other, and at the points of saturation momentary unbalance occurs in the induction fields of the two cores and voltage pips appear across a secondary winding surrounding both. It is, however, simple to show that, when the capacity of the secondary and cable is neglected, the theoretical pulse width becomes extremely small in low ambient fields ($\simeq 3 \times 10^{-9}$ sec for $H = 10$ gammas when $f = 400$ c/s) and the cores must be extremely evenly balanced. A better explanation is that partially illustrated in Fig. 10. Because of saturation, the effective permeability of the two cores together changes $2f$ times per second, and therefore in the presence of an

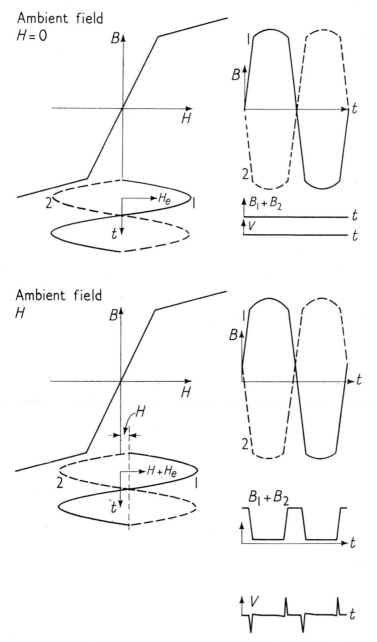

Fig. 10. Illustration of generation of a spike pattern from a two-element inductor in presence of ambient field.

ambient field a voltage is induced in the secondary with an amplitude and phase which depend on the magnitude and sense of H. In Fig. 10 the periodic exciting current and hence field is assumed to be sinusoidal, i.e. derived from a high-impedance source. When the exciting voltage is sinusoidal, the peaks on one side of zero increase (those corresponding to entering saturation when the inductance decreases), whereas those on the other side decrease (corresponding to leaving saturation when the inductance increases). The peak voltage of the large voltage pips is proportional to H, which can therefore be measured using infinite impedance detectors with suitable time constants feeding a strip-chart recording voltmeter, as illustrated in Fig. 11. In practice, as illustrated in the insert to Fig. 11, the primary winding can be wound on one strip or rod of Permalloy and the use of a separate secondary winding avoided. Furthermore, it is usual to avoid the noise problem in zero ambient field by deliberately unbalancing the two elements by means of a shunt across one so that alternate positive and negative spikes of equal magnitude are obtained in zero ambient field. An ambient field then introduces a difference in the positive and negative spikes, which is measured by a differential detector. The system illustrated in Fig. 11 is basically that used in early airborne total-intensity magnetometers.[59] The axis of the detector must be suitably oriented, and most of the field is compensated by means of another winding fed with direct current. Step switches, activated by the recorder, can be arranged to adjust this compensation in steps to keep the pen record automatically on scale.

A good sensitive inductor gives a peak signal amplitude of about 100 μV/gamma with a background noise level of about 10 to 20 μV. This magnetic noise and its reduction are discussed in Section IV-5. The peak voltage sensitivity is proportional to the self-inductance of the primary windings in free air, the frequency of excitation, and parameters which involve the magnetization characteristics of the core material but are a maximum when a sharp knee occurs in the B/H curve and the cores are driven well beyond saturation. To minimize demagnetization effects, the length/cross section ratio of the cores should be large, and the strips used should be thin to avoid eddy currents. Audio range frequencies from 400 to 1000 c/s are best.

Recently Maxwell [30] has described a station recording magneto-meter employing peak detection in which feedback is used to keep the ambient field unchanged at the sensitive head. Wickerham [58] has described an airborne magnetometer in which the feedback current is controlled by a servo-system geared to a rate generator. The rectified output of the rate generator is proportional to the

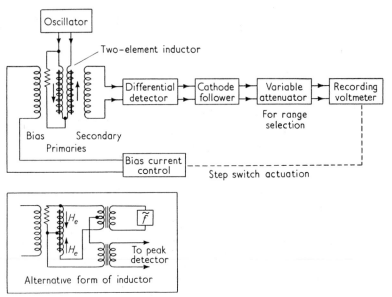

Fig. 11. Schematic diagram of peak voltage magnetometer using a two-element–three-winding inductor.

horizontal gradient of the total field when the magnetometer is operated from a moving support. Simple calculations show that the accuracy of such a gradiometer far exceeds that feasible by using two saturable-core magnetometers separated in space. The use of feedback in saturable-core magnetometers is more fully discussed in Sections IV–4–A, B below.

4. Second Harmonic Methods

Usually, the more recently developed magnetometers use the second harmonic component only of the unbalance voltage. A large number of magnetometers of this type have been described

for different uses, but in general they can be considered in two
classes according to whether untuned or tuned inductors are used.
The latter have great advantages in sensitivity and simplicity.

A. *Untuned systems*

Either a single-element magnetometer or a bridge of two
matched elements oppositely excited can be used. The use of a
bridge simplifies the filtering problem by approximately cancelling
out the odd harmonics and leaving only the even harmonics, which
are sensitive to the sign of the ambient field and vanish when it is
zero. Thus, referring to Fig. 12, if the magnetization curve in the

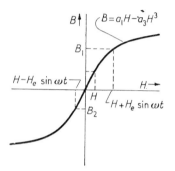

Fig. 12. Illustration of magnetization
curve for two saturable cores of an untuned second harmonic magnetometer.

region of interest can be approximately written $B = a_1 H - a_3 H^3$,
then the induced voltage is proportional to

$$-d(B_1 + B_2)/dt = 6a_3 \omega H_e^2 H \sin 2\omega t$$

for the two element inductor and

$$-dB_1/dt = 3a_3 \omega H_e^2 H \sin 2\omega t$$
$$+ \omega H_e \cos \omega t (3a_3 H_e^2/4 + 3a_3 H^2 - a_1)$$
$$- \omega H_e \cos 3\omega t (3a_3 H_e^2/4)$$

for the single element inductor.

In general, three types of operation are clear. In the first, which
was mentioned above, the largest part of the field component to
be measured is cancelled out by means of a winding, and variations
from this known base, which is made as drift-free as possible,
recorded. In the second negative feedback is used and the d.c. output of the amplifier-detector is fed back to a winding about the
sensitive elements in such a way as to minimize the resultant

ambient field change there. In the third case negative feedback is used together with the cancellation of the largest part of the ambient field by a suitable winding. Separate windings can be used for cancellation or bias, feedback, the secondary and the primary, or one winding can serve all four purposes.

A single-element system, typical of those in this class employing feedback, has been described by Schonstedt and Irons [45] and is illustrated schematically in Fig. 13. Two band-pass filters are required; one, tuned to the excitation frequency f, situated in the driving circuit, to minimize the second harmonic content in the driving current which could produce false zero ambient field signals, and the second, tuned to the second harmonic, used to suppress the odd harmonics before major amplification. This is necessary to avoid the first and other unwanted harmonics saturating the later stages of the amplifier and producing non-linearity. The feedback action should be clear from the figure.

A second harmonic output of 10 to 35 μV/gamma is typical with a magnetic noise level sometimes as low as 0·03 gamma. The principal disadvantage is the need to use two critically tuned circuits. If any comparatively simple filters with sufficient discrimination in one octave are used, a phase shift is introduced which changes rapidly with changes in the excitation frequency and with variations in the components of the filter. When a phase-sensitive detector is used, such phase shifts become serious. Furthermore, some of the filters used have had to be specially constructed,[40] and their input and output impedances must be matched.

The resistive feedback situation is illustrated in the insert to Fig. 13. When the product $SGA \gg R$, the sensitivity becomes R/A and is largely independent of the amplifier gain and variations caused by changes in tube characteristics, and the linearity of response is increased, since the resulting change in ambient field at the detector is SGA/R times less than the change without feedback. The scale value can be adjusted by changing R. To obtain 1000 gammas full scale in a recording magnetometer, R/A must be in the range 150 to 1000 V/oersted for many inexpensive recording voltmeters and milliameters. For $S = 25 \mu$V/gamma, $G \gg 60$ to 400. The voltage gain can easily be obtained, but despite the band-pass filter, the amount of fundamental frequency present in the second harmonic signal with a single-element

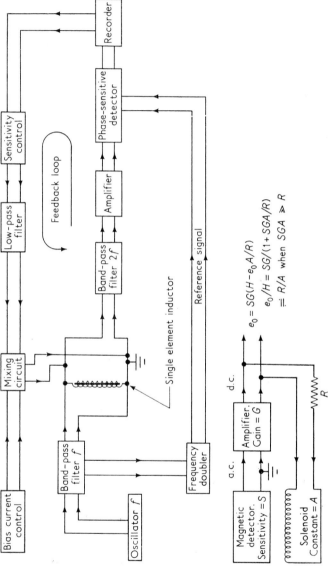

Fig. 13. Schematic diagram of an untuned second harmonic magnetometer using feedback and a single-element-single-winding inductor.

inductor is so large that the amplifier may become saturated. Also the narrower the pass band of the filter used, the smaller is the feedback which can be applied before oscillations occur because of the frequency shift produced by the filter inside the feedback loop. In one magnetometer [40] a voltage gain is used before the phase-sensitive detector which is sufficiently low to avoid amplifier saturation by unwanted harmonics. The output of the detector is then chopped, amplified and used to control a servomotor geared to a potentiometer which controls the feedback current.

Some of the difficulties can be minimized by the use of a balanced two-element inductor, and feedback factors up to 25 have been reported.[18]

B. *Tuned systems*

By means of a suitable condenser across the secondary winding of a balanced two-element inductor, the second harmonic component of the signal can be so greatly enhanced that it is unnecessary to use band-pass filters [48, 49] Infinite sensitivity can be obtained because of the presence of a fourth harmonic component in the effective time-dependent permeability of the two cores, and the system becomes unstable if the resistance of the secondary winding is below a critical value. In order to find operating conditions which do not change critically with small variations in the frequency and amplitude of excitation, or with small changes in the tuning capacity, the tuned system must be shunted with a sufficiently low resistance to restore optimum stability. The sensitivity is then found to be still at a conveniently high value of 1 to 2 mV/gamma. Serson and Hannaford [47] have computed the Fourier coefficients in terms of two permeability parameters, and shown that, in their approximation, the sensitivity remains greater than 1 mV/gamma and variations in phase less than ~1° for variations of a few per cent in the above parameters provided the exciting field is only about 10 per cent greater than the field required to saturate the cores.

Fig. 14 shows schematically such a tuned system with feedback. The signal is amplified and detected by a phase-sensitive detector. Quite commonly a simple low-Q resonant circuit is used in the input stage, which is followed by a limiting stage before the detector. The output of the phase-sensitive detector is fed to a d.c. amplifier with capacitive feedback and consisting of a balanced input stage and cathode follower. The output of this amplifier is recorded in a suitable way, and fed back to a solenoid surrounding the sensitive head of the magnetometer. Detailed consideration of the feedback loop together with the amplifier lags produced by the time constant of the phase-sensitive detector shows that the system behaves like a simple servomechanism. Serson, Mack and Whitham [48] have shown that it is possible to obtain feedback factors as high as 4×10^5 for specialized applications.

Typical station recording magnetometers have been described with feedback factors from 20 (Meek and Hector [31]) to 10^3 (Serson [49]). In a practical design the time constant of the inte-

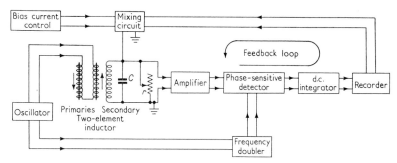

Fig. 14. Schematic diagram of a tuned second harmonic magnetometer using feedback and a two-element–two-winding inductor.

grator can be adjusted to obtain suitable damping (half critical) at the requisite sensitivity determined by R/A as before. The natural frequency is largely determined by the time constant of the phase-sensitive detector, and can be as high as 20 c/s. The response to very quick field changes is usually limited by the saturation of the phase-sensitive detector, and d.c. drifts at the input to the d.c. amplifier can be kept to a fraction of one gamma.

The details of different magnetometers [31, 48, 49] vary in the thermal treatment of the cores, their mounting, the size of the sensitive head and windings (commonly 5 to 15 cm in length, and 2 to 5 cm in diameter), the frequency of excitation, the type of oscillator used and so on. In general, it is desirable to use oscillator circuits at a frequency from 400 to 1 000 c/s, with a low second harmonic output, and in a three-element magnetometer to use three separate driving circuits if the waveform of each is required to be adjusted to obtain zero signal in zero ambient field.[48]

Battery-operated magnetometers using one pentode stage of amplification only have been built.[47] The phase-sensitive detector drives a centre-zero meter, and the sensitive inductor is mounted on a theodolite telescope. The device is used as a null indicator. In the measurement of D and I the directions are found which are perpendicular to **H** in the horizontal plane and perpendicular to **F** in the vertical plane of the magnetic meridian. The axis of the detector is then placed parallel to **F** and the total field reduced to zero by means of a bias field whose magnitude is measured. Absolute accuracies of $\pm 0 \cdot 3'$ in D, $\pm 0 \cdot 2'$ in I and ± 50 gammas in **F** are obtained. The uncertainty in **F** can be considerably improved by frequent standardization and is produced by changes in the coil constant and in the standard cell and resistance characteristics. These changes occur with small coil forms and in rough field use.

Palmer [35] has described a battery-operated magnetometer in which the cores consist of Mumetal wire carrying sufficient alternating current to saturate all but the inner part. A pulse-type excitation current is used at a frequency of 10 kc/s. At the output of the coupling transformer used, the sensitivity is about $0 \cdot 1$ mV/ gamma and efficient filter circuits are not required.

5. Limitations in Saturable-core Magnetometers

The fundamental limitation is that imposed by magnetic noise, the magnitude of which has been given earlier in Sections IV–3 and IV–4–A. This noise is produced by small-scale hysteresis effects in the cores, and can be reduced to the low values quoted earlier only if the cores have been suitably heat-treated, handled carefully and mounted inside the primary windings in a strain-free way. Thus it is usual to cement the cores in place at one point only.

In most magnetometers other limitations are more important. It is, however, important to note that some of these, such as effects which produce zero offsets, are of importance in absolute measurements only, whereas other effects, such as those produced by temperature variations, are important in relative measurements in space and time.

The two strips in the detectors and their primary windings can never be made exactly identical, although they can be balanced to within about 1 per cent. Consequently if the excitation current contains 1 per cent of second harmonic, a zero field signal corresponding to $3 \times 10^5 \times 10^{-2} \times 10^{-2} = 30$ gammas is obtained. Reversing the excitation to the primary windings reverses this offset signal, and this can be used to balance out any second harmonic by adjusting the driving circuit, when necessary. With an untuned single-element system the need for an excellent filter in the excitation circuit is clear. The cores can also become permanently magnetized and produce zero field signals if the a.c. exciting field is too low. There is evidence that such effects are, in general, less than 5 gammas.[48] Usually, the cores can be wiped in a large solenoid by a large a.c. field before mounting. Because of end effects in the cores and local strains, the inductance/unit length is usually less at the ends than at the centre of the cores, and this can cause a quadrature voltage at the null. Consequently any phase shifts in the reference signal can produce small zero field outputs. This effect can be minimized by careful handling and strain-free mounting of the core or cores, and by winding additional primary turns near the ends. The quadrature voltage can then be reduced to the equivalent of a few gammas.

When bias currents are used, drifts occur. In early airborne magnetometers these amount to 1 to 3 gammas/h.[59] Schonstedt and Irons [45] have described a constant-impedance system with both electronic and battery regulation in which the drift is reduced to about 1 gamma/12 h. Serson [49] has described a station magnetometer in which, using electronic regulation, baseline drifts of 10 gammas in 10 h occur. Using gas-regulator reference tubes, systematic drifts of this magnitude can be expected for the first 100 to 300 h of operation, after which the drifts are largely random. It should also be noted that because the feedback current required to cancel an ambient field depends very slightly on the magnitude of the excitation current, the latter should be kept constant to a few per cent.

Various temperature effects occur. The effect of temperature variation on coil constants can be simply calculated, and kept suitably small by thermostatting the sensitive head,[48] by using special spools with a low coefficient of thermal expansion [45] or by using thermistor compensation. Temperature changes also affect the bias current, if any, and the standard cell used to measure the magnitude of any fed-back current. Standard cells must be thermostatted to keep the temperature coefficient from this cause less than 1 gamma/°C. In the control of bias currents, it should be recalled that typical voltage reference tubes have temperature coefficients of minus 3 to 4 $\times$ 10^{-5}/°C or 2 gammas/°C. A temperature-controlled battery is probably reliable to approximately 5 gammas. Second-order temperature effects of 0·1 gamma/°C approximately occur because of the change in resistance of the coil winding, and temperature-dependent residual hysteresis effects.

Mis-orientation errors cannot be fully discussed here. In total-intensity aeromagnetic work such errors are more important than drift because drift errors can be automatically removed in the flight-reduction programme.[3] The axis of the magnetometer must be aligned within $\pm$20′ with the total field to keep mis-orientation errors to $\pm$1 gamma. To do this a reference plane perpendicular to **F** is usually established by magnetic means of one sort or another.[2, 3, 5, 9] Alternative devices have been used.[32, 55] In principle, using three orthogonal detectors it is possible to determine **F** by squaring their outputs, adding and extracting the square root, and no orientation is required. The computation can be done with the required accuracy by digital means, but the maximum deviation from orthogonality must not exceed 20′, and the output of each detector must be linear to 1 part in 5 $\times$ 10^4. If it is done by electrical circuits the errors in squaring, summation and square-root extraction must be a few parts or less in 10^6, which is a formidable requirement. Orientation errors in three-component airborne magnetometers have been discussed by Serson and Whitham.[50] Finally, errors from aircraft magnetization in the best compensated inboard installations are of the order of 10 gammas.

6. Impedance Methods using Saturable Cores

Several magnetometers have been developed by Butterworth [9, 10] and others which depend on the variation of the permeability with ambient field in highly permeable cores. The increase in the resistance of a wire to alternating current because of the skin effect is proportional to $(\mu f)^{1/2}$. Large changes in the a.c. resistance of a Mumetal wire occur at audio frequencies in small ambient fields superposed on a suitable bias field of about 0·4 oersted.

Using a symmetrical bridge circuit, with opposite magnetic field bias on the pair of balanced elements, and a phase-sensitive detector, it is possible to obtain an output voltage which is proportional to the magnitude and depends on the sign of the ambient field along the common axis. The bias field is reversed automatically, and the out-of-balance voltages are stored in condensers and connected in series to obtain the difference, which is proportional to the ambient field. In this way variations in the frequency and amplitude of the oscillator output and bias current variations are eliminated. Feedback can be used to eliminate drifts in sensitivity, and 1 gamma accuracy is possible with temperature effects of about 0·02 per cent/°C. It is doubtful if the method has any advantages in sensitivity, linearity or simplicity over that described in Section IV–4–B above, but it might be further developed.

A method has been described [20] in which the change in inductance in an ambient field of a Permalloy-cored coil has been used to measure that field.

V. HALL EFFECT METHODS

1. General Principle

In 1879 Hall discovered that a potential could be produced across a strip of metal which carried a current by placing the metal in a strong magnetic field. The force exerted on a charge e moving with velocity $\mathbf{v}$ in a magnetic field $\mathbf{B}$ is $e\mathbf{v} \times \mathbf{B}$. This force causes the electrons to travel in curved paths, thus charging up the sides until a transverse electric field of the right magnitude exists to cancel the effects of the magnetic field. The use of the Hall effect is usually limited to the measurement of large laboratory-produced magnetic fields, but recently semi-conducting materials have become available in which the earth's field is strong enough to produce measurable effects, and an experimental Hall effect compass has been described by Ross, Saker and Thompson.[41] However, at the present stage of their development the best Hall effect magnetometers for geomagnetic investigations are appreciably less sensitive and have much poorer signal/noise ratios than the electrical magnetometers described in Section IV. The sensitive head can, however, be made very small.

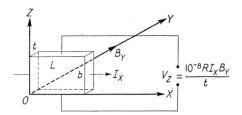

Fig. 15. Illustration of Hall effect in single crystal.

With the notation of Fig. 15, the Hall e.m.f. developed across the xy faces of the crystal is V_z. The Hall constant of the material is R cm³/coulomb.

2. Power-matching Devices

If the resistance between the electrodes and the crystal is low, for power matching the load resistance must match the internal resistance and equal $r = \sigma b/Lt$, where σ is the specific resistance in ohm-cm. The ratio of the output to input power

$$W_0/W_i = 10^{-16}(R/\sigma)^2 B^2/4$$

Indium antimonide is the best material to use, since it has a very large value of $(R/\sigma)^2$, much greater than that of the more commonly used n-type germanium.[36]

Using low-impedance milliammeters, small crystals give tolerable matching and with $W_i \sim 10^{-2}$ W, useful readings can be obtained in fields of about 10 gauss. Using highly permeable rods as field concentrators parallel to the O_Y axis, it is possible to increase the earth's field by a factor of 10^3 for low ambient fields and obtain sufficient power to activate a relay. In this way an experimental compass has been built [41] in which mis-alignment of 1 degree of arc from a position perpendicular to the meridian ($\pm 4 \times 10^{-3}$ gauss) can be used to activate a relay. Hysteresis effects can be reduced to about 0·5°, and might be reduced further with special thermal treatment of the concentrator material.

3. Some a.c. Devices

It can be simply shown that for a high-impedance input circuit $V_z = 10^{-8}(W_i b/\sigma Lt)^{1/2}RB$. If the input current is alternating, the a.c. voltage output can be amplified using a suitable narrow-band amplifier. The greatest sensitivity is obtained by selecting a thin crystal with the largest value of $R\sigma^{-1/2}$. Theoretically n-type germanium is the best-known semi-conductor, but in low fields the crystal noise becomes important and it can be shown that indium antimonide in this respect is again superior.

Using indium antimonide and an input transformer with a high turns ratio, fields of 10^{-3} gauss give quite detectable signals.[44] The sensitivity can be made greater than this by the use of positive feedback, but the system becomes rather unstable.

4. Limitations in Hall Effect Magnetometers

The thermal noise output of indium antimonide crystals at room temperature is the equivalent of about 10^{-4} gauss for a bandwidth of 1 c/s, and this represents the ultimate sensitivity of present Hall effect magnetometers for a 1 sec response time. Temperature effects are caused by the temperature dependence of R, and the change in electron mobility with degree of thermal scattering. The temperature variation of R is smaller if the electron or hole concentration in the material is dominant (e.g. n-type germanium) than if both are important, as in indium antimonide. Furthermore, inhomogeneities or geometrical effects produce zero-field Hall signals, which must be accurately cancelled in absolute measurements.

5. Magneto-resistive Methods

The proportional change $\Delta\sigma/\sigma$ in the resistivity of semi-conductors is proportional to B^2 for fields up to 10^4 gauss, and is produced by effects similar to the Hall effect. For germanium $\Delta\sigma/\sigma$ is about equal to 2×10^{-9} only for $B = 1$ gauss, and so the method [37] cannot easily be used in the earth's field. In indium antimonide the magneto-resistive effect is ten times larger than for bismuth, which previously was commonly used, but the output from a bridge exceeds the Hall effect output only for fields greater than 5×10^3 gauss.

VI. MAGNETOSTRICTION METHODS

In these methods material is used which exhibits a change in dimensions with magnetization. In general, the change in length of a suitable ferromagnetic material in the geomagnetic field is too small to detect. However, when an a.c. field is applied to a centre-clamped partially pre-magnetized magnetostrictive rod a change in the amplitude of vibration occurs with a change in the ambient field, and when the frequency of the a.c. field matches that of the

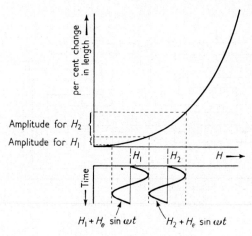

Fig. 16. Illustration of non-linear change in amplitude of magnetostrictive vibration with change in ambient field.

natural frequency of the rod for longitudinal vibration this change can be detected by means of vibration pickups. This is illustrated in Fig. 16, where the effect of non-linearity can be seen to produce a large change in the amplitude of vibration when the ambient field changes from H_1 to H_2.

Rowe [43] used a balanced arrangement of two rods of annealed steel with the same natural frequency which were aligned perpendicular to the magnetic meridian. The d.c. bias field and the exciting a.c. fields were in opposite directions in each rod. In the presence of an ambient field the signal output from piezoelectric pickups becomes unbalanced. Changes in the d.c. bias field cancel each other. Perls [38] measured the magnetostrictively excited

L

vibrations in long rods of various materials using a small barium titanate accelerometer attached to one end. The rods were excited at resonance by a coil driven at a constant power of 5 W from an audio amplifier. Under certain conditions amplitude changes equal to the noise level in a narrow-band detector were measured for field changes of 4 gammas, and signals of 1 μV/gamma were obtained. The ultimate resolution was limited by frequency changes, but could be improved by the use of feedback to stabilize the excitation in frequency and amplitude (see Fig. 17). With an extremely low

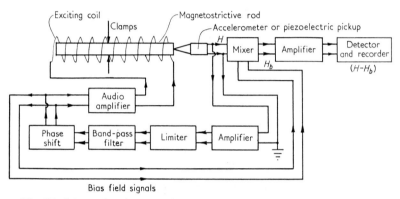

Fig. 17. Schematic diagram of a magnetostrictive magnetometer with negative feedback.

noise level pre-amplifier and a bandwidth of 4 c/s, the ultimate sensitivity should be about 0·3 gamma.

It has been suggested [43] that at high amplitude excitation fields or near zero intensity of magnetization, frequency doubling should occur, the amount depending on the magnitude of the ambient field. The variation in the amount of second harmonic in the fundamental output should be measurable.

At present magnetostrictive methods are of more interest in solid-state investigations than in geomagnetic studies, but the best materials to use and their heat-treatment is still obscure, and further development may lead to more sensitive magnetometers.

VII. METHODS USING THE DEFLECTION OF FREE ELECTRONS IN A MAGNETIC FIELD

1. General Principle

These methods depend on the measurement of the force **F** exerted on an electron of charge e, moving with velocity **v** in a field **B**. In contrast to the use of this law in Hall effect magnetometers, these methods involve electrons only and the measurement of their deflection *in vacuo* by some combination of electrical fields and geometrical effects. Although several different techniques have been suggested, only two really practical methods have survived.

The first uses coaxial-diode magnetron tubes, and the second cathode-ray tubes. Both these purely electronic methods can be used to measure very quick field changes without the limitations imposed by the audio-frequency excitation described in Sections IV and VI above. However, drift and the need sometimes for a stable auxiliary field has limited the use of the method for good absolute observations. Electronic magnetometers are among those most likely to undergo rapid advances. For example, it appears that, by the choice of a suitable operating point, it should be possible to obtain a linearly field-dependent frequency output from a magnetron, and fluctuations in any auxiliary field could be automatically cancelled in a gradiometer device. Electron magnetometers are sensitive to the field component in one direction and require appropriate orientation.

2. Magnetron Methods

In a coaxial-diode magnetron the cathode, in the shape of a straight filament heated by a current, is situated at the axis of a cylindrical anode. The current across the diode can be stopped by applying a field **B** parallel to the cathode, because the paths of the electrons are bent by the magnetic field. Below a critical value of **B**, i is independent of **B**, but near the critical value it rapidly decreases, and a few gammas can produce a large change in the diode current. With the notation of Fig. 18, since the magnetic field contributes no energy,

$$e \int_a^r E dr = \tfrac{1}{2}m[(dr/dt)^2 + r^2(d\theta/dt)^2]$$

The torque is

$$e\mathbf{B}r\,dr/dt = m\,d/dt[r^2 d\theta/dt]$$

If $d\theta/dt = 0$ at $r = a$ (radial emission), then by integration

$$r\,d\theta/dt = e\mathbf{B}(r^2 - a^2)/2mr$$

The critical field $\mathbf{B}_c$ is obtained when $dr/dt = 0$ at b and $\mathbf{B}_c{}^2 = 8mb^2V/e(b^2 - a^2)^2$ where V is the potential between cathode and anode.

Rössiger [42] used a magnetron with an auxiliary field coil producing a field $\mathbf{B}_c$ and rigidly mounted inside a pair of Helmholtz coils. By appropriate rotations and measuring the changes in the

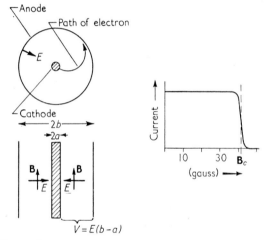

Fig. 18. Illustration of a coaxial-diode magnetron and its current variation with an axial magnetic field.

Helmholtz coil current to restore the magnetron current, H and Z could be determined with an absolute accuracy of 40 gammas. The method has all the limitations described in Section II–3–B, together with effects due to voltage fluctuations, emission fluctuations and variations in the constancy of the large (about 40 gauss) auxiliary field. Selzer and Neel [52] are reported to have described a field multiplier which concentrates the geomagnetic field to obtain a suitably large, near-critical field at the magnetron. The apparatus is very large, very magnetic, is sensitive to mechanical effects and hysteresis effects, and large variations in sensitivity occur.

3. Cathode-ray Tube Method

Cragg [14] has described a magnetometer in which the deflection of an electron beam by a magnetic field $\mathbf{B}$ is automatically compensated by a voltage applied to the electrostatic deflection plates of the miniature cathode-ray tube used. The light spot on the short-persistence screen passes a shutter and falls on a photomultiplier, the output of which is amplified and fed back to the electrostatic plates to keep the position of the spot unchanged. If the magnetic field acts over an effective length L_1, and electric field over an effective length L_2, for equal and opposite deflections

$$(ev\mathbf{B}/2m)(L_1/v)^2 = (eE/2m)(L_2/v)^2 \text{ with } v = (2eV/m)^{1/2}$$

Therefore $\mathbf{B} = E(L_2/L_1)^2(m/2eV)^{1/2}$. An output of $12 \cdot 5$ V/gauss has been obtained which is linear for fields up to 10 kc/s. Changes in the acceleration voltage, V, produce drifts of some 8×10^{-5} gauss/min, which could probably be reduced. The use of a separate phosphor and photomultiplier cathode could be eliminated by a vacuum system using an electron multiplier.

Hessler [24] has successfully operated an electron beam magnetometer based on a commercial magnetic pickup tube for the study of rapid fluctuations. There is, of course, no indication of absolute values.

VIII. PROTON-PRECESSION METHODS

1. General Principle

Nuclear precession magnetometers have been developed from the experimental study by physicists of the phenomena of nuclear resonance and nuclear induction, which have been used for some years in investigating nuclear magnetic moments, isotope analysis, the measurement of nuclear relaxation times and the calibration of intense magnetic fields. Nuclear magnetic resonance occurs when nuclear spins of moment β are placed in a magnetic field $\mathbf{H}$, and a high-frequency field f is applied. If the nuclear spin angular momentum is I, there exist $(2I + 1)$ energy levels defined by the magnetic quantum number m ($-I$ to I) and separated by frequency intervals $\beta\mathbf{H}/I$. When $2\pi f = \beta\mathbf{H}/I = \gamma H$, where γ is the gyromagnetic ratio, absorption phenomena are observed corresponding to changes in the equilibrium distribution among energy levels and involving the spin–lattice interaction with a relaxation time which can vary widely but is of the order of 1 sec for most proton-containing liquids. When $\mathbf{H}$ is about 10^3 oersteds, f is about 4 Mc/s. In the nuclear induction process the field $\mathbf{H}$ is along the O_Z axis and an a.c. field with angular frequency ω is applied along the O_X axis. When $\omega = \gamma\mathbf{H}$, the alignment of the nuclear magnets parallel to $\mathbf{H}$ is disturbed and weak magnetization parallel to the O_Y axis can be produced and easily detected because of the high frequency.

In 1954 Packard and Varian [34] reported the observation of a free audio-frequency induction signal from 500 cm³ of water persisting for 1 sec or more after the polarizing field $\mathbf{H}_p$, perpendicular to the earth's field $\mathbf{F}$, was quickly reduced to zero. The nuclear moments then precessed about the earth's field, inducing a voltage in a receiving coil perpendicular to both $\mathbf{F}$ and $\mathbf{H}_p$. The signal-to-noise ratio was 20 using an initial polarizing field $\mathbf{H}_p = 100$ oersteds. Since this demonstration, the method has been quickly developed for use as a field measuring device in airborne and seaborne surveys and in rocket and satellite experiments and as an observatory standard for total field intensity. In principle, the time of signal decay can be used to measure small magnetic gradients. These rapid developments have occurred largely because of the following advantages of this method over other electronic methods:

(a) The precession frequency, $f = \gamma\mathbf{F}/2\pi$, is a measure of the magnitude of $\mathbf{F}$ and is independent of the orientation in the field. The signal strength does, however, depend on the orientation, and this is discussed in Section VIII–3 below.

(b) The gyromagnetic ratio of protons in water, γ_p, has been determined [53] to a high precision: $\gamma_p = 2 \cdot 67523 \pm 0 \cdot 00006 \times 10^4$ sec⁻¹ oersted⁻¹ when uncorrected for the diamagnetic effect in a water molecule and $2 \cdot 67528 \pm 0 \cdot 00006 \times 10^4$ when corrected. Convenient standards of frequency reliable to 1 in 10^8 are available in crystal oscillators. Consequently, provided suitable means can be devised to measure the precession frequency, the method is presently capable of providing extremely accurate absolute determinations of $\mathbf{F}$ (to ± 1 gamma). These determinations should be independent of coil forms, standard cells and standard resistances, and provided the frequency standards are reliable different proton precession magnetometers must always agree in the determination of the same field. Furthermore, frequency standards are the easiest to check, using for comparison the carrier frequencies of certain standard time signals.

Since the ampere is known to 5 parts per million, using extremely accurately constructed coils, it should ultimately be possible to determine γ_p to 1 part per million with respect to the ampere in some national standards institution, and so reduce its present absolute uncertainty some 3 to 4 times.

(c) The frequency instead of voltage-output signal has technical advantages in rocket and satellite experiments because no errors arise from uncertain amplitude calibration of telemetering systems. Also no alignment or matching problems comparable to those with saturable-core magnetometers occur in the use of proton precession magnetometers.

One fundamental disadvantage is that the time taken for one observation is at least 1 sec, and hence the method cannot be used to investigate very short-period phenomena. With the higher frequencies involved in paramagnetic resonance this objection may be overcome in the near future.

2. Description of the Operation of a Typical Magnetometer

If a polarizing d.c. magnetic field $\mathbf{H}_p$ perpendicular to $\mathbf{F}$ is applied to a sample of water, the total nuclear magnetic moment at time t is $M_t = M_0[1 - \exp(-t/T_1)]$, where T_1 is the spin–lattice thermal relaxation time. If t is much larger than T_1, M_t becomes equal to M_0. If χ is the nuclear susceptibility, $M_0 = v\chi\mathbf{H}_p$ where v is the volume of the sample. For a sample of several hundred cubic centimetres and $\mathbf{H}_p$ of about 10^2 oersteds, M_0 is about 10^{-5} c.g.s.u. If $\mathbf{H}_p$ is reduced to zero in a time short compared to one precession period, the moment M_0 precesses about $\mathbf{F}$ at the Larmor frequency $f = \gamma_p \mathbf{F}/2\pi$ where γ_p is the nuclear gyromagnetic ratio of the protons in water. Consequently a voltage proportional to $M_0 f$ is induced in a receiving coil with its axis perpendicular to $\mathbf{F}$. This voltage decays exponentially as precessional coherence is lost as $V_t = V_0 \exp(-t/T_2)$, where T_2 is the transverse or spin–spin relaxation time. If the pickup coil consists of N turns of area

A with a filling factor a between sample and coil, $V_0 = 10^{-8}\omega N A 4\pi a M_0 \sin(\omega t)$ where $\omega = 2\pi f$. With samples of a few hundred cubic centimetres and quite small receiving coils with $N \sim 10^3$, V_0 is a few microvolts.

It is usual to use the same coil for polarizing and receiving. On tuning the receiving coil to frequency f and considering it as a solenoid without end corrections, the signal-to-noise ratio can be written

$$V_s/V_n = Qav\chi 4\pi[W_i/4kT\Delta f]^{1/2}$$

where W_i is the input power on polarizing, Δf is the receiving bandwidth and Q is that of the tuned receiving coil. The receiving bandwidth need only be a few cycles per second for faithful reproduction of the signal. Signal-to-noise ratios greater than 100 are theoretically possible in laboratory designs and the measurable signal should persist for a period of between 2 to $3T_2$. In general, T_2 is less than T_1, but for distilled water T_2 is very nearly equal to T_1 and lies between 2 and 3 sec.

In practice, in laboratory units the polarizing field is usually obtained from a car battery, and sufficiently rapid removal of the field (collapse of $\mathbf{H}_p$ from a few oersteds to zero in a time less than 50 μsec) is achieved with a sequence timer and DPDT relay combination which switches the coil from its polarizing to tuned receiving state.

The precession signal is pre-amplified and then amplified in a suitable high-gain, narrow-bandwidth amplifier (typically of the order 10^2 c/s bandwidth). The range of field values to be measured determines the pass band of the system, and whether the amplifier should be tuneable.[57] Cahill and Van Allen [11] used a tuned transformer for critical impedance transformation and amplification. In an observatory instrument to be used as an $\mathbf{F}$ standard in one location it is theoretically advantageous to reduce the bandwidth as much as possible, in order to decrease the noise signal and increase the length of time for which a measurable signal exists. However, because of impulse noise (Section VIII–3) not much is gained.

Several methods have been used to measure the precession frequency f which is commonly in the range 1·3 to 2·6 kc/s. Those suitable for laboratory instruments are described below. It should be clear that they can easily be modified for use with telemetered signals stored on magnetic tape. All the methods are, of course, limited in accuracy by the signal-to-noise ratio at the amplifier output.

The amplifier output can be fed to a counter which counts the cycles for a pre-set time interval, often 1 sec. With a very favourable signal-to-noise ratio the cycles could be counted for as long as 4 sec. The pre-determined time interval is provided by circuits locked to a standard crystal. The accuracy is usually ± 1 c/s or ± 25 gammas and would be increased to $\pm\frac{1}{4}$ c/s, or ± 6 gammas, for a 4-sec count. The method is simple but obviously does not fully utilize the accurate information contained in the signal.

Alternatively the signal can be used to open and close an electronic gate, which in the open position feeds a 100-kc/s signal from a standard crystal to a time interval meter.[57] This gate can be pre-set to remain open for a fixed number of cycles $= n \times 10^3$, where $n = 1, 2, 3$, etc., and can be varied according to the noise conditions. The gate is opened with a variable delay, for example of 1000 cycles, to avoid errors due to relay or other noise associated with switching from polarizing to receiving. The time-interval meter reading is thus $10^8 n/f \pm 1$, and the uncertainty from this cause is ± 1 gamma for a useful signal lasting ~ 1 sec, and $\pm 0\cdot 2$ gamma for a useful signal lasting ~ 4 sec. A block diagram of a proton precession magnetometer using such a frequency-measuring method is shown in Fig. 19. This system can be converted to read out on a punched tape or operate a recording meter. Suppose $n = 4$ and $f = 2$ kc/s. If the read out operates from the last three decade scaling stages in the time-interval meter the range is 250 gammas and the resolution is $0\cdot 25$ gamma. By reducing n, the resolution is decreased and the range increased. In this method random noise introduces errors into the time gate determined by the precession signal. Provided V_s/V_n is greater than 10 at the end of the counting period the error from noise fluctuations can be shown to be $\sim 0\cdot 4$ gamma only. In general the best compromise between a long time gate and a reduced signal-to-noise ratio is obtained when $n \times 10^3 \simeq fT_2$, provided the initial signal-to-noise ratio is sufficiently high.

Finally, the precession frequency can also be measured by beating it with the second harmonic of a suitable well-constructed tuning fork.[56] Such a fork has a frequency reliable to 1 part in 10^6. Alternatively the stepped-down frequency of a standard crystal oscillator can be used as a reference. The amplified beat frequency pattern can then be photographed on a cathode-ray tube and compared with a crystal-derived frequency. A beat frequency of a few cycles per second can be estimated to one part in several hundred, and the error in the determination of the precession frequency is

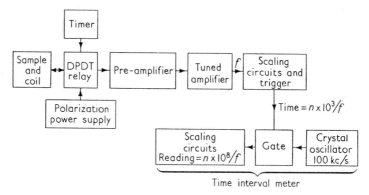

Fig. 19. Schematic diagram of a proton precession magnetometer for the absolute laboratory determination of **F**.

less than 1 gamma if the beat frequency is less than ~20 c/s. Alternatively the difference frequency can be converted to a voltage by a frequency meter, and this voltage, filtered with a time constant of several seconds, recorded on a moving-chart meter. If the field changes during the course of a frequency measurement the precessional frequency also changes, and in general, the first two methods described above determine the mean value of the field.

3. Difficulties in the Proton-precession Method

The effect of a field gradient across the sample is to de-cohere the signal more rapidly effectively reducing T_2. For example a difference of 10 gammas across the sample should de-cohere the signal within about 1 sec. In general, very accurate field measurements require small field gradients of less than about 0·1 gamma/cm across the coil. It has been suggested that this effect be used in a gradiometer device,[57] but such a gradiometer would appear to have few advantages over astatic means in laboratory installations, and to be too insensitive for most airborne uses.

External noise pickup, which depends strongly on the location, the closeness to power lines, the nature of the terrain, etc., can become troublesome in observatory installations. Some noise cancellation can be obtained by using two parallel samples connected oppositely so that the signals add whereas external noise subtracts. A toroidal specimen and coil minimizes the external noise pickup. In practice, however, the choice of a suitable location can best be made by the application of common sense and by a little experimenting. It appears easiest to place the magnetometer several feet above the ground. Normally the use of shielded cable and a shielded pre-amplifier near the sample is necessary for the best results.

The signal amplitude, but not frequency, depends on the magnetometer orientation. If the axis of a solenoidal receiving and polarizing coil is at an angle θ with the direction of $\mathbf{F}$, the component of magnetic moment which precesses is proportional to $\sin \theta$ and the flux cutting the receiving coil is proportional to $\sin \theta$. Hence the signal amplitude is proportional to $\sin {}^2\theta$, and falls by 50 per cent for $\theta = 45°$. If two mutually perpendicular coils are used, and $\mathbf{F}$ makes an angle θ with the normal to the plane defined by the axes of the coils, the signal amplitude is proportional to $\frac{1}{2}(1 + \cos {}^2\theta)$. Beteen $\theta = 0°$ and $\theta = 90°$, the amplitude is reduced only two times. This result holds for a toroidal sample and coil. It can be shown by an extension of the same theory that the signal obtained from a mutually perpendicular three-coil configuration is completely independent of orientation.

The angular rotation $\dot{\phi}$ of the magnetometer coil in balloon, rocket and satellite magnetometers produces an apparent precessional frequency error of $\dot{\phi}/2\pi$ or an error in the field of about $4\dot{\phi}$ gammas.[11]

4. Choice of Sample

Water is a very convenient proton-rich material to use in laboratory instruments because of its convenient relaxation times (which can, if necessary, be changed by the addition of paramagnetic salts) and the accurate knowledge of the gyromagnetic ratio of protons in water.[53] Furthermore, by the removal of dissolved oxygen, the transverse relaxation time T_2 can be increased, if necessary. By the use of different hydrocarbons, rich in hydrogen atoms, it is possible to select other relaxation times more suitable for some applications. Thus in airborne total-intensity magnetometers materials are chosen which can conveniently withstand low ambient temperatures and which have somewhat shorter relaxation times than water, in order to minimize the time for a complete cycle of one **F** determination.

A number of materials, such as alcohols and kerosene, have been used in rocket and airborne magnetometers. The relaxation times of these can be adjusted by introducing various amounts of relatively viscous oils. It should be remembered that in satellite magnetometers another complication which arises is that the power consumed per cycle rises with T_1 for the same moment, and a compromise is necessary between the accuracy which is acceptable for such a fast-moving body and the number of observations which can be made with batteries of a given weight.

5. A Proposed Two-component Magnetometer

The uncertainties in the present world standards of magnetic field intensity (see Section II–3–B) are such that it seems inevitable that the present instruments will ultimately be replaced by proton precession units. The accuracy of such magnetometers should be so great that the errors in the determination of I using present techniques (see Section III–2) will provide the largest uncertainties in the determination of H and Z. For this reason, and to avoid the use of two instruments, the possibility of using proton precession magnetometers to measure force components has been discussed.[33]

In principle, a two-component magnetometer could be built by placing a proton magnetometer in the centre of a Helmholtz coil system with its axis accurately horizontal and in the direction of the magnetic meridian. When the current through the coil system is varied the measured value of the resultant field changes and a minimum field value can be obtained equal to Z. Such a determination of Z would be independent of the precise coil dimensions and observatory electrical standards. If the axis of the Helmholtz system is at a small angle a to the horizontal, but the system is rotated through 180° about an accurately vertical axis and the current reversed, errors from this cause cancel. However, the mean value of Z is in error by $\delta Z = H^2\beta^2/2Z$ if the axis of the system is at a small angle β to the magnetic meridian. In theory, when β is less than 10', δZ is less than 0·2 gamma for locations where the inclination exceeds 45°. This error corresponds to that imposed by the uncertainty in the absolute ampere. However, the fact that the applied field need not accurately equal minus H for a good determination of Z makes this method a poor one for measuring H accurately. At lower latitudes it would be preferable to use the Helmholtz coils with their axis vertical, and determine H by a minimum method.

Because of time variations it may not be possible to determine the minimum to the accuracy quoted above. One way of avoiding this difficulty is to take a rapid sequence of five measurements corresponding, for the horizontal Helmholtz system described above, to a determination of the field with no current, $\mathbf{F}_1$, current on, $\mathbf{F}_2$, current reversed, $\mathbf{F}_3$, coils rotated through 180°, $\mathbf{F}_4$, and current again reversed, $\mathbf{F}_5$. Then it can be shown that

$$H = [(\mathbf{F}_2{}^2 - \mathbf{F}_3{}^2) + (\mathbf{F}_4{}^2 - \mathbf{F}_5{}^2)]$$
$$[1 + \tfrac{1}{2}(\alpha^2 + \beta^2)]/8(\mathbf{F}_2{}^2 + \mathbf{F}_3{}^2 - 2\mathbf{F}_1{}^2/2)^{1/2}$$

and if α, β are less than 10', which should not be difficult to achieve, the error in H from coil mis-alignment is less than 0·4 gamma. By making the Helmholtz axis vertical, and a similar experiment, Z can be determined. If the resolution in each $\mathbf{F}$ measurement is dF, and the field of the Helmholtz system, H_c, is approximately equal to H, $dH = \mathbf{F}dF/H_c$. If H_c much exceeds H, $dH = d\mathbf{F}$. In either case to avoid the need for measurements with a very high resolution, an appreciable applied field is required.

A number of practical difficulties would require solution. A suitably small gradient must be maintained across the sample, which should therefore be small and the Helmholtz coils large. The signal amplitude must be maintained as the direction of the resultant field is changed. This might necessitate the use of a toroid or even a three-coil configuration (see Section VIII–3 above). Finally, the amplifier used must have a variable band-width to deal with the different field values.

However, there seems no doubt that an instrument of this sort could make perfectly possible uniform world magnetic standards independent of precise coil dimensions and observatory electrical standards and give results superior to those obtained by the torque methods described in Section II–3–B.

IX. DISCUSSION

In the last decade the most important developments in the methods of measuring the geomagnetic elements have been in the saturable-core and proton-precession methods. In exploration geophysics, in rocket and satellite geomagnetic measurements and in much work done by university departments in geophysics, these two methods have been rapidly developed and fully exploited in the study of spatial and time variations from a moving support.

In general, most of the detailed observations of time variations in the geomagnetic field are made at magnetic observatories. Many of these observatories have neither the trained personnel nor the facilities and equipment to take advantage of some of the recent developments. Using the classical methods, good results with a sensitivity adequate for most purposes can usually be obtained if the operators are careful and patient. Furthermore, with the exception of the proton-precession method, the classical methods are considerably more free from drift than the best electrical methods. They are also more reliable in operation, consume relatively little power and make fewer demands on the technical competence of the operators: these are all important at small and isolated observatories. Consequently there is a definite bias towards methods which do not involve electronics, and efforts to develop fully automatic observatories have been largely limited to the construction of small and very stable magnet variometers capable of operating unattended for some weeks or months.

Despite these considerations, the use of electronic methods could very profitably be increased. Saturable-core recording magnetometers for standard sensitivity and automatic storm recording, proton-precession magnetometers for absolute force observations and the use of negative feedback photocell recording systems with magnet variometers in gradient measurements are all examples in use nowadays at one or two places. Furthermore, one advantage of the electrical magnetometers is the possibility of more simple adaptation to automatic processing of the data. Voltage outputs or frequency outputs which are proportional to the field intensity or field gradients can be more conveniently analysed by digital means from punched tape, or by using magnetic tape recording than can photographic outputs, even if variable-area recording were used. It is clear that if many aspects of the subject of transient magnetic disturbance are to progress quickly, automatic means must ultimately be developed of handling the very large amount of data which continually accumulates.

Finally, it should be emphasized that electronic methods should be only used if they are both worthwhile and sensible. One suspects that the opinions of many older geomagneticians concerning the reliability and worth of the electrical methods were formed from experience with unreliable apparatus sometimes incapable in principle of giving good results. An example might be the use of a good magnet variometer with an inferior photocell recording system without feedback. Similarly, designers of electronic apparatus sometimes forget that nearby ferromagnetic material influences the measurement being taken, and the fields of galvanometer magnets or of recording meters may be appreciable at a distance of a few metres. This sort of effect from electrical apparatus becomes important in the design of small and inexpensive observatories in which interactions are required to be very small.

Acknowledgements

The author wishes to thank his colleagues E. R. Niblett and P. H. Serson for carefully reading the manuscript and for their many helpful suggestions.

References

1. Aschenbrenner, H. and Goubau, G. *Hochfrequenztech. u. Electroakust.*, **47**, 177–181 (1936).
2. Bailey, R. *Canad. J. Res. F*, **26**, 523–539 (1948).
3. Balsley, J. R. *Advances in Geophysics*, Vol. I, pp. 313–349. Academic Press Inc.: New York, (1952).
4. Barnett, S. J. *Res. Dept terr. Magn. Carnegie Inst.* **4**, 373–394 (1921).
5. Bartels, J. *Ann. internat. geophys. Yr*, **4**, 209–214 (1957).
6. Bates, L. F. *Proc. phys. Soc. Lond.* **45**, 180–193 (1933).
7. Bozorth, R. M. *Rev. mod. Phys.* **25**, 42–48 (1953).

8. Bruckshaw, J. M. *Geophys. Prospecting*, **1**, 259–271 (1953).
9. Butterworth, A. *J. Instn elect. Engrs*, **94** Part II, 325–332 (1947).
10. Butterworth, A. *J. Instn elect. Engrs*, **95** Part II, 645–652 (1948).
11. Cahill, L. J. and Van Allen, J. A. *J. geophys. Res.* **61**, 547–558 (1956).
12. Chapman, S. and Bartels, J. *Geomagnetism*, Vol. I. Oxford University Press: London, 1940.
13. Chapman, S. and Nelson, J. H. *Ann. internat. geophys. Yr*, **4**, 237–245 (1957).
14. Cragg, B. G. *J. sci. Instrum.* **32**, 385–386 (1955).
15. Dye, D. W. *Proc. Roy. Soc. A*, **117**, 434–458 (1928).
16. Espersen, J., Andreasen, P., Egedal, J. and Olsen, J. *J. geophys. Res.* **61**, 593–624 (1956).
17. Frowe, E. *Geophysics*, **13**, 209–214 (1948).
18. Gerard, V. B. *J. sci. Instrum.* **32**, 164–166 (1955).
19. Gordon, D. I. *Rev. mod. Phys.* **25**, 56–57 (1953).
20. Gregg, E. C. *Rev. sci. Instrum.* **18**, 77–80 (1947).
21. Grenet, G. *Ann. Géophys.* **5**, 188–195 (1949).
22. Haalck, F. *Geophys. Prospecting*, **4**, 424–441 (1956).
23. Heiland, C. A. *Geophysical Exploration*, pp. 318–355. Prentice-Hall: New York, 1946.
24. Hessler, V. P. Private communication (1958).
25. Kalashnikov, A. G. *Ann. internat. geophys. Yr*, **4**, 304–305 (1957).
26. La Cour, D. *Commun. Magnét. No. 15*. Danish Meteorological Institute: Copenhagen, 1936.
27. La Cour, D. *Commun. Magnét. No. 19*. Danish Meteorological Institute: Copenhagen, 1942.
28. Logachev, A. A. *Geophysics*, **11**, 135–147 (1946).
29. Lundbak, A. *Tellus*, **3**, 69–74 (1951).
30. Maxwell, A. *Ann. internat. geophys. Yr*, **4**, 281–286 (1957).
31. Meek, J. H., and Hector, F. S. *Canad. J. Phys.* **33**, 364–368 (1955).
32. Muffly, G. *Geophysics*, **11**, 321–334 (1946).
33. Nelson, J. H. *Report* of Committee on Magnetic Instruments, I.A.G.A., I.U.G.G., Toronto meeting (1957).
34. Packard, M., and Varian, R. *Phys. Rev.* **93**, 941 (1954).
35. Palmer, T. M. *J. Instn elect. Engrs*, **100** Part II, 545–550 (1953).
36. Pearson, G. L. *Rev. sci. Instrum.* **19**, 263–265 (1948).
37. Pearson, G. L., and Suhl, H. *Phys. Rev.* **83**, 768–776 (1951).
38. Perls, T. A. *Phys. Rev.* **87**, 230 (1952).
39. Roman, I. and Sermon, T. C. *Trans. Amer. Inst. min. (metall.) Engrs*, **110**, 373–390 (1934).
40. Rose, D. C. and Bloom, J. N. *Canad. J. Res. A* **28**, 153–163 (1950).
41. Ross, E. M., Saker, E. W. and Thompson, N. A. C. *J. sci. Instrum.* **34**, 479–484 (1957).
42. Rössiger, M. *Z. Geophys.* **4**, 371–372 (1928).
43. Rowe, R. G. *Electronics*, **18**, 123–125 (1945).
44. Saker, E. W., Cunnell, F. A. and Edmond, J. T. *Brit. J. appl. Phys.* **6**, 217–220 (1955).

45. Schonstedt, E. O. and Irons, H. R. *Trans. Amer. geophys. Un.* **36**, 25–41 (1955).
46. Selzer, E. *Ann. internat. geophys. Yr*, **4**, 287–301 (1957).
47. Serson, P. H. and Hannaford, W. L. W. *Canad. J. Technol.* **34**, 232–243 (1956).
48. Serson, P. H., Mack, S. Z. and Whitham, K. *Publ. Dom. Obs. Ottawa,* **19**, 15–97 (1957).
49. Serson, P. H. *Canad. J. Phys.* **35**, 1387–1394 (1957).
50. Serson, P. H. and Whitham, K. *Handbuch der Physik,* Vol. 49. Springer: Berlin, 1959.
51. Smith, F. E. *Phil. Trans. A*, **223**, 175–200 (1922).
52. Thellier, E. *Ann. internat. geophys. Yr*, **4**, 255–280 (1957).
53. Thomas, H. A., Driscoll, R. L. and Hipple, J. A. *Phys. Rev.* **78**, 787–790 (1950).
54. Tsubokawa, I. *Bull. geogr. Surv. Inst., Japan*, **2**, 325–329 (1951).
55. Vacquier, V., Simons, R. F. and Hull, A. W. *Rev. sci. Instrum.* **18**, 483–487 (1947).
56. Waters, G. S. *Nature, Lond.* **176**, 691 (1955).
57. Waters, G. S. and Phillips, G. *Geophys. Prospecting*, **4**, 1–9 (1956).
58. Wickerhan, W. E. *Geophysics*, **19**, 116–123 (1954).
59. Wycoff, R. D. *Geophysics*, **13**, 182–208 (1948).

M

MEASUREMENTS IN PALAEOMAGNETISM

D. W. COLLINSON and K. M. CREER, *King's College,*
Newcastle-on-Tyne

CONTENTS

I. MEASUREMENT OF NATURAL REMANENT MAGNETIZATION

1. Introduction

Methods of measuring the very small magnetic fields associated with the remanent magnetization of sedimentary and igneous rocks were described by Nagata.[22] Of these only two have been developed to the high degree of sensitivity necessary for the study of the natural remanent magnetization (n.r.m.) of the more weakly magnetized igneous rocks and of sediments. These are the spinner magnetometer, sometimes known as the rock-generator, and the astatic magnetometer.

In 1952 Blackett [1] made a detailed study of the design of astatic magnetometers, and at Manchester University constructed instruments admirably suited to the measurement of the n.r.m. of sedimentary rocks. Before this, workers in sedimentary rock magnetism, e.g. in America, Johnson [17] and Johnson, Murphy and Michelsen,[18] and in Japan, Nagata, Akasi and Rikitake [23] had constructed instruments of the rock-generator type for the most sensitive work. The ultimate sensitivity of the latter type of instrument is limited by the thermal noise of the pickup coil and by the noise of the first valve of the amplifiers, and Blackett compared the lowest detectable intensity of magnetization of the Johnson instrument with that of his own astatic magnetometer fitted with Alcomax IV magnets. Resistivity of existing conductors in the rock-generator and the retentivity of existing magnetic materials in the astatic magnetometer impose natural limitations on the practical sensitivities such that there is little to choose between them.

2. Astatic Magnetometers

A. *General considerations*

The factors governing the general lay-out of these instruments may be briefly mentioned. These are chiefly concerned with the size of the sample to be measured and its position relative to the magnet system, the main requirement being to obtain maximum signal from a specimen of given intensity of magnetization in the shortest possible time.

In the computation of results the assumption is usually made that the magnetization of the specimen may be represented by a single dipole. In order that this should be a reasonable assumption one is faced with the choice of using a sample of small volume close to the magnetometer or, alternatively, a large sample far from the magnetometer, the limitation being that the specimen should not subtend more than a certain solid angle at the centre of the magnet system. Thus the maximum field produced at the magnet system by a small specimen will be the same as that produced by a larger system under these conditions.

The location of the equivalent dipole within a rock specimen depends on the shape and size and distance from the magnet system as shown by Collinson *et al.*[7] Homogeneity of magnetization is also important. For small specimens close to the magnetometer, machining accurately to the chosen shape is important. Larger specimens at greater distances, however, can be more or less roughly chipped to the required cubic, cylindrical or spherical form. Inhomogeneity of magnetization, due to uneven distribution of ferromagnetic grains or to vesicles, etc., is more likely to be observed in small specimens than in large, where small clusters or concentrations of grains of given type tend to be so numerous that the specimen becomes quasi-isotropic. Hence, in cases where specimens are difficult to machine to shape and where magnetization is not homogeneous, workers have resorted to using specimens of large sample size despite serious disadvantages in instrument design which are pointed out below. Larger specimens at greater distance must also be favoured when the susceptibility is high and the remanent magnetization low, because induced magnetization becomes troublesome. The effect on the magnet system of such induced magnetization falls off as z^6 where z is the distance separating the two. Hence this effect is much less for large specimens far off than for small ones close to the magnetometer. On the other hand, small specimens can be more easily manipulated by remote control near the magnetometer and are to be favoured on these grounds.

There are three positions relative to the magnet system in which the specimens may be placed for measurement. These are as follows:

(a) beneath the lower magnet of the astatic pair (Blackett,[1] Collinson *et al.*[7]);
(b) to one side of the lower magnet;
(c) to one side of the magnet system mid-way between the astatic pair.

The sensitivity of magnetometers is calculated in later paragraphs in terms of the magnetic field required to produce a given deflection. The question considered here is whether better use can be made of a given sensitivity by adopting one of the above specimen positions rather than another, the most practical measure of sensitivity being given by the intensity of magnetization of a rock sample required to produce the minimum readable deflection.

Specimen position (a). Let the specimen be represented by a small dipole P having horizontal and vertical components P_x and P_z respectively situated on the vertical axis of the magnet system at a distance z below the lower magnet (Fig. 1). Such a position is known as an 'on centre' position. If P_x makes an angle θ with the moment of the lower magnet H_x, the horizontal field tending to produce a deflection is given by

$$H_x = P_x \sin \theta / z^3 \qquad (1)$$

P_z has no effect in the on-centre position, but may be measured because it produces a field having a horizontal component H_z at the magnet system when the specimen is traversed horizontally a distance x in a direction at right angles to the moment of the lower magnet

$$H_z = 3P_z \cos^4 \psi \sin \psi / z^3 \qquad (2)$$

$$= 3P_z x / z^4 \qquad (3)$$

for small values of ψ where $\psi = \tan^{-1} (x/z)$.

Combining equations 1 and 3 we get ϕ, the angle of dip of the dipole P as follows:

$$\tan \phi = P_z/P_x = H_z z/H_x 3x \qquad (4)$$

In the above the effect of the specimen on the upper magnet of the astatic pair has been neglected. Now it has been found that in practice induction and shape effects limit the distance z of a

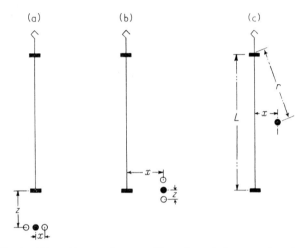

Fig. 1. Alternative specimen positions for astatic magnetometer.

small specimen of diameter 3 cm to about 3 cm. If the separation of the magnets of the astatic pair is L, then the ratio between the fields H_x at the upper and lower magnet is given by

$$H_x \text{ (upper)}/H_x \text{ (lower)} = z^3/(z + L)^3 \qquad (5)$$

For the effect at the upper magnet to be 1 per cent of that at the lower, $(z + L) \gg 100^{\frac{1}{3}}$ $z = 4.65z$, and for $z = 3$ cm, the magnet separation should be about 11 cm. At $z > 3$ cm, the ratio 5 will be greater than 1 per cent, and this means a reduction in sensitivity in terms of deflection per unit intensity of magnetization of specimen. However, at $z > z_{min.}$ this is not important, as the specimen may always be brought closer to the magnet system to obtain a measurable deflection. For a large specimen of diameter say 30 cm, $z_{min.} = 30$ cm and the separation L of the magnet system should be about 110 cm. This is a great disadvantage because of the practical difficulties of astaticizing such a magnet system and because, as is shown below, magnet systems should be as small as possible for great sensitivity.

Specimen position (b). Again the assumption is made that the effect of the specimen on the upper magnet is negligible in comparison with that at the lower. Here we have

$$H_x = 2P_x \sin \theta / z^3 \qquad (6)$$

As in position (a) P_z has produced no horizontal component of magnetic field in the 'in plane' position—that is with the specimen in the horizontal plane containing the lower magnet. However, P_z produces a small horizontal component H_z if the specimen is moved a distance x vertically up or down, given by

$$H_z = 3P_z x / z^4 \qquad (7)$$

if x is small.

Again as for case (a) consideration that the horizontal field on the upper magnet due to P_x should be less than 1 per cent of that at the lower at the closest position ($z = 3$ cm again) for a 3-cm specimen leads to the conclusion that L should be greater than about 10 cm. Also it is advantageous to use small specimens for the same reason as mentioned for specimen position (a).

Specimen position (c). The horizontal dipole P_x produces equal horizontal fields at the upper and lower magnets, and consequently there is no couple on the magnet system as a whole due to this component of the total dipole. However, P_z produces equal but opposite horizontal fields at upper and lower magnets producing a total horizontal field H_z given by

$$H_z = (12P_z / L^3) \cos^4 \psi \sin \psi \qquad (8)$$

For a given magnet separation L, H_z is a maximum at $\psi = \tan^{-1} \frac{1}{2}$, since at this value of ψ, $dH_z/d\psi = 0$ and $d^2H/d\psi^2$ is negative.

Taking $x = 3$ cm to be the minimum permissible horizontal distance between the centre of the specimen and the centre of the magnet system, we find that L should be equal to 12 cm for maximum sensitivity in terms of specimen moment per unit deflection.

If the specimen is displaced a small distance along the vertical axis the horizontal fields at the magnets due to P_x are no longer equal, but the deflecting couple on the magnet system will be extremely small, since the couples on the individual magnets oppose each other. For this reason the technique of measurement using this position is different from that found suitable for the other two. It is necessary to take measurements about three mutually perpendicular axes (in both directions to remove any effects due to induced magnetization). In positions (a) and (b) the specimen is turned round into different azimuths in the principle (symmetrical) setting and the deflection plotted against azimuth gives a sine curve. If deflections in the two unsymmetrical positions are recorded at different azimuths, P_x, $\sin \theta$ and P_z may be found. Measurements must be repeated with the specimen inverted to correct for induced effects.

The relative effectiveness of the three positions is given in Table 1, where it would appear that positions (a) and (b) provide

Table 1.   Ratios of horizontal field at magnet system to magnetic moment of specimen for the three specimen positions

Position	Symmetrical setting (e.g. 'on centre')	Unsymmetrical setting (e.g. 'off centre')	Notes
(a) Vertically beneath magnet system	$H_x/P_x = \sin \theta/z^3$ (= 0·037 for $z = 3$ cm $\theta = \pi/2$)	$H_z/P_z = 3x/z^4$ (= 0·0093 for $x = 0·25$, $z = 3$ cm)	See Fig. 1 (a)
(b) In horizontal plane containing lower magnet, and to one side	$H_x/P_x = 2 \sin \theta/x^3$ (= 0·074 for $x = 3$ cm $\theta = \pi/2$)	$H_z/P_z = 3z/x^4$ (= 0·0093 for $z = 0·25$, $x = 3$ cm)	See Fig. 1 (b)
(c) In horizontal plane midway between magnets and to one side	$H_z/P_z = 3Lx/r^5$ (= 0·0078 for $x = 3$ cm, $L = 12$ cm and $\psi = \tan^{-1} \frac{1}{2}$)	H_x/P_x extremely small	See Fig. 1 (c)

for considerably more sensitivity than position (c). Although the ratio H_x/P_x for position (b) is twice that for position (a), it has been found in practice much easier to design and build remote control devices to bring the specimen up from below the magnet system than from the side. The ratio H_z/P_z is the same for both positions.

Rock samples cannot be represented accurately by dipoles at

their centres, and the theory outlined above requires modification to take into account the finite size of the sample. For position (a) Papapetrou (quoted in Blackett [1]) has shown that the magnetization of a sample in the form of a cylinder can be represented by dipoles P_x, P_z at the centre and the deflecting fields due to P_x, P_z are then given by expressions of the forms

$$H_x = P_x F(x)/z^3 \tag{9}$$

$$H_z = P_z x F(z)/z^4 \tag{10}$$

where $F(x)$, $F(z)$ are functions depending on the ratio of the height of the cylinder and its diameter to z, measured from the lower magnet to the centre of the cylinder. An expression is given for the limiting value of x for which the expression for H_z is valid. Alternatively it has been shown in Collinson et al.[7] that for samples in the form of discs of radius a, a good approximation is given by substituting z_0 for z in (6) and (7), where $z_0^2 = z^2 + a^2$. This is applicable to cases where the minimum value of z is approximately equal to the radius of the disc.

A further complication arising in rock specimens is their inhomogeneity of magnetization. Collinson, Creer, Irving and Runcorn have shown that inhomogeneity can be represented by a small displacement of the equivalent dipole and that, by taking a sufficient number of readings with the sample upright and inverted, and traversed on either side of the axis of the magnetometer, the effects due to inhomogeneity can be meaned out.

For samples of very weak magnetization, where close approach ($z < 2$ cm) to the lower magnet is necessary, the best results have been obtained by measuring the components along three perpendicular axes, with the sample in the on-centre position, sets of readings being taken with the specimen in the upright and inverted position in each case. Cubes or cylinders may be used in positions (a) or (b), although (a) is preferable because the specimen can be brought closer to the magnet system. In position (c) the closest possible position of a specimen to one of the magnets is rather greater than for positions (a) and (b). However, great care must be taken to recognize the effects of magnetization induced in the specimen by the magnet system. As a rule it is not advisable to place the specimen closer than about 3 cm from one of the magnets.

B. *Description of the Cambridge instrument*

Fig. 2 gives a general view of the instrument constructed at the Department of Geodesy and Geophysics, University of Cambridge, in 1952 (see Creer,[8] Collinson *et al.*[7])

Fig. 2. General view of astatic magnetometer.

The magnetometer case A is made of ebonite-impregnated beech wood and consists of two parts. The upper part A[1] (Fig. 3) houses the suspension strip and rests kinematically on the tripod stand T, the legs of which are rigidly attached to the isolated concrete

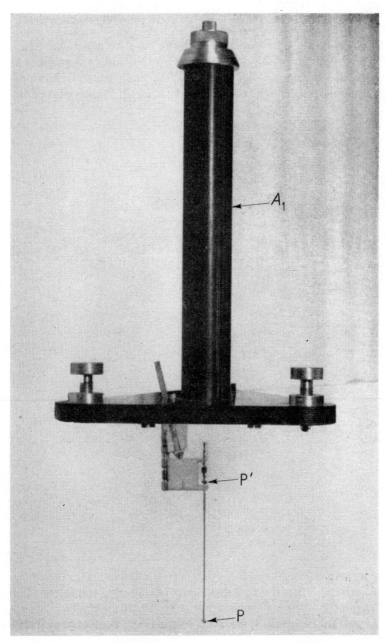

Fig. 3. Magnet system, clamp and upper part of case.

block (Fig. 2). The lower part of the case A^2 is attached to the upper by means of bayonet sockets and encloses the magnet system. It contains a small window W through which deflections of the magnet system are observed. A copper damping plate D may

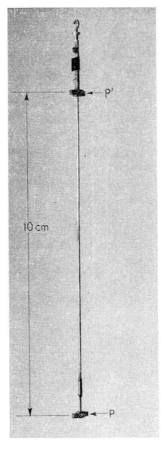

Fig. 4. Magnet system.

be adjusted for critical damping. The torsion head (Fig. 3) is made of Dural and fits into the upper part of the case, and from it hangs the phosphor–bronze suspension strip, 20 cm in length. The magnet system PP' (Fig. 4) hooks on to the lower end of the suspension strip.

In Fig. 3 the magnet system is shown held between the jaws of the clamping device, which is made of Perspex. The jaws are held together by a beryllium–copper spring and may be forced apart by screwing down a cone. In clamping, the magnet system is raised slightly because the jaws press against the cone-shaped projection at the top of the magnet system (Fig. 4), thus taking the tension off the suspension strip. The specimen mounting is shown in Fig. 5. The nature of the measurements to be made requires that the specimen be raised and lowered beneath the magnet system, rotated to different azimuths and traversed horizontally short distances (up to 1 cm) in a direction at right angles to the direction of magnetization of the magnet system. A string and pulley remote control system allows these adjustments to be made from the reading table 5 m away, thus eliminating thermal and magnetic disturbances which are inevitably produced when the instrument is approached and also enabling measurements to be made more rapidly.

A horizontal table runs kinematically on two vertical guides. Height control is by a stop which is threaded on the rod between the guides and which may be rotated by means of the lower pulley seen at the bottom of the picture. The height of the table may in this way be repeated to 0·1 mm and can be read by observing the Vernier scale through a telescope. The base is free to slide in a groove in the table in a direction at right angles to the plane of the vertical guides. It is spring-loaded and bears against a cam which can be rotated about the same axis as the height-adjusting rod. With the table in the lowered position the hub of the cam engages with the dog seen on the top of the pulley. Nine steps are provided on the cam, each step corresponding to a displacement of 0·25 cm. The rotating head fits over a column fixed to the base. The azimuth can be altered by means of a string passing through flexible cables. The azimuth and traverse positions are read from the reading table through a telescope and the additional magnifying lenses can be seen in Fig. 5. The specimen fits into the self-locating cap which is placed in position from outside the magnetometer room. The whole system is supported on a Dural girder which is secured to the floor of the hut, provision being made for accurate centring with respect to the magnetometer and coil system.

An Alcomax IV magnet system is shown in Fig. 4. Two magnets

6 mm $\times$ 1·5 mm $\times$ 1·5 mm are supported 10 cm apart in a
Dural former. Near the top of the system are two trimming

Fig. 5. Specimen mounting.

magnets which fit into rotatable heads, the axes of which are
perpendicular to one another and also a plane mirror 4 mm square.
Just below the hook at the extreme top the Dural former broadens

out into the cone. The lower magnet may be rotated relative to the upper in the collar to permit high astaticization.

High values of astaticism, i.e. extremely small total moment of the magnet system, are required for good performance of the instrument. The magnets are first aligned, and the stronger one demagnetized until a maximum period of swing is obtained in the earth's field. The trimming magnets are then rotated to position as described by Blackett,[1] until the effect of changing the magnetic field over the system is as small as possible. By this means it is possible to reduce the effective moment of the system to 0·01 per cent of the moment of one magnet.

C. *Design of magnet system*

Consider a small dipole placed at a point on the axis of and below the magnet system at a distance z from the lower magnet A, which is separated from the upper, A′, by a distance L. If the dipole is at right angles both to this axis and to the direction of magnetization of the magnets it will produce magnetic fields H and H' at A and A′ respectively such that

$$H/H' = (L + z)^3/z^3 \qquad (11)$$

In the following discussion it is assumed that

$$H/H' \ll 1 \qquad (12)$$

and the effect on the upper magnet A′ is neglected. In these circumstances the sensitivity S may be written:

$$S = \theta/H = T^2P/4\pi^2I \qquad (13)$$

because the condition for a steady deflection θ is

$$\sigma\theta = PH \qquad (14)$$

and

$$T = 2\pi(I/\sigma)^{\frac{1}{2}} \qquad (15)$$

In the above θ is the deflection in radians produced by field H acting on bottom magnet; T, the free period of the magnet system; P, the magnetic moment of one of the magnets of the astatic pair; I, the moment of inertia of the suspended system; and σ the torsional constant of the suspension strip.

(i) *Design for maximum sensitivity.* It is advantageous to discuss this in terms of the minimum field H required to produce a

given deflection θ, since it is conventional to compare magnetometers by discussing their reciprocal sensitivities measured in
oersteds per radian deflection. It would appear that H/θ might be
decreased indefinitely by increasing T. However, T is about equal
to the time required to make an observation, since the instrument
is used near the condition of critical damping. Hence T must be
kept short for an adequate speed of measurement, and also so that
drift of the zero reading can be kept small.

It is convenient to write

$$I = aI_0 \qquad (16)$$

where I_0 is the moment of inertia of a single magnet, a being necessarily greater than 2. Then, having decided on an upper limit for
the period T, the reciprocal sensitivity depends only on I_0/P.
Since $I_0 \propto l^5$ and $P \propto l^3$ where l is a length, $I_0/P \propto l^2$. H/θ cannot, however, be reduced indefinitely by reducing the size of the
magnets, since there is a lower practical limit to the size of the
magnet support and to the width of the mirror. The smaller the
mirror, the less bright the reflected image and the broader the
principal maximum of the diffraction pattern. The thinner the
mirror, the greater the tendency to warp. A mirror 4 mm wide
produces a principal maximum of width about 1 mm on a screen
5 m away, and since deflections of the order of millimetres have
to be measured, it is not advisable to use a mirror much smaller
than this. By blacking out the central strip of the mirror we obtain an interference pattern due to the pair of strips so formed
superimposed on the diffraction pattern so that the accuracy of
reading can be improved in this way. It has been found practicable to make a as small as 2·5, and a value of 3 is not too difficult
to achieve. Another factor restricting the degree of scaling down
is due to the grain size of magnetic materials. When this becomes
comparable with the magnet size the material can no longer be
regarded as isotropic and it is extremely difficult to make a pair of
magnets identical in weight, size, shape and magnetic moment.
Sintered magnetic materials have been found preferable to cast
magnetic materials for this reason.

Obviously both I_0 and P for a given magnet mass depend on
shape, and we now proceed to discuss the effect of magnet shape
on the sensitivity. Consider a magnet of square cross section, side

a and length l. Such a magnet may be magnetized either longitudinally (along l) or transversely (along one of the sides a). In the former case the fineness ratio $\beta = l/a \gg 1$ and the moment of inertia about an axis perpendicular to the direction of magnetization and through the centre of gravity is given by

$$I_0 = (Ml^2/12)(1 + \beta^{-2}) \tag{17}$$

In the latter case the fineness ratio $\beta = a/l \ll 1$ and

$$I_0 = Ma^2/6 \tag{18}$$

In either case, following Blackett,[1] we may write

$$I_0 = M^{\frac{5}{3}}\rho^{-\frac{2}{3}}f(\beta) \tag{19}$$

where

$$f(\beta) = \beta^{\frac{2}{3}}(1 + \beta^{-2})/12 \quad (\beta \gg 1) \tag{20}$$

and

$$f(\beta) = \beta^{\frac{2}{3}}/6 \quad (\beta \ll 1) \tag{21}$$

and ρ is the density of the material.

$f(\beta)$ is shown in Fig. 6, and the discontinuity in slope at $\beta = 1$ should be noted. The intensity of magnetization of a given

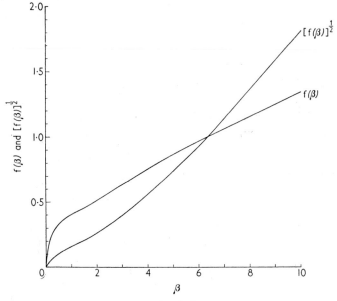

Fig. 6. Variation of $f(\beta)$ and $[f(\beta)]^{\frac{1}{2}}$ with fineness ratio.

N

magnetic material varies with shape and may be calculated for different materials from their B/H curves. Stoner [25] has tabulated demagnetizing coefficients D for prolate ellipsoids, so it is convenient to represent a magnet of fineness ratio β by such an ellipsoid of axial ratio β. When a magnetic material is removed from

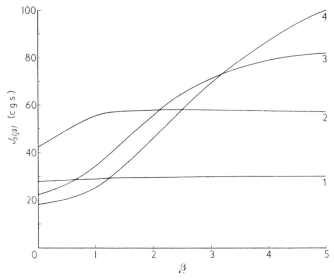

Fig. 7. Intensity of magnetization per unit mass, $J_s(\beta)$, plotted against values of β. Curve 1: Platinax II; 2: Magnadur II; 3: Ticonal K; 4: Alcomax IV.

a magnetizing field its intensity of magnetization corresponds to a point on the B/H curve such that

$$B/H = (1 - D)/D \tag{22}$$

The intensities of magnetization per unit mass, $J_s(\beta)$, of those materials we have found most useful have been calculated, and these are shown in Fig. 7.

We write

$$P = M J_s(\beta) \tag{23}$$

thus

$$I_0/P = P^{\frac{2}{3}} Q_s(\beta) \tag{24}$$

where

$$Q_s(\beta) = f(\beta)/\rho^{\frac{2}{3}}[J_s(\beta)]^{\frac{2}{3}} \tag{25}$$

and is purely a function of shape for a given material of density ρ. It has been plotted for four materials in Fig. 8, and the fineness ratio chosen should be such that $Q_s(\beta)$ is a minimum. Thus for Alcomax IV, $\beta \approx 3 \cdot 25$ should be chosen, for Ticonal K $\beta \approx 2 \cdot 5$, while for Magnadur II and Platinax II transversely magnetized

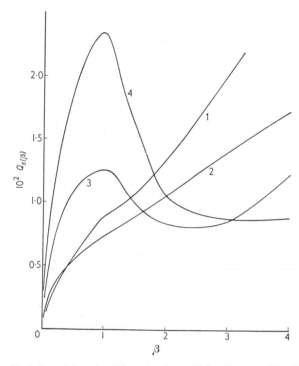

Fig. 8. Variation of $Q_s(\beta)$ for different values of β for the materials of Fig. 7.

magnets may be employed ($\beta < 1$). It is not practicable to use $\beta < \frac{1}{3}$, since the field produced by a weak specimen placed very close to the magnetometer falls off noticeably over the length of such a magnet.

(ii) *Design for maximum signal/noise ratio.* This has been fully discussed by Blackett,[1] who pointed out that the r.m.s. deflection θ_0 of the system due to thermal noise is given by

$$\tfrac{1}{2}\sigma\theta_0{}^2 = \tfrac{1}{2}k\tau \qquad (26)$$

where k is Boltzmann's constant and τ the temperature in degrees absolute. H_0, the magnetic field which will produce a deflection equal to θ_0, is given by

$$PH_0 = \sigma\theta_0 \qquad (27)$$

and by using equation 26 we get

$$H_0 = (2\pi\epsilon^{\frac{1}{2}}/T)(I^{\frac{1}{2}}/P) \qquad (28)$$

where $\epsilon = k\tau$. H_0 may be regarded as the minimum detectable field and may be decreased by increasing T. However, as explained previously, this is usually not desirable. Having chosen a value for T, we see that $H_0 \propto I^{-1/2} \times P^{-1/6}$ so that the magnet size should be large. However, as H_0 is increased in this way θ_0 diminishes rapidly ($\theta_0 \propto I^{-5/2}$) and becomes immeasurable unless the mirror is made large, when a will become so large as to reverse any gain in H_0. The optimum shape may be deduced as in Blackett,[1] where it is shown that

$$H_0 = (2\pi\epsilon^{\frac{1}{2}}a^{\frac{3}{2}}/TP^{\frac{1}{2}})G_s(\beta) \qquad (29)$$

where

$$G_s(\beta) = [f(\beta)]^{\frac{1}{2}}/\rho^{\frac{3}{2}}[J_s(\beta)]^{\frac{5}{3}} \qquad (30)$$

$[f(\beta)]^{1/2}$ is plotted against β in Fig. 6. $G_s(\beta)$, like $Q_s(\beta)$, depends only on the magnetic properties of the material and on the fineness ratio. In Fig. 9, $G_s(\beta)$ is shown plotted against β for the four materials considered at present to be the most suitable (Platinax II, Magnadur II, Ticonal K, and Alcomax IV). There is nothing to choose between Alcomax IV and Ticonal K used at fineness ratios of 4·0 and 2·2 respectively. Transversely magnetized Magnadur II and Platinax II are slightly better.

D. *Details of some other designs*

In palaeomagnetism it has been found more important to produce magnetometers having high sensitivity and low free period, rather than instruments having the smallest possible minimum detectable field. In the following are described designs using those materials which are considered to be the best available at present and these designs are compared with two of Professor Blackett's designed for maximum signal/noise ratio. It will be shown that the minimum detectable field of these instruments is much smaller than the field expected even from the weaker sediments yet studied and that the r.m.s. thermal noise deflection is certainly much less than zero drift due to other causes which are not easily avoidable.

We suppose it is desired to obtain maximum sensitivity with a reading time of T_0 sec. We use

$$I_0 = T_0{}^2\sigma/4\pi^2a \qquad (31)$$

and if we choose a suitable suspension, I_0 may be calculated easily. Phosphor–bronze strip 0·002 in. × 0·0001 in. has frequently been

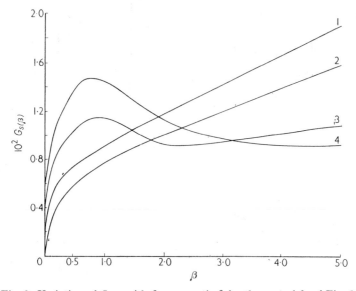

Fig. 9. Variation of $G_s(\beta)$ with fineness ratio β for the materials of Fig. 3.

used. Quartz fibres can be drawn with torsional constants of the same order as that of this strip. The latter are more constant in physical properties but considerably more difficult to handle. σ depends on the length of the fibre, about 20 cm being convenient. A value of 2·5 is considered to be a practical minimum for a and is substituted in equation 31. Hence I_0, the moment of inertia of a single magnet, may be calculated. The optimum fineness ratio is determined for the chosen magnetic material by finding the minimum $Q_s(\beta)$ from Fig. 8, and so the mass and dimensions of the magnets are found. Having done this, it is now necessary to check

Table 2. Details of astatic magnetometers

	Creer				Blackett	
	Alcomax IV	Ticonal K	Magnadur II	Platinax II	Alcomax IV	Vectolite
I_0		$4 \cdot 51 \times 10^{-3}$			$10 \cdot 0 \times 10^{-3}$	37×10^{-3}
α		$2 \cdot 5$			$4 \cdot 1$	$4 \cdot 5$
M	$0 \cdot 137$	$0 \cdot 178$	$0 \cdot 347$	$0 \cdot 589$	$0 \cdot 19$	$2 \cdot 5$
β	$3 \cdot 5$	$2 \cdot 3$	$0 \cdot 4$	$0 \cdot 4$	$4 \cdot 5$	$0 \cdot 16$
b, l	$0 \cdot 17 \times 0 \cdot 17 \times 0 \cdot 60$	$0 \cdot 22 \times 0 \cdot 22 \times 0 \cdot 50$	$0 \cdot 31 \times 0 \cdot 31 \times 0 \cdot 77$	$0 \cdot 24 \times 0 \cdot 24 \times 0 \cdot 59$	$0 \cdot 18 \times 0 \cdot 18 \times 0 \cdot 80$	$0 \cdot 50 \times 0 \cdot 50 \times 3 \cdot 20$
P	$10 \cdot 8$	$10 \cdot 9$	$16 \cdot 5$	$16 \cdot 8$	$15 \cdot 0$	$60 \cdot 0$
H/β	$2 \cdot 6 \times 10^{-5}$	$2 \cdot 5 \times 10^{-5}$	$2 \cdot 0 \times 10^{-5}$	$2 \cdot 0 \times 10^{-5}$	$1 \cdot 5 \times 10^{-4}$	$1 \cdot 2 \times 10^{-4}$
Field for 1 mm deflection	$2 \cdot 6 \times 10^{-9}$	$2 \cdot 5 \times 10^{-9}$	$2 \cdot 0 \times 10^{-9}$	$2 \cdot 0 \times 10^{-9}$	$1 \cdot 5 \times 10^{-8}$	$1 \cdot 2 \times 10^{-8}$
H_0	$3 \cdot 6 \times 10^{-10}$	$3 \cdot 5 \times 10^{-10}$	$2 \cdot 3 \times 10^{-10}$	$2 \cdot 2 \times 10^{-10}$	$6 \cdot 7 \times 10^{-10}$	$2 \cdot 9 \times 10^{-10}$

that the suspension selected will support the weight of the magnet system and that the magnets are not so small as to make the value taken for a impossible to achieve. The former may possibly not be true if silver suspension strip has been chosen and the latter if too small a fineness ratio $(\beta \lesssim \frac{1}{3})$ has been assumed. The other quantities listed in Table 2 may be calculated using the formulae given above. $T_0 = 40$ sec and $\sigma = 1 \cdot 1 \times 10^{-2}$ dyne cm/radian per cm length of fibre have been chosen. It has been assumed in the above analysis that the control is purely torsional, and this condition is possible in practice. It is convenient to provide means of introducing a variable amount of magnetic control as a means of decreasing sensitivity when measuring more strongly magnetized rocks with a corresponding reduction in period T_0 and time of measurement, and this can be done by means of a small permanent magnet.

For the measurement of igneous rocks and very strongly magnetized sediments of intensity higher than 10^{-4} gauss, an instrument having a time constant of about 1 sec was constructed at Cambridge (see Collinson et al.[7]). For a short period, I_0 should be as small as possible, and the condition that P/I_0 should be a maximum is no longer of primary importance. Alcomax IV magnets of fineness ratio 2 were used.

Table 3.   Details of a short period astatic magnetometer

Length of magnets (e) (sintered Alcomax IV)	3 mm
Breadth of magnets (b) (square cross section)	1·5 mm
Magnet mass (M)	$5 \cdot 07 \times 10^{-2}$ g
Magnetic moment (P)	2·3 gauss cm^3
Moment of inertia of magnet system (I)	$1 \cdot 2 \times 10^{-3}$ c.g.s.u.
Sensitivity (light path 1 m)	$0 \cdot 2 \times 10^{-6}$ oersted/mm deflection
Time constant (T)	1·4 sec
Degree of astaticism	500
Suspension strip (phosphor–bronze)	0·010 in. $\times$ 0·0005 in.
Length of suspension	6 cm
Torsional constant of suspension strip (σ)	4·1 dyne cm rad^{-1}
Magnetic restoring force due to geomagnetic field	$8 \cdot 2 \times 10^{-4}$ dyne cm rad^{-1}

With such a small period, the direction of magnetization of a cylindrical specimen can be determined by turning it, first about a vertical axis until maximum deflection is obtained, and then about a horizontal axis parallel with the magnetic axis of the suspended system, until zero deflection is obtained. Then the magnetization vector is vertical and its direction with respect to orientation lines on the specimen can be read directly.

It is important to support the specimen holder independently of the tripod carrying the magnetometer so that vibrations due to manipulating the specimen holder while readings are being taken are not transferred to the magnet system. The lay-out of the instrument is shown in Fig. 12 and particulars are listed in Table 3.

3. Rock-generator Magnetometers

A. *Principle of operation*

In these instruments a rock sample is rotated within or near a pickup coil system. After amplification of the weak voltage induced in the coil, its phase is compared with that of a voltage of known phase, obtained from the same rotating system. This phase difference determines the direction of the magnetic component perpendicular to the axis of rotation, referred to some fixed line on the rock sample. Rotation about two further mutually perpendicular axes enables the direction of the total vector to be fixed. The intensity of magnetization of the rock can be obtained from the amplitude of the amplified signal.

B. *Design factors*

Thermal noise in the pickup coil is the ultimate factor limiting sensitivity in the a.c. magnetometer. For the measurement of very weak specimens, it is desirable to pay some attention to obtaining the maximum signal/noise ratio for this part of the instrument.

Two types of pickup coils suggest themselves: a solenoidal shape, with the sample rotating inside, or a flat, disc-shaped coil, with the sample rotating on its axis, and as near to it as possible. Calculations show that the signal/noise ratios obtainable with a given magnetic moment are comparable. It might be supposed that the signal/noise ratio could be improved by increasing the inducing moment, i.e. by increasing the volume of the sample. With the solenoidal coil, this involves increasing the mean radius of the coil, and an approximate calculation shows that the signal/noise ratio is nearly independent of size. Similarly, with the flat coil, an improved signal/noise ratio is obtained (within certain

limits) by using a small sample, the loss in moment being offset
by the decrease in distance between the coil and the centre of the
rock. It is assumed that the rocks are being rotated at high speed
in some form of air-turbine, and that larger rocks cannot be
rotated at such high speeds as small ones.

The flux, F, through a circular coil of radius r due to a magnetic
moment P situated on and directed along the axis of the coil perpendicular to its plane and distant z from it, is given by

$$F = 2\pi P r^2/(r^2 + z^2)^{\frac{3}{2}} \tag{32}$$

Consider a coil of rectangular winding area, with dimensions as
shown in Fig. 10.

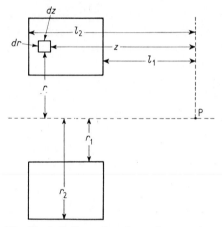

Fig. 10. Coil dimensions for rock-generator.

If the wire has a cross sectional area a, and the packing factor
is k, the number of turns in the small area $dr.dz$ is given by

$$dN = dr.dz.\, k/a \tag{33}$$

and the flux turns $d\phi$, threading this element of the coil, is given
by

$$d\phi = (2\pi Pk/a)r^2(r^2 + z^2)^{-\frac{3}{2}}dr.dz \tag{34}$$

and for the whole coil

$$\phi = 2\pi Pk/a\int_{r_1}^{r_2}\int_{l_1}^{l_2} r^2(r^2 + z^2)^{-\frac{3}{2}}dr.dz \tag{35}$$

$$= \frac{2\pi Pk}{a}\left[l_2 \log\frac{r_2 + (r_2{}^2 + l_2{}^2)^{\frac{1}{2}}}{r_1 + (r_1{}^2 + l_2{}^2)^{\frac{1}{2}}} - l_1 \log\frac{r_2{}^2 + (r_2{}^2 + l_1{}^2)^{\frac{1}{2}}}{r_1 + (r_1{}^2 + l_1{}^2)^{\frac{1}{2}}}\right] \tag{36}$$

If the specimen is rotating at f revolutions per second, the r.m.s. voltage, e_s, induced in the coil, is given by

$$e_s = \frac{\pi^3 Pkf \cdot 10^{-8}}{a\sqrt{2}}$$
$$\left[l_2 \log \frac{r_2 + (r_2^2 + l_2^2)^{\frac{1}{2}}}{r_1 + (r_1^2 + l_2^2)^{\frac{1}{2}}} - l_1 \log \frac{r_2 + (r_2^2 + l_1^2)^{\frac{1}{2}}}{r_1 + (r_1^2 + l_1^2)^{\frac{1}{2}}} \right] \quad (37)$$

The resistance, R_c, of the coil expressed in the same terms is

$$R_c = (\pi^2 \rho k/a^2)(l_2 - l_1)(r_2^2 - r_1^2) \quad (38)$$

where ρ is the resistivity of the wire used. The r.m.s. random noise voltage, e_n, arising from this resistance is given by:

$$e_n = 1 \cdot 27 \times 10^{-10} (R_c \Delta f)^{\frac{1}{2}} \quad (39)$$

where Δf is the effective bandwidth of the circuit. If the signal from the coil is fed via a transformer into the amplifier, the reflected noise resistance at the first valve can be made large compared with the equivalent noise resistance of the valve.

Then from equations 37 to 39, the signal/noise ratio is

$$\frac{e_s}{e_n} = \frac{APk^{\frac{1}{2}}f}{\rho^{\frac{1}{2}}} \cdot \frac{1}{(l_2 - l_1)^{\frac{1}{2}}(r_2^2 - r_1^2)^{\frac{1}{2}}}$$
$$\left[l_2 \log \frac{r_2 + (r_2^2 + l_2^2)^{\frac{1}{2}}}{r_1 + (r_1^2 + l_2^2)^{\frac{1}{2}}} - l_1 \log \frac{r_2 + (r_2^2 + l_1^2)^{\frac{1}{2}}}{r_1 + (r_1^2 + l_1^2)^{\frac{1}{2}}} \right] \quad (40)$$

where A is a constant.

Thus, the signal/noise ratio is independent of the number of turns, except in so far as an improved packing factor is obtained with thick wire.

Johnson [17] has developed a similar expression for a coil in which $(l_2 - l_1)$ is small compared with r_1 and r_2, and the signal is passed directly to the grid of the first valve of the amplifier. He shows that the coil should have many turns of fine wire, and $(r_2 - r_1)$ should be small.

For a hollow cylindrical coil, with the sample rotating at its centre, $l_2 = -l_1 = l$ and equation 40 becomes

$$\frac{e_s}{e_n} = \frac{APk^{\frac{1}{2}}f}{\rho^{\frac{1}{2}}} \times F(r_1, r_2, l) \quad (41)$$

where

$$F(r_1, r_2, l) = \frac{l^{\frac{1}{2}}}{(r_2^2 - r_1^2)^{\frac{1}{2}}} \log \frac{r_2 + (r_2^2 + l^2)^{\frac{1}{2}}}{r_1 + (r_1^2 + l^2)^{\frac{1}{2}}}$$

In equation 41 the magnitude of P has been discussed, and ρ and k are not variable through very wide limits. In practice there are also limits to the speed of rotation of the rock sample. Use of air-turbines of the Beams type enable frequencies of up to 1 kc/s to be used, but the practical limit is considerably below this owing to breakage of samples, excessive noise and the time taken to accelerate to and decelerate from the required speed.

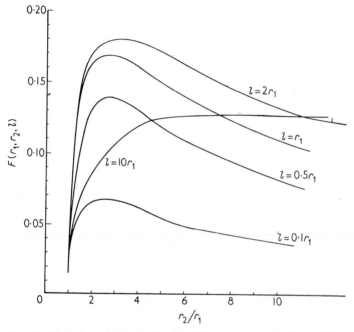

Fig. 11. Variation of $F(r_1, r_2, l)$ with different values of r_2/r_1 and l/r_1.

Fig. 11 shows graphs of $F(r_1, r_2, l)$ against varying values of r_2/r_1 and l. r_1 is effectively fixed by the size of the rock sample chosen, and here $r_1 = 4$ cm. The graphs show that there is considerable variation in the value of signal/noise ratio with the shape of the coil. A similar result is obtained with flat coils.

Stray fields from a.c. mains circuits will induce unwanted voltages in the pickup coil. These can be reduced to a low level by winding a compensating coil of the same number of area turns around or near to the main coil. The specimen, being more closely coupled to the main coil, will induce a net output voltage in the system, but the output due to a uniform disturbing field will be nearly zero. In a practical system the decrease in the signal/noise ratio is small. Electromagnetic screening of the coil system is also useful, and the use of narrow-band filters reduces the effects of fields due to harmonics of the mains.

The various methods used to determine the direction of magnetization from the phase of the induced voltage are conveniently described with reference to instruments that have been constructed or are in use.

C. *Description of instruments*

In 1937 Kruger and Brasack [19] used a type of spinner magnetometer to measure the intensity of magnetization of crystals. The crystal was rotated at 400 c/s by means of a geared-up motor, the pickup coil being similar in principle to a Gramme-ring armature. A vibration galvanometer was used as detector after several stages of amplification, the limiting sensitivity set by the galvanometer being $9·2 \times 10^{-7}$ gauss.

Johnson [17] has described an instrument used for measurements of magnetic directions in rocks. A 30-cm^3 sample was rotated at 10 c/s, and the signal fed to a synchronous commutator in series with a milliammeter, the brushes being adjusted to give maximum signal. A similar instrument has been used by Nagata.[22]

An improved method of phase discrimination was introduced by Bruckshaw and Robertson [4] in 1948. A reference voltage was obtained from a pair of coils surrounding a magnet rotating on the same shaft as the specimen. By rotating the coils to different positions, the phase of the induced voltage could be varied, and when it was the same as that of the signal voltage a balance was possible on a potentiometer, using a vibration galvanometer as detector. In this method the amplifier is used only to amplify a signal, the phase of which is immaterial, and thus the accuracy does not depend on its stability or phase/frequency characteristics.

A similar method of generating the reference voltage was used by Johnson *et al.*,[18] an electronic wattmeter being used to measure phase differences, zero output indicating that the two signals were 90° out of phase. The wattmeter acts as a very narrow band detector which enables signals to be measured which are of the same order as the noise in the first valve, but which are undergoing rapid and random changes in phase. A frequency of 10 c/s was used and amplication was by a series of eight unit amplifiers with RC filter networks. The whole unit was capable of being built into and used in the back of a truck for work in the field.

The generation of a reference voltage by means of a rotating magnet has certain disadvantages, chief of which is the field it produces at the sample pickup coil. In more recent instruments, e.g. those of Gough,[13] and of Tatel and Michelson (described in a paper by Graham [12]) a photoelectric method is used. Both these instruments employ air-turbines to spin the sample, at 525 and 282 c/s respectively. A beam of light is reflected off the rotor, on which a suitable pattern is marked and the voltage from the photocell varies accordingly. In Gough's instrument the reference voltage is passed through a phase-shifting network, and it and the signal voltage are displayed on the X and Y plates of an oscilloscope, the phase of the reference voltage being varied until the resulting ellipse is reduced to a straight line. Brynjolfsson [5] describes a 5-c/s instrument, using larger specimens of up to 1 200 cm³ in volume. The specimen is rotated until zero signal is obtained in the output, a commutator and d.c. galvanometer being used as detector. External field disturbances are reduced by the use of Mumetal screens.

D. *Performance of a.c. magnetometers*

There is little to choose between astatic and a.c. magnetometers from the point of view of sensitivity and accuracy of measurement. In both, the chief sources of errors are external disturbing fields; these can usually be reduced to a sufficiently low level for all but very weak rocks, by good astaticism in the astatic instrument, and by compensation coils and screening in the a.c. magnetometer. There is a possible additional source of error in the latter type arising from changes in the characteristics of electronic circuits, such as variation of phase with frequency and waveform. A method of detecting phase differences without the use of narrow-pass filters and phase-shifting networks is being explored at Newcastle.

Further sources of error at low levels are magnetic contamination of the specimen holder and electrostatic charges accumulating on the holder. The fact that the a.c. magnetometer can be used in the presence of a.c. magnetic fields and mechanical vibration, as exist in the average laboratory, is the chief advantage of this type of instrument. Under optimum conditions intensities of magnetization of 10^{-7} gauss can be measured, a level which includes the great majority of rocks now being examined.

II. THE INVESTIGATION OF OTHER MAGNETIC PROPERTIES OF ROCKS

1. Measurement of Susceptibility

A. *The a.c. method*

Bruckshaw and Robertson [4] have described an instrument for the measurement of the susceptibility of igneous rocks in fields of the order of 0·5 oersted. The specimen is placed in an a.c. magnetic field from a Helmholtz coil system, its susceptibility causing a distortion in the exciting field. This is detected by a coil of two windings, the turns being adjusted so that there is no output from the system due to the uniform field of the Helmholtz coils. There will be an induced voltage due to the magnetization of the specimen, it being more closely coupled to the inner coil. By means of a potentiometer, this voltage is measured in terms of that set up in a further coil wound on the outside of the main coil, and excited by the Helmholtz system. The balance point is found by a vibration galvanometer on the output of a high-gain amplifier connected to the potentiometer.

Values of susceptibility down to 10^{-5} e.m.u. per c.c. can be measured, using an exciting field at 50 c/s, noise in the amplifier limiting the accuracy. The same coil system and detecting circuits are used in the a.c. magnetometer of Bruckshaw and Robertson, described in Part I.

B. *The d.c. method*

Blackett [1] has described how the astatic magnetometer may be used for the measurement of susceptibility. A known uniform field is applied to the specimen by means of secondary windings on the Helmholtz coils. The magnetization then measured will be the sum of the permanent and induced magnetizations, and by subtracting the former, the susceptibility can be derived. There is a small loss of sensitivity, depending on the degree of astaticism, due to the uniform field over the magnet system.

C. *Anisotropic susceptibility*

Ising's [16] method has recently been developed by D. B. Stone (private communication). A small cylindrical specimen of rock hangs at the end of a phosphor–bronze suspension strip

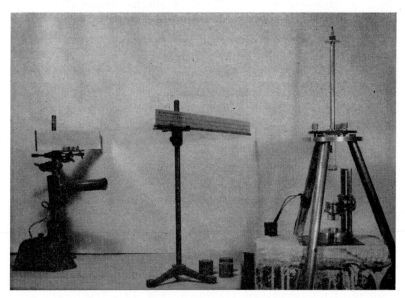

Fig. 12. Lay-out of igneous magnetometer.

and is placed in a horizontally directed alternating field, the frequency of which must be considerably greater than that of the suspended system and much less than that appropriate to the time of relaxation of the magnetic particles in the rock. The specimen is deflected by the couple due to the applied alternating field and the moment induced in the rock at right angles to it due to anisotropy. Deflections are measured in three planes mutually at right angles, by rotating the applied field through 360° and turning the specimen. The ellipsoid of susceptibility may be calculated, but the calculations involved are tedious.

Howell *et al.*[15] have recently developed a method of using the rock-generator magnetometer for the determination of anisotropy of susceptibility. The sample is rotated at half-normal speed in an inducing field, the signal due to the permanent magnetization being filtered out, while that due to the susceptibility, being of twice the rotational frequency, can be measured. Measurements about three mutually perpendicular axes enable the principal axes to be determined.

2. Measurement of Saturation Magnetization and Hysteresis Plotting at Different Temperatures

The simple form of magnetometer cannot be used, as compensation at the magnetometer for the effect of the high fields necessary to produce saturation in rocks and minerals is impossible. Two methods which have been recently developed to a high degree of sensitivity are outlined below.

A. *Balance methods*

(i) *The torsional balance.* The principle, first employed by Curie and Chèneveau,[10] is to measure the force on the specimen due to an inhomogeneous magnetic field by means of a torsion fibre. A uniform magnetic field strong enough to saturate the specimen is also applied, so that the temperature at which the magnetization disappears is the true Curie point and not a blocking temperature.

In the original apparatus described by Chevallier and Pierre,[6] an electromagnet with truncated conical pole pieces of 1 in. diameter provides a magnetic field of up to 500 oersteds and a gradient of 150 oersted/cm maximum (Fig. 13). The total movement of a specimen so caused is about 1 cm and this is designed to be within a furnace situated between the poles of the magnet. Both intensity of magnetization and temperature are recorded on a photographic plate, changes in intensity causing the light beam to be deflected from left to right and changes in temperature up or down. Temperature marks are placed on the photographic record by cutting off the light for a short interval as required.

A balance of similar design sufficiently sensitive for measuring sedimentary rocks is being constructed by Parry.[24] In place of the electromagnet, a coil system has been designed. Residual magnetism of the former prevented an accurate zero being attained on the magnetic axis of the record and could also cause vertical movement

of the specimen, since the field gradient produced is not unidirectional. Two gradient coils carrying current in opposite directions
are contained within two main field coils. Both sets are wound
with wire with braided glass-fibre insulation. The main field coils
(22 s.w.g. wire) can take 3 kW at 240 V producing a field of up to
2 000 oersteds and the gradient coils (30 s.w.g. wire) can take 1 kW
at 240 V producing a field gradient of up to 1 000 oersted/cm. The
coil systems are water-cooled. Inside the gradient coils is a
Nichrome tubular former 13·5 cm long and 1·25 cm in radius

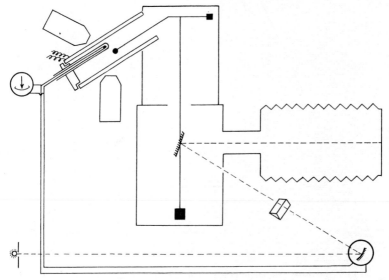

Fig. 13. The torsional balance.

wound with a 1-kW heating element of Nichrome wire in five
sections.

The specimen is carried in a small cup at the end of a silica rod.
The beam of the balance is of $\frac{1}{4}$-in. Dural tubing and the suspension of 26 s.w.g. copper wire. Four plates immersed in oil damp
the suspended system.

(ii) *The translational balance.* This device, which has previously
been used successfully and with high accuracy by Foex and
Forrer [11] and by McKeehan,[21] has been adopted by Parry [24] in an
apparatus in which a specimen, magnetized to saturation, is

o

acted upon by a force due to an applied field gradient (Fig. 14). The specimen is attached to one end of a thin silica rod S, which fits into a light Dural beam ($\frac{1}{8}$ in. tubing) of length 33 cm and total mass 10 g. This is suspended from a rigid tetrapod framework by five threads, only allowing movement parallel to the length of the beam. The period of oscillation of the suspended

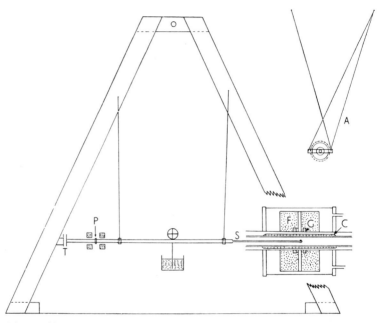

Fig. 14. The translational balance. The method of suspending the beam is shown at A.

system is about 1 sec. A small tubular furnace C of internal diameter 1 cm surrounds and is aligned with the line of movement of the specimen (of approximate volume 0·25 cm³). A carefully designed system of coils F, G, surrounds the furnace and is capable of applying a magnetic field gradient of up to 350 oersted/cm at the same time as a uniform field of maximum intensity 7100 oersted. By connecting the gradient coils in series to an a.c. source an alternating magnetic field can be obtained for an hysteretic measurements. The coil system is water-cooled, 15 kW being dissipated for a temperature rise of 10°C. The force on the specimen is measured either by restoring the pendulum to its rest position by applying a known magnetic field gradient to a permanent magnet P (made from Magnadur III) fixed to the other end of the beam, or by automatically recording the deflection of the beam by measuring changes in the capacity of a small parallel-plate condenser T consisting of a plate fixed to the baseplate and a light metal plate fixed to the far end of the beam.

The minimum detectable force on a specimen is estimated at 0·02 dyne, which is the force per unit field gradient on a magnetic moment of about 2×10^{-2} gauss cm³. The gravitational restoring force on the pendulum is 45 dynes per millimetre deflection.

B. *Ballistic and a.c. methods*

A simple ballistic method has been used by Thellier (described in Nagata [22]), in which the specimen is moved from one to the other of two identical coaxial pickup coils connected in opposition and placed between the poles of an electromagnet. The signal is recorded on a ballistic galvanometer. This method, though simple, is not capable of great sensitivity, since the signal cannot be amplified.

P. M. S. Blackett [2] and D. J. Sutton at the Imperial College of Science and Technology have designed an apparatus based on the same principle in which the specimen is set in transverse simple harmonic vibrations of amplitude 1 or 2 mm at about 30 c/s (to avoid 50 c/s mains interference) in a holder at the end of a Perspex rod between two pickup coils situated near opposite pole faces of an electromagnet capable of producing 14000 oersteds from 4 kW. The signal from the pickup coils is fed into a three-stage amplifier and cathode follower and then to a vibration galvanometer. Hysteresis curves and saturation magnetization can be measured over a range of temperature from $-80°C$ to $+100°C$ by circulating a stream of hot or cold air around the specimen, which is surrounded by a Perspex box. The instrument is calibrated by substituting a small current-carrying element for a specimen. Frequent calibration is necessary, since the sensitivity depends on the amplitude of the vibrations, and this is difficult to control precisely. The minimum detectable dipole as set by thermal noise due to the resistance of the coils is calculated to be about 3×10^{-6} e.m.u. but the actual error of a single reading in the apparatus constructed is 10^{-4} e.m.u. Another instrument of this type is being constructed with a redesigned coil system, a furnace capable of attaining 600°C and in which the frequency of vibration is increased to 75 c/s and a better magnet employed. Also the untuned amplifier and vibration galvanometer may be replaced by a homodyne with circuit synchronous switching.

3. Apparatus for the Study of Temperature Effects

A. *Introduction*

Investigations of thermo-remanent magnetization (t.r.m.) and of the effects of temperature on the natural remanent magnetization (n.r.m.) of igneous rocks have been carried out by a large number of workers in palaeomagnetism. There are two approaches to the problem. In the first, the rock is heated to successively higher temperatures and then cooled to room temperature either in zero field or in a field of the desired strength. After each successive step the rock is removed from the furnace and its remanent magnetization is measured by means of a standard magnetometer. In the second, the remanent magnetization of the rock specimen is measured while it is hot and therefore while it is in the furnace. The latter method is more suitable for experiments on the decay of remanent magnetization of sediments with temperature, because the t.r.m. acquired by many sediments in a magnetic field of intensity as low as 0·1 per cent of the earth's field is greater than the n.r.m., and consequently elaborate apparatus is necessary to adjust the current in the coil system to compensate for the diurnal variation, since this may amount to 0·1 per cent of the total field.

It is important that heating should be carried out in a neutral atmosphere to prevent oxidation, and sometimes it may be necessary to evacuate the air from the pores of the specimen prior to heating as an additional precaution. Heater windings should be non-inductive to reduce the intensity of a.c. fields near the specimen which may be placed in a non-magnetic metal container to reduce temperature gradients over it. Temperature is most conveniently measured by means of a thermocouple. Chromel–Alumel is sufficiently magnetic to distort the magnetic field in the furnace, and may be used only in experiments where the rock is measured out of the furnace at room temperature and must be removed from the apparatus during cooling. Where the furnace is installed underneath the magnetometer platinum-platinum–rhodium thermocouples have been found satisfactory, but other steps are necessary to render negligible the effects of the furnace on the magnetometer. The resistance element must be highly non-magnetic, and since none of the more commonly used resistance materials, such as Constantan, Manganin or Nichrome, are sufficiently non-magnetic, platinum or silver–palladium have been employed. Since the external magnetic field due to the current flowing in the heater is proportional to the current flowing, for a given power the heater should be designed to have maximum re-sistance and therefore thin wire should be used. However, the wire should have a high tensile strength to withstand the stresses due to relative expansion of the wire and the former and be re-sistant to corrosion. Fire cements usually employed in furnace building have been found to acquire a t.r.m. after successive heat-ings and coolings. Mixtures of pure magnesium oxide and pure boric acid in the proportion six to one, and of sodium silicate and aluminium oxide have been used successfully. A mixture of ethyl silicate and pure quartz has also been used, but is unsuitable mechanically.

B. Description of some existing furnaces

Parry [24] has constructed a tubular-type electric furnace which has been used for work on igneous rocks. It was not designed for use under a magnetometer and specimens must be cooled and removed for measurement. The specimen R (Fig. 15) is placed in-

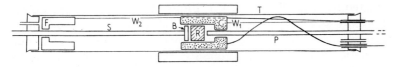

Fig. 15. Tubular furnace for igneous rocks.

side a copper tube, round which is wound a non-inductive Nichrome heater C developing 200 W at 270 V. This is placed in a transparent silica tube T of diameter 1·5 in. closed at both ends with rubber bungs. Dry nitrogen is drawn through the tube by means of a filter pump and temperatures are read by means of a Chromel–Alumel thermocouple cemented into the copper block B, which bears against one end of the specimen. The small thermal capacity of the apparatus ensures rapid heating. Cooling is achieved by pulling the furnace C away from the specimen by means of a wire W_1 passing through a gas-tight seal in the rubber bung, at the same time sliding the copper block F along the thermocouple sheath S on to the specimen with another wire W_2. The silica rod P holds the specimen in position during this operation. Cooling is speeded up by blowing compressed air over the part of the silica tube covering the specimen and cooling block.

A hot-air furnace suitable for placing under a magnetometer has been constructed by J. H. Leng.[20] Air is passed, first through a heat exchanger, where it is heated by the exhaust gases, then through a furnace which is about 2 ft away from the specimen to avoid magnetic effects both on the specimen and on the magnetometer, then through silica tubes to the specimen and finally through the heat exchanger into the atmosphere. All hot parts are insulated by diatomaceous earth. The top of the furnace is separated from the magnetometer by a water-cooled copper plate, this precaution being necessary, since Thomson currents set up in the copper damping plate of the magnetometer due to temperature gradients induced by the furnace can produce fluctuations in the reading of the magnetometer greater than the signal expected. The main disadvantages of this type of furnace are, first, the difficulty of achieving air-tight joints to withstand 800°C, and secondly, the large time constant.

Furnaces suitable for measuring the magnetization of strongly magnetized sediments while hot have been designed and constructed by Leng [20] and by D. J. Blundell [3] at the Imperial College of Science and Technology, and by K. M. Creer and G. Turnbull at King's College, Newcastle. These furnaces are not completely non-magnetic, but by making 'dummy' runs with no specimens the magnetization of the furnace can be corrected for. Leng's furnace was designed to allow specimens to be heated to 700°C in about 45 min. The power input is kept as small as possible to ease the problems of thermal lagging, but even so an external cooling system by water flow is necessary to prevent the creation of Thomson currents in the damping plate of the magnetometer. Specimens

Fig. 16. Sedimentary furnace beneath magnetometer.

are moved by remote control into the necessary positions inside the furnace which itself remains fixed in position. Blundell's furnace, which was developed from Leng's design, is shown in Fig. 16. The specimen, when in position in the furnace, occupies a position 3 cm below the lower magnet of the magnetometer, allowing only 2 cm for thermal lagging and insulation. Therefore the specimen is arranged to sit on the heater and both are rotatable together. The heater consists of 6 m of 30 s.w.g. platinum wire wound almost non-inductively inside a disc of diameter 37 mm and

Fig. 17. Method of winding furnace.

height 10 mm, and tests were made to ensure that specimens are not demagnetized by an external alternating field due to it. All direct current is blocked by connecting an 80-microfarad con-denser in series. With a power input of 95 W specimens may be heated to 650°C in less than an hour. Difficulty with this furnace has been experienced due to short-circuiting caused by expansion, at high temperatures, but has been overcome in the furnace designed by Creer and Turnbull in which the platinum wire of the heating element is wound through silica tubes, and temperatures of 900°C can be reached without breakdown. A photograph is shown in Fig. 17. Silica wool is used for insulation. Radiation of heat is reduced by silvering the insides of the various layers of insulation.

Since haematite undergoes a transition in its magnetic properties at a temperature in the region of −30°C, it has been found neces-

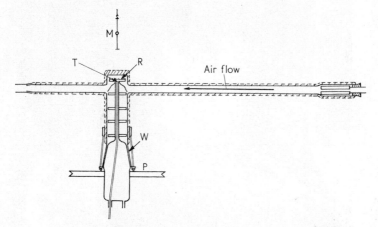

Fig. 18. Apparatus for measurements below room temperature.

sary to design and construct apparatus for measuring remanent magnetization below room temperature. Apparatus designed by G. Haigh [14] is shown in Fig. 18. The direction and intensity of magnetization of a disc-shaped specimen may be measured at temperatures down to −100°C. Dry air is passed through a copper tube immersed in liquid oxygen and the temperature of the specimen R controlled by governing the flow of cold air by means of a fine-adjustment diaphragm valve. By circulating hot air instead of cold, the specimen can be heated up to about 100°C. A platinum/copper thermocouple T is used to record temperature. The specimen can be rotated to any azimuth by means of the pulley P, working in the ground-glass joint W.

4. Demagnetization by alternating magnetic fields

The study of the decay of n.r.m. of igneous and sedimentary rocks in alternating magnetic fields leads to important conclusions about the stability of this magnetization, an example having been given by Creer.[9] For igneous rocks a peak field of about 300 oersteds is sufficient to distinguish between stable and unstable rocks, the unstable or 'soft' component of magnetization being

Fig. 19. Demagnetizing coil and rotating specimen holder.

destroyed by alternating fields of about 100 oersteds. However, for sediments in which the ferromagnetic mineral is most frequently haematite which has a high coercivity, changes in direction of magnetization begin to occur only after treatment in alternating magnetic fields of peak value 500 oersteds and above, and apparatus capable of producing magnetic fields of peak value up to about 2000 oersteds is necessary. It is most convenient to use the a.c. mains supply (at 50 c/s and 240 V in England). The demagnetizing coil is used in series resonance with a condenser to minimize the power consumed. The specimen is placed in a holder which is free to rotate about two axes at right angles, both of which are perpendicular to the axis of the coil. In this way all directions in the specimens are demagnetized. Special consideration must be given to the smoothness with which the current supply is reduced, and an electrolytic resistance has been used for this purpose. The rate must be slow compared with the speed of rotation of the specimen, which in turn must be much slower than the frequency of the a.c. supply. In the apparatus constructed at Newcastle by Creer the specimen is rotated at 1·1 and 1·2 rev/sec about each of the axes, a photograph being shown in Fig. 19.

III. CONCLUSION

In recent years work in palaeomagnetism has expanded so rapidly that acquaintance through personal contact with all of the latest developments and techniques in the subject is impossible. The apparatus described is, however, for the most part, known to the authors, and where this is not so they have had personal contact with the workers concerned in the design and construction. This has been an important consideration in the choice of particular pieces of apparatus for detailed description. Measurements of the direction and intensity of permanent magnetization are now invariably made by means of either astatic or spinner magnetometers similar to those described in Part I, and many such instruments are now in use. The only type of instrument which appears capable of challenging the sensitivity and ease of use of the astatic or spinner instruments is the resonance type of magnetometer as constructed in Tokyo by Kawai (see Nagata [22]). Improvement of the astatic instrument by means of an electronic feedback system is a possibility in the future. Because of variations in lithology of rocks and possibilities of local undetected tectonic movements, the quantity of measurements it is possible to make is believed to be of prime importance, aiming of course at an accuracy of 2° to 3° in direction.

The instruments and measurements described in Part II are concerned with the principal outstanding problems in the subject today, namely the origin of magnetization of sediments, the cause of reversal of magnetization and the removal of unstable components of magnetization to reveal the true fossil component. For these purposes various techniques and standard pieces of apparatus such as the separation of ferromagnetic grains, ore microscopy, x-ray methods, electron microscopy, neutron diffraction and others have been employed. No attempt, however, has been made to describe any of these, this account being limited to a description of apparatus specially constructed for the purpose of palaeomagnetic measurements.

References

1. Blackett, P. M. S. *Phil. Trans.* **245**, 309 (1952).
2. Blackett, P. M. S. *Lectures on Rock Magnetism*. Weizmann Science Press of Israel, Jerusalem, 1956.
3. Blundell, D. K. *Thesis*, University of London (1956).
4. Bruckshaw, J. McG. and Robertson, E. I. *J. sci. Instrum.* **25**, 444 (1948).
5. Brynjolfsson, A. *Advanc. Physics*, **6**, 247 (1957).
6. Chevallier, R. and Pierre, J. *Ann. Phys.*, Paris, **18**, 383 (1932).
7. Collinson, D. W., Creer, K. M., Irving, E. and Runcorn, S. K. *Phil. Trans.* **250**, 73 (1957).
8. Creer, K. M. *Thesis*, University of Cambridge (1955).
9. Creer, K. M. *Ann. Géophys.* **14**, 373 (1958).
10. Curie, P. and Chèneveau, C. *J. Phys. Radium*, **4**, 769 (1903).
11. Foex, G. and Forrer, R. *J. Phys. Radium*, **7**, 180 (1936).
12. Graham, J. W. *J. geophys. Res.* **60**, 329 (1955).
13. Gough, D. I. *Mon. Not. R. astr. Soc. Geophys. Suppl.* **7**, 196 (1956).
14. Haigh, G. *Thesis*, University of London (1957).
15. Howell, L. G., Martinez, J. D. and Statham, E. H. *Geophysics*, **23**, 285 (1958).
16. Ising, G. *Ark. Mat. Astr. Fys.* **29**, No. 5, 1 (1942).
17. Johnson, E. A. *Rev. sci. Instrum.* **9**, 263 (1938).
18. Johnson, E. A., Murphy, T. and Michelsen, P. F. *Rev. sci. Instrum.* **20**, 429 (1949).
19. Kruger, F. and Brasack, F. *Ann. Phys., Lpz.* **30**, 113 (1937).
20. Leng, J. H. *Thesis*, University of London (1955).
21. McKeenhan, L. W. *Rev. sci. Instrum.* **5**, 265 (1934).
22. Nagata, T. *Rock Magnetism*, Maruzen Co., Tokyo (1953).
23. Nagata, T., Akasi, K. and Rikitake, T. *Bull. Earthq. Res. Inst. Tokyo*, **21**, 276 (1943).
24. Parry, J. H. *Thesis*, University of Cambridge (1957).
25. Stoner, E. C. *Phil. Mag.* **36**, 805 (1946).

THE MEASUREMENT OF GRAVITY AT SEA

J. C. HARRISON, *Institute of Geophysics,*
University of California

CONTENTS

I. INTRODUCTION

The instrumental difficulties in the measurement of gravity at sea arise from the large magnitude of the disturbing wave accelerations relative to the accuracy desired. The useful instrumental accuracy is set by the difficulties of navigation when out of sight of land and in the absence of accurate aids to navigation; in general, the uncertainties in position and in east–west component of velocity during a measurement contribute at least 3 mgal to the standard error of the free-air anomaly. An instrumental accuracy of 2 mgal is sufficient to reduce the instrumental errors below those of navigation, and greater accuracy would be superfluous except in a very limited number of cases. On the other hand, instrumental errors cannot exceed about 5 mgal without detracting considerably from the value of the measurements. The disturbing accelerations may exceed 100000 mgal in a surface ship, but decrease with depth below the surface and are typically less than about 5000 mgal at 250 ft depth. The energy in the ocean wave spectrum is mainly contained in the range between 3 and 18 sec period, and the short-period disturbances decrease more rapidly with depth than do those of longer periods.

In designing an apparatus to measure gravity at sea one may be prepared to face the full accelerations experienced in a surface ship or may operate under quieter conditions in a submarine or unmanned pressure-tight container put over the side of a surface vessel. Operation on the surface is much more convenient, but also much more difficult instrumentally.

Hecker made the first attempts to measure gravity at sea about the turn of the century using a barometric method on board a surface ship. Duffield also constructed a sea-going gravity meter working on this principle, but neither of them really functioned satisfactorily. An apparatus of this type constructed by Haalck was tested during the summer of 1938 on four trips between Hamburg and Bremen.[8] It gave results accurate to 3 to 5 mgal under very calm sea conditions, but this work has not been followed up. However, the first measurements with better than 10 mgal accuracy were made shortly after the First World War by Vening Meinesz using his specially developed pendulum apparatus in a submarine. This apparatus proved to be thoroughly reliable and has been used very extensively. Its accuracy is between 1 and 2 mgal when operated under reasonably calm conditions. It must, however, be used in a submarine, and the computation of the photographic records is laborious and time-consuming.

Promising tests of R. L. G. Gilbert's vibrating-string gravity meter were made on a submarine expedition in 1948, and since then successful tests of the Graf and LaCoste spring gravity meters have been made in submarines. These gravity meters are basically suited for development for use on surface vessels, and both the Graf and LaCoste instruments have been used successfully on surface ships. The results, however, must be treated with some caution until more is known about the acceleration limits under which these meters are capable of giving accurate results. Their future is most promising and it is very probable that most measurements will in future be made using this type of meter on board surface ships.

The measured gravity value is significant only when compared

with the value given by the International Formula for the latitude
of observation. The value of gravity according to the International
Formula varies at approximately 1·5 mgal/mile change in latitude
in middle latitudes, so that a navigational error of 1 mile in latitude is equivalent to an error of 1·5 mgal in the measured value of
gravity. A body moving in an east–west direction on the rotating
earth experiences a vertical Coriolis force. Measured gravity must
be corrected for this Eötvös effect, which amounts to 7·5 cos ϕ
mgal/knot, to be added to observed gravity for an eastward
velocity. ϕ is the latitude of observation. For 2 mgal accuracy,
the east–west component of velocity must be known to about one-
quarter of a knot. This is often difficult to achieve in practice, and
the Eötvös correction usually furnishes the most important source
of error in the free-air anomaly.

A gravity-measuring apparatus cannot distinguish between
gravity and a vertical acceleration. It measures

$$\frac{1}{T} \int_0^T (g + \ddot{z})dt$$

over the observations of length T. $\ddot{z}$ is the vertical acceleration.
This integral is

$$g + \left[\dot{z}\right]_0^T / T$$

so that measured gravity must be corrected by an amount

$$\frac{\dot{z}_2 - \dot{z}_1}{T} = \frac{\text{change in vertical velocity during observation}}{\text{length of observation}}$$

unless the observation is long enough for this first-order correction
to be negligible.

II. THE VENING MEINESZ PENDULUM APPARATUS

The horizontal components of the wave accelerations have the
greatest effect on the swinging of a pendulum. Vening Meinesz
designed his apparatus to eliminate these to the first order by using
the difference between the angular displacements of two identical
pendulums. The equations of motion of two pendulums of equivalent length l, when their knife edges are moving with equal

horizontal accelerations $\ddot{x}$ in the swinging plane, are, to the first order,

$$l\ddot{\theta}_1 + g\theta_1 + \ddot{x} = 0 \tag{1}$$

and

$$l\ddot{\theta}_2 + g\theta_2 + \ddot{x} = 0 \tag{2}$$

so that subtracting

$$l(\ddot{\theta}_1 - \ddot{\theta}_2) + g(\theta_1 - \theta_2) = 0 \tag{3}$$

It is seen that the difference $(\theta_1 - \theta_2)$ obeys the equation of motion of an undisturbed pendulum with the same equivalent length as the two original pendulums. This undisturbed pendulum is known as a 'fictitious' pendulum.

The Vening Meinesz pendulum apparatus [15] contains three pendulums on a single rigid support and free to swing in the same plane. The outer two are set swinging in antiphase and the middle one starts at rest, so that the pendulums initially transmit no sway to the apparatus. Two fictitious pendulums are formed by pairing the centre pendulum with each of the outer pendulums, and the motion of each fictitious pendulum is determined by reflecting a light beam from mirrors on the two pendulums in turn. The motion of the centre pendulum relative to a short-period damped pendulum is determined in the same way and the three motions are recorded photographically. Timing marks are made by interrupting the light beams at regular intervals, which were controlled in the original apparatus by a mechanical chronometer. The chronometer has since been replaced by a quartz crystal clock. The box containing the pendulums is mounted in gimbals and therefore remains approximately aligned along the direction of the total resultant acceleration (the apparent vertical). The generally small departures of the swinging plane of the pendulums from the apparent vertical are recorded on the photographic paper. A second short-period damped pendulum, able to swing at right angles to the swinging plane of the other pendulums, is used to establish the direction of the apparent vertical.

A 30-min observation is long enough to remove the first-order effects of the vertical wave accelerations, though it may be necessary to apply a correction for the changing vertical velocity of the submarine caused by imperfect depth keeping. Browne [2] pointed out that the second-order effects, which depend on the mean square values of the vertical and the horizontal components of the wave accelerations, are too large to be ignored. The second-order correction due to the vertical accelerations arises because the pendulum periods do not depend linearly on the value of apparent gravity, but rather vary as the inverse of its square root. Thus the mean period of the pendulums during a disturbed observation does not yield the correct mean gravity value. Browne showed that the correction to be applied to the gravity value obtained from the mean pendulum period is $+ \ddot{z}^2/4g$, provided the wave periods are long compared with those of the pendulums. ($\ddot{z}$ is the vertical acceleration.) The second-order correction for horizontal accelerations arises because the apparatus measures the mean of the total apparent acceleration $(g^2 + \ddot{y}^2)^{\frac{1}{2}}$, which is always larger than g ($\ddot{y}$ is the total horizontal acceleration). The correction amounts to $- \ddot{y}^2/2g$, again provided that the wave periods are long. Some controversy has arisen over the theory of the second-order correction for horizontal accelerations in the swinging plane of the pendulums when the wave period is only several times that of the pendulums.[19, 17, 13, 14] However, laboratory experiments [9] have shown that the Browne corrections are adequate for horizontal accelerations of period as short as 3·3 sec, so that the simple Browne corrections are good enough for observations made in submarines.

The vertical wave accelerations affect the pendulum periods and therefore cause fluctuations in the timing marks on the photographic records. The second-order correction for vertical accelerations can be estimated from these fluctuations, so that a second vertical accelerometer is not strictly necessary. The horizontal accelerations, however, have been eliminated from the record, and hence must be determined using a separate accelerometer. The accelerometers used for determining the horizontal accelerations have measured the angle between short-period pendulums able to follow the apparent vertical and the true vertical. The direction of the true vertical has been obtained from pendulums with natural periods much larger than the wave periods, or from a gyroscope.[3] Vening Meinesz added pendulums of about 25 sec period to his pendulum apparatus.[16] He recorded the angle between these pendulums and the apparatus itself, which was free to swing in

P

gimbals, on the same photographic paper as the fictitious pendulum traces.

This apparatus has proved very reliable when used on submarines, and has an instrumental accuracy of about 1·5 mgal under good conditions. The pendulums themselves are very stable. The apparatus should not be used when the disturbing accelerations exceed about 7 000 mgal, or when there is much energy of less than 6 sec period present. It is unsuited for use on surface ships because the accelerations on the surface are larger and because the shorter periods are more prominent. There is also the probability of the pendulum knife edges slipping on their agate planes. For these reasons, and because of the lengthy computations needed, the pendulum apparatus is rapidly being replaced by gravity meters for the measurement of gravity at sea.

III. THE USE OF GRAVITY METERS AT SEA

Gravity meters, in which the force Mg on a mass M is balanced in some way against the elastic force in a spring, have replaced pendulums for gravity measurements on land except for the establishment of calibration intervals and for absolute measurements. They have the advantages of greater accuracy, portability, ease and speed of reading, and simplicity of computation of the gravity values. At sea they promise the advantages of ease of reading and simplicity in the computation of the gravity values, they are easier to install than the pendulum apparatus and above all, they can probably be used on surface ships. The land meter must, however, be considerably modified before it can be used at sea.

The meter must be sufficiently sensitive to measure to 1 mgal and yet be so heavily damped that it does not hit its stops when subjected to periodic vertical accelerations of 50 000 mgal or more. The output of the meter must be very closely linear over the range of movement of the beam, so that this output may be averaged over the observation without introducing an error. The meter must be very stable as regards drift and sudden jumps in reading, as it may be necessary to go for several weeks or even months between base-station checks.

Given a meter satisfactory in these respects there are two ways in which it can be used to measure gravity at sea.

(1) It can be stabilized in direction so that it always remains aligned along the direction of the true vertical. In this case it measures the sum of gravity and the vertical accelerations and, providing this sum is averaged over a sufficiently long time, a true gravity reading will be obtained.

(2) The meter may be suspended in a gimbal mounting which will swing to follow the direction of the instantaneous apparent vertical. The quantity measured is the average of the total resultant acceleration, which is greater than the true value of gravity. A second-order Browne correction must be made, as for the Vening Meinesz pendulum apparatus.

1. Theoretical Consideration of a Gravity Meter Stabilized in the Vertical Direction

Suppose a meter is stabilized along the true vertical but that, owing to imperfections in the stabilization, the axis of the meter makes a small angle $\theta = \theta_0 + \theta_1 \cos{(pt + \phi)}$ with the vertical in the plane containing the vertical and the horizontal accelerations $\ddot{x} = \ddot{x}_0 \cos{(\omega t + \lambda)}$. Let the vertical acceleration be $\ddot{z} = \ddot{z}_0 \cos{(\omega t + \epsilon)}$ and suppose the meter to be unaffected by a component of acceleration at right angles to its axis.

Then (see Fig. 1) the total acceleration measured by the meter is

$$(g + \ddot{z}) \cos{\theta} - \ddot{x} \sin{\theta} \tag{4}$$

which, θ being small, is

$$g\{1 - \tfrac{1}{2}[\theta_0 + \theta_1 \cos{(pt + \phi)}]^2\} + \ddot{z}_0 \cos{(\omega t + \epsilon)}$$
$$- \ddot{x} \cos{(\omega t + \lambda)}[\theta_0 + \theta_1 \cos{(pt + \phi)}] \tag{5}$$

When averaged over a time long with respect to the periods involved this becomes

$$g\{1 - \tfrac{1}{2}\theta_0{}^2 - \tfrac{1}{4}\theta_1{}^2\} - \tfrac{1}{2}\theta_1\ddot{x}_0\{\overline{\cos{[(\omega + p)t + \phi + \lambda]}} + \cos{[(\omega - p)t + \lambda - \phi]}\} \tag{6}$$

The second term will become vanishingly small on averaging unless $\omega = p$, when the whole expression becomes

$$g\{1 - \tfrac{1}{2}\theta_0{}^2 - \tfrac{1}{4}\theta_1{}^2\} - \tfrac{1}{2}\theta_1\ddot{x}_0 \cos{(\lambda - \phi)} \tag{7}$$

For 1 mgal accuracy θ_0 must be less than 5′, but the requirements on θ_1 are very much more stringent unless $(\lambda - \phi)$ should happen to equal $\frac{1}{2}\pi$. If $\ddot{x}_0 = 100\,000$ mgal and $(\lambda - \phi) = 0$, then for 1

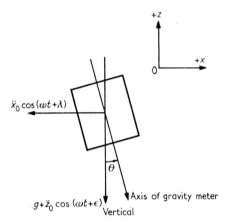

Fig. 1. Stabilized gravity meter.

mgal accuracy θ_1 must be less than 4″. The error introduced into the measured value of gravity for a given value of θ_1 is proportional to $\ddot{x}_0$.

A. *Cross-coupling*

A gravimeter beam is deflected by a periodic vertical wave acceleration, the deflection having the same period as the acceleration. Horizontal accelerations acting on the beam in its deflected position produce a couple which may be predominantly in one direction if the vertical and horizontal accelerations have the same period. This cross-coupling effect may produce a large error in the gravity reading, as was pointed out by LaCoste.

A gravity meter beam is pivoted about a point O and has its centre of gravity at G (see Fig. 2). Let OG be a, the horizontal acceleration be $\ddot{x}_0 \cos{(\omega t + \lambda)}$, the vertical acceleration be $\ddot{z}_0 \cos{(\omega t + \epsilon)}$ and the angle ϕ that the beam makes with the horizontal be $\phi = \phi_0 + \phi_1 \cos{(\omega t + \psi)}$. Then the anti-clockwise couple on gravity meter beam is

$$aM\{\ddot{x}_0 \cos{(\omega t + \lambda)} \sin{\phi} + [g + \ddot{z}_0 \cos{(\omega t + \epsilon)}] \cos{\phi}\} \quad (8)$$

Retaining terms in ϕ^2 and taking an average over a time long with respect to the periods concerned this couple is

$$aMg\{1 + \tfrac{1}{2}\phi_1(\ddot{x}_0/g) \cos (\psi - \lambda) - \tfrac{1}{2}\phi_0{}^2 - \tfrac{1}{4}\phi_1{}^2\} \qquad (9)$$

Substitute

$$\phi_1 = S\ddot{z}_0/F \qquad (10)$$

where S is the static sensitivity of the gravity meter in radians/mgal and F the ratio of the static sensitivity of the meter to the

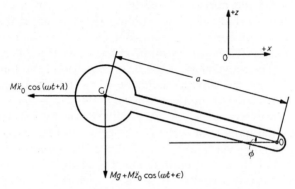

Fig. 2. Cross-coupling on a beam gravity meter.

sensitivity for changes occurring with angular frequency ω. Then the couple equals

$$aMg\{1 + (S/2F)(\ddot{x}_0\ddot{z}_0/g)\cos (\psi - \lambda) - \tfrac{1}{2}\phi_0{}^2 - \tfrac{1}{4}(S\ddot{z}_0/F)^2\} \qquad (11)$$

For typical values of $S = 5 \times 10^{-6}$ radians/mgal, $F = 50$, $\phi_0 = 10^{-4}$ radians, and putting $\ddot{x}_0 = \ddot{z}_0 = 100000$ mgal, the third and fourth terms in equation 11 are seen to be negligible with respect to the second. Dividing this equation by the couple, aMg, acting on the beam in its zero position when the meter is stationary,

$$\frac{\text{Couple acting when meter is moving}}{\text{Couple acting when meter is stationary}} = 1 + \frac{S}{2F}\frac{\ddot{x}_0\ddot{z}_0}{g} \cos (\psi - \lambda) \qquad (12)$$

This increase in couple is equivalent to an apparent increase in g, Δg, given by

$$\Delta g = (S/2F)\ddot{x}_0\ddot{z}_0 \cos (\psi - \lambda) \qquad (13)$$

which, using the values given above, becomes

$$\Delta g = 500 \cos (\psi - \lambda) \text{ mgal} \qquad (14)$$

Thus the error introduced by the cross-coupling effect in the above example can be between 0 and 500 mgal depending on the value of $(\psi - \lambda)$.

$(\psi - \lambda) = (\psi - \epsilon) + (\epsilon - \lambda) =$ phase difference between movement of beam and vertical accelerations plus phase difference between vertical and horizontal accelerations. $(\epsilon - \lambda)$ is $\frac{1}{2}\pi$ for circular motion, so that the cross-coupling effect is zero if the movement of the beam is 0 or π radians out of phase with the vertical accelerations, and has a maximum value when this phase difference is $\frac{1}{2}\pi$. The movement of the beam lags $\frac{1}{2}\pi$ on the forcing accelerations when the wave period is equal to the natural period of the undamped gravity meter beam, and this lag is zero for very slow accelerations and π for very-high-frequency accelerations. The heavy damping means, however, that the phase lag lies between $\frac{1}{4}\pi$ and $\frac{3}{4}\pi$ over a wide range about the undamped natural period, so that the cross-coupling effect is likely to be large if the undamped natural period is comparable with the wave periods.

B. *Effect of horizontal accelerations on a gravity-meter spring*

The effect of wave accelerations on the spring of a gravity meter depends on the geometry of the instrument in use. The elementary example treated below may frequently give the order of magnitude of this effect. The mass M, constrained to move only in the vertical direction, is supported by a zero length spring OM of mass m and is kept in its zero position by adjustments of a secondary spring. The gravity meter is subjected to a horizontal acceleration $\ddot{x} = \ddot{x}_0 \cos (\omega t + \lambda)$ and the inertial forces cause the spring to bow outwards as shown in Fig. 3. If the bowing is small the spring can be assumed to take the form of the arc of a circle of radius R given by

$$m\ddot{x}/l = T/R \qquad (15)$$

T being the mean tension in the spring and l its length. The angle θ that this arc makes with the vertical at its upper and lower ends is given by

$$\theta = m\ddot{x}/2T \qquad (16)$$

The bowing of the spring increases its length, thus increasing the tension at any point, but the spring acts at an angle θ with the vertical so that the vertical component acting on the mass is reduced. The increase in tension ΔT at any point in the spring is given by

$$\Delta T = T\Delta l/l = T[2Rl^{-1} \sin^{-1} (l/2R) - 1]$$
$$= \tfrac{1}{24}Tl^2/R^2 = \tfrac{1}{24}T(m\ddot{x}^2/T^2) \quad (17)$$

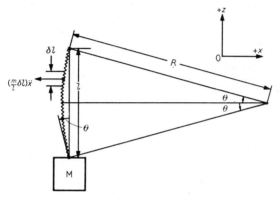

Fig. 3. Effect of horizontal acceleration on a gravity meter spring.

On taking a time average it is seen that there is an increase in the mean tension given by

$$\Delta T = \tfrac{1}{48}T(m^2\ddot{x}_0/T^2) \quad (18)$$

The fractional increase in the vertical component of tension acting on M is given by

$$\{(T + \Delta T) \cos\theta - T\}/T = - (1/12)m^2\ddot{x}^2/T^2 \quad (19)$$

Taking the time average, there is a net mean fractional decrease of vertical force on M of

$$- (1/24)m^2\ddot{x}_0^2/T^2 \quad (20)$$

Neglecting the tension in the secondary spring, it is possible to substitute $T = Mg$, and if $\ddot{x}_0 = 100\,000$ mgal, the decrease in vertical component is

$$m^2/2400M^2 \quad (21)$$

and if this is to be less than 10^{-6}, m/M must be less than 5×10^{-2}.

Thus the effect of the bowing of the spring under the influence of horizontal accelerations contributes a negligible error at 100000 mgal acceleration provided that the ratio of the mass of the spring to the mass it supports is less than 1 to 20.

2. Theoretical Consideration of a Gravity Meter Suspended in Gimbals

In a stabilized gravity meter, the importance of stabilization errors with the same period as the horizontal wave accelerations arises because a component of the horizontal acceleration $\ddot{x} \sin \theta$, or approximately $\ddot{x}\theta$, is introduced into the measured vertical acceleration. In the absence of horizontal accelerations the levelling error amounts to $g(1 - \cos \theta)$, or approximately $- \frac{1}{2}g\theta^2$, and so depends on the square rather than the first power of the small angle θ. Misalignment errors enter only as $G(t)[1 - \cos \alpha]$ when the gravity meter is suspended in gimbals and allowed to follow the direction of the total apparent acceleration $G(t)$. α is the angle between $G(t)$ and the axis of the gravity meter. Thus the requirements for α are a great deal less stringent than those for θ. However, the response of the gimbals to the forcing accelerations and the accelerations introduced by the swinging of the meter in its gimbals need further consideration. The theory as given below was developed by LaCoste.

The meter suspended in gimbals behaves as a pendulum with its own natural period (see Fig. 4). It is suspended at O. Let its centre of gravity be at G and the gravity sensing element be at P. Let OG = L, OP = l and suppose P to lie in OG. Let OG make an angle θ with the vertical, let the mass of the suspended system be M and its radius of gyration about O be k. Suppose the horizontal wave acceleration in the plane of the paper to be $\ddot{x} = \ddot{x}_0 \cos (\omega t + \lambda)$ and the vertical acceleration to be $\ddot{z} = \ddot{z}_0 \cos (\omega t + \epsilon)$. Put $(L^2 + k^2)/L = L_0 = g/\omega_0^2$, so that $2\pi/\omega_0$ is the natural swinging period of the gimbals.

Then the equation of motion for the suspended system is

$$\ddot{\theta} + \beta\dot{\theta} + (1/L_0)\{g + \ddot{z}_0 \cos (\omega t + \epsilon)\} \sin \theta$$
$$= -(\ddot{x}_0/L_0) \cos (\omega t + \lambda) \cos \theta \quad (22)$$

where β is a frictional term.

To obtain an approximate solution for this equation put $\sin \theta = \theta$, $\cos \theta = 1$ and neglect the vertical accelerations $\ddot{z}$ with respect to g.

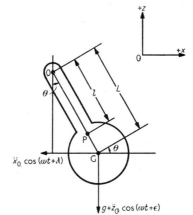

Fig. 4. Gravity meter suspended in gimbals.

The equation becomes

$$\ddot{\theta} + \beta\dot{\theta} + \omega_0^2\theta = -(\ddot{x}_0/L_0) \cos (\omega t + \lambda) \qquad (23)$$

the solution of which consists of two parts, damped free oscillations

$$\theta_n = A \exp (-\tfrac{1}{2}\beta t) \cos \{(\omega_0^2 - \tfrac{1}{4}\beta^2)^{\frac{1}{2}}t - \lambda\} \qquad (24)$$

and forced oscillations

$$\theta_d = -(\ddot{x}_0/L_0[(\omega_0^2 - \omega^2)^2 + \beta\omega^2]^{-\frac{1}{2}} \cos (\omega t - \phi) \qquad (25)$$

A and γ are arbitrary, ϕ is the phase angle of the forced oscillations given by

$$\tan (\phi - \lambda) = \beta\omega/(\omega_0^2 - \omega^2) \qquad (26)$$

The natural oscillations will be damped out after the gravity-meter gimbal system has been released for a sufficiently long time unless they are maintained by energy of the correct period reaching the gimbal system. It will be assumed that sufficient energy of this period is present to maintain the natural oscillations at a constant level. It will also be assumed that the friction in the gimbals is sufficiently small for β to be neglected. In this case

$$\theta_n = B \cos (\omega_0 t - \gamma)$$
$$\theta_d = - \ddot{x}_0/\{L_0(\omega_0^2 - \omega^2)\} \{\cos (\omega t + \lambda)\} \qquad (27)$$
$$\theta = \theta_n + \theta_d$$

Then the component of acceleration along the axis of the gravity meter, which is the measured acceleration, is

$$\{g + \ddot{z}_0 \cos(\omega t + \epsilon)\} \cos\theta - \ddot{x}_0 \cos(\omega t + \lambda) \sin\theta + l\dot{\theta}^2 \quad (28)$$

or approximately

$$\{g + \ddot{z}_0 \cos(\omega t + \epsilon)\}(1 - \tfrac{1}{2}\theta^2) - \ddot{x}_0\theta \cos(\omega t + \lambda) + l\dot{\theta}^2 \quad (29)$$

On taking an average over a time long with respect to the periods involved equation 29 becomes

$$g - \tfrac{1}{2}g\overline{\dot{\theta}^2} + \ddot{x}_0^2/\{2L_0(\omega_0^2 - \omega^2)\}$$
$$+ \tfrac{1}{2}l\{B^2\omega_0^2 + \ddot{x}_0^2\omega^2/[L_0^2(\omega_0^2 - \omega^2)^2]\} \quad (30)$$

The second-order corrections are difficult to evaluate from this expression, but great simplification is possible if l is put equal to $L_0 = g/\omega_0^2$. Substituting this value in equation 30, we obtain for measured gravity the expression

$$g - \tfrac{1}{2}g\overline{\dot{\theta}^2} + \tfrac{1}{2}g\{B^2 + \ddot{x}_0^2\omega_0^4/[g^2(\omega_0^2 - \omega^2)]\} \quad (31)$$

but

$$\overline{\dot{\theta}^2} = \overline{\{B\cos(\omega_0 t - \gamma) - [\ddot{x}_0/\{L_0(\omega_0^2 - \omega^2)\}]\cos(\omega t + \lambda)\}^2} \quad (32)$$
$$= \tfrac{1}{2}\{B^2 + \ddot{x}_0^2\omega_0^4/g^2(\omega_0^2 - \omega^2)\}$$

so that the acceleration measured is

$$g + \tfrac{1}{2}g\overline{\theta^2} \quad (33)$$

An identical expression is obtained if the disturbing accelerations consist of the sum of a number of simple harmonic disturbances with different amplitudes and periods. θ is approximately $\ddot{x}/g$, and the usual formula for the Browne correction is obtained if this is substituted in equation 33.

The angle θ may be measured by using a gyroscope, or long-period pendulums of the type devised by Vening Meinesz, to establish the direction of the true vertical. It must be squared and averaged to obtain the second-order correction.

The acceleration perpendicular to the axis of the gravity meter is

$$\{g + \ddot{z}_0 \cos(\omega t + \epsilon)\} \sin\theta + \ddot{x}_0 \cos(\omega t + \lambda) \cos\theta + l\ddot{\theta} \quad (34)$$

which, if θ is small and putting $l = L_0 = g/\omega_0^2$, becomes

$$\theta\{g + \ddot{z}_0 \cos(\omega t + \epsilon)\} + \ddot{x}_0 \cos(\omega t + \lambda) + l\ddot{\theta} \quad (35)$$

Substituting for θ and $\ddot{\theta}$ derived from equation 27 this expression becomes $\ddot{z}_0 \theta \cos{(\omega t + \epsilon)}$, which is a small quantity with respect to accelerations like $g\theta$ or $\ddot{x}$. Thus to the first order the acceleration perpendicular to the axis of the gravity meter is zero. Hence the cross-coupling effect described in connection with the stabilized gravity meter is much less important when the meter is free to swing in gimbals.

LaCoste has carried these calculations to a higher order of accuracy, making an approximate solution of equation 22 retaining the $\ddot{z}_0 \cos{(\omega t + \epsilon)}$ term and retaining terms of order $(\ddot{x}_0/g)^4$ throughout the calculations. He concludes that equation 33 is accurate to 1 mgal for $\ddot{x}_0$ and $\ddot{z}_0$ up to 60000 mgal provided that there is no important component of disturbing acceleration present with period near, or less than, the natural period of the gimbal system. This natural period is typically of the order of 1 sec, and the assumption is true in all but rather rough conditions, or on very small ships.

3. Conclusions Concerning the Use of Gravity Meters at Sea

A gravity meter for use at sea may be stabilized along the true vertical or be allowed to swing in a gimbal suspension. In the former case errors in alignment with the same period as the horizontal accelerations are extremely important, and they must either be reduced below 5 sec amplitude or made to be $\frac{1}{2}\pi$ out of phase with the horizontal accelerations, if an accuracy of 1 mgal is to be obtained in the presence of horizontal accelerations of 0·1 g. In the case of a beam gravimeter, the cross-coupling effect can contribute an error up to the order of 500 mgal, depending on the phase difference between oscillations of the gravity meter beam and the horizontal accelerations. This error can be reduced if this phase difference be made to vary during a measurement.

If the meter is suspended in gimbals it is necessary to make a second-order correction for the horizontal accelerations. This correction takes on a particularly simple form if the gravity sensing element is suspended at a distance equal to the length of the simple equivalent pendulum below the point of suspension of the gimbal system. In this case the second-order correction can be determined from the mean square value of the angle between the gravity meter and the true vertical. In this case, also, forces perpendicular to the axis of the gravity meter vanish to the first order, so the cross-coupling effect is drastically reduced.

4. A Brief Description of the Graf, LaCoste and Vibrating-string Gravity Meters

The sea-going gravity meter designed by Graf [6, 7, 12] (see Fig. 5) consists of an aluminium beam 30 cm long maintained in a horizontal position by the couple provided by horizontal cylindrical springs under torsion near one end. Movements other than rotation about a horizontal axis are prevented by restraining filaments

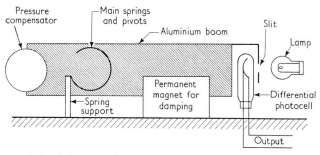

Fig. 5. Construction of Graf sea-going gravity meter.

and the position of the beam is read photoelectrically. The beam moves in the field of a powerful permanent magnet which provides eddy current damping. The static sensitivity of the instrument is 1″/mgal and the damping is such that the response at 6 sec period is reduced by a factor of 50. An initial coarse adjustment of the cylindrical springs brings the beam approximately to its null position, and thereafter the position of the beam is recorded on an Enograph recorder. The recorder contains further electrical damping, so that the response to accelerations of 6 sec period is reduced by an overall factor of 10000. The difference between observed gravity and the value corresponding to the initial spring setting is read from the Enograph recorder as the difference between the mean of the beam-position trace and the null line. The meter contains no means of measuring the second-order correction. In the comparisons on board a submarine [18] the meter was suspended in gimbals and the values from the gravity meter were compared with those from the pendulum apparatus before correcting the pendulum values for the second-order corrections for horizontal accelerations. In subsequent tests on board a surface ship [12] the meter was mounted on a gyroscopically stabilized platform. The results from both these tests are extremely encouraging.

The LaCoste sea-going gravity meter is an adaption of the LaCoste suspension [10, 11] used in land meters, employing a beam of increased moment of inertia with damping and a photoelectric reading system.[4] The instrument is suspended in gimbals and the second-order correction is determined using long-period pendulums of 60 sec period to establish the direction of the true vertical. The deflections of the gimbals are measured, and the second-order corrections computed, electrically. This correction is automatically and continuously applied to the measuring screw through a differential gearbox, so that the measuring-screw reading is the sum of the gravity reading and the second-order correction (see Fig. 6).

The equation of motion of the gravity-meter beam, when the gravity reading counter is set to a value corresponding to a gravity reading S in a static case, is of the form

$$m\ddot{\phi} + \beta\dot{\phi} + k\phi = (g + \ddot{z}) - S \tag{36}$$

ϕ is the deflection of the beam and m, β and k are instrumental constants. A quantity proportional to $\int (m\ddot{\phi} + \beta\dot{\phi} + k\phi)\, dt$ is computed and shown on a timing indicator microammeter. Occasional changes are made in S so that the timing indicator passes through zero at about 10-min intervals. Integrating equation 36 between two times at which the timing indicator shows zero

$$\int_{T_1}^{T_2} (m\ddot{\phi} + \beta\dot{\phi} + k\phi)\, dt = 0 = \int_{T_1}^{T_2} (g + \ddot{z})dt - \int_{T_1}^{T_2} S\, dt \tag{37}$$

so that

$$\frac{1}{T_2 - T_1}\int_{T_1}^{T_2}(g + \ddot{z})dt = \frac{1}{(T_2 - T_1)}\int_{T_1}^{T_2} S\, dt \tag{38}$$

The value of S is recorded in digital form by an Esterline Angus 20 pen recorder which is also marked at the instants when the timing indicator passes through zero. The integral of the RHS of equation 38 can be determined from this record, and this is equal to the average value of $(g + \ddot{z})$ during the interval $T_2 - T_1$.

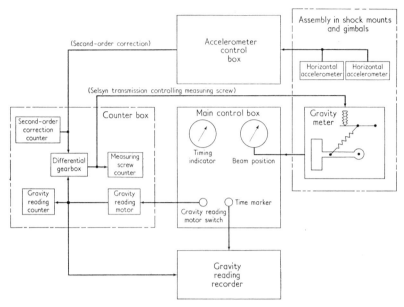

Fig. 6. Block diagram of LaCoste–Romberg sea-going gravity meter.

This meter has been used on submarines, and comparisons with the results of simultaneous pendulum measurements [1] indicate that the standard error of a gravity-meter measurement is much the same as that of a pendulum measurement. It has also been used successfully on oceanographic surface vessels and on an aircraft.

A vibrating-string gravity meter made by Gilbert was tested against pendulums on board a submarine in 1948.[5] In this meter a vertical string is tensioned by the weight Mg of a mass M. The frequency of its fundamental, $F = [1/2L](Mg/m]^{\frac{1}{2}}$, where L is the length of the string and m its mass per unit length, varies with g and enables variations therein to be measured. A beryllium–copper strip is used, hanging vertically between the poles of a permanent magnet. The lines of force are horizontal and parallel to the plane of the strip, so that when the strip vibrates an alternating e.m.f. is generated between its ends: conversely, if an alternating e.m.f. is applied, the amplitude and phase of the vibrations, and hence the current in wire, depend on the frequency. The wire behaves as a resonant circuit element and vibrations in the string can be maintained using an amplifier and feedback circuit.

The results of the tests made in 1948 were very promising but were not immediately followed up. An improved version was tested on a submarine late in 1957, but no details of its performance on this trip are yet available. The meter would appear to be suitable for use on a surface ship, and it has the advantage that the output is in the form of a frequency which is easy to work with electronically. The meter appears to be rather unstable as regards drift and occasional sudden changes not related to changes in gravity. A second-order correction for vertical accelerations is necessary, as the frequency is proportional to the square root of g and not to g directly.

References

1. Brown, G. L. and Spiess, F. N. *Trans. Amer. geophys. Un.* **39**, 391–396 (1958).
2. Browne, B. C. *Mon. Not. R. astr. Soc., Geophys. Suppl.* **4**, 271–279 (1937).
3. Browne, B. C. and Cooper, R. I. B. *Trans. Roy. Soc. A*, **242**, 243–310 (1950).
4. Clarkson, H. N. and LaCoste, L. J. B. *Trans. Amer. geophys. Un.* **38**, 8–16, 1957.
5. Gilbert, R. L. G. *Proc. phys. Soc. Lond. B*, **62**, 445–454 (1949).
6. Graf, A. *Z. Geophys.* **23**, 4–25 (1957).
7. Graf, A. *Z. InstrumKde*, **8**, 151–161 (1958).
8. Haalck, H. *Beitr. angew. Geophys.* **7**, 418–448 (1939).
9. Harrison, J. C. *Mon. Not. R. astr. Soc., Geophys. Suppl.* **7**, 22–31 (1954).
10. LaCoste, L. J. B. *Physics*, **5**, 178–180 (1934).
11. LaCoste, L. J. B. *Bull. seismol. Soc. Amer.* **25**, 176–179 (1935).
12. National Academy of Sciences. *I.G.Y. Bull. No. 8, Trans. Amer. geophys. Un.* **39**, 175–178 (1958).
13. Romanyuk, V. A. *Izvestia Akad. Nauk S.S.S.R. Ser. geofiz.*, No. 3, 341–350 (1957).
14. Romanyuk, V. A. *Izvestia Akad. Nauk S.S.S.R. Ser. geofiz.*, No. 4, 458–470 (1957).
15. Vening Meinesz, F. A. *Theory and Practice of Pendulum Observations at Sea*. Waltman: Delft, 1929.
16. Vening Meinesz, F. A. *Theory and Practice of Pendulum Observations at Sea*, Part II. Waltman: Delft, 1941.
17. Vening Meinesz, F. A. *Verh. Akad. Wet. Amst. Ser. B*, **56**, 218–227 (1953).
18. Worzel, J. L. and Graf, A. *Bull. geod. int. N. S.*, No. 45, 38–53 (1957).
19. Worsley, B. H. *Proc. Camb. phil. Soc.* **48**, 718–732 (1952).

THE DETECTION OF EARTH
MOVEMENTS

P. L. WILLMORE, *Dominion Observatory, Ottawa*

CONTENTS

I. INTRODUCTION

In seismology one is not concerned with the motion of the earth as a whole, but rather with movements of a selected point relative to the centre of gravity. Any such motions necessarily represent distortions of the earth, and as such will be associated with rotation or tilt, with changes in g (due to the changing figure of the earth) and with stress and strain. A record which shows any of these parameters as a function of time will serve to describe the earth movement, and any instrument used for obtaining such records may properly be called a 'seismograph'.

By far the most widely used type of seismograph consists of a weight, mounted on resilient supports, so that any movement of the ground will displace the frame of the instrument relative to the mass. These relative displacements are detected by lever trains or by electrical 'transducers', and ultimately recorded on moving paper or on some other recording medium. In seismographs of this type any change of acceleration acting on the frame in a direction along which the mass is free to move will disturb the system, and we can therefore draw no distinction in principle between ordinary seismographs, which are designed primarily to detect earth movements, and the gravimeters and tiltmeters which are supposed to record components of acceleration. In practice, a broad distinction can be drawn in terms of the duration of the phenomena which are observed. Both classes of instrument can detect accelerations of the order of 10^{-5} cm/sec^2, but the seismographs are designed to respond most strongly to accelerations which have an oscillatory character with periods of less than a few minutes, whereas tiltmeters and gravimeters are designed to record accelerations which persist for hours or more.

In the early days of seismology the 'ideal' seismograph was considered to be one in which the steady mass would be supported against the continuous force of gravity, but would otherwise be free from any constraints in its direction of operation. Such an instrument would yield a faithful reproduction of the ground displacement. For a vertical seismograph, a mass on a very long spring would approximate to the ideal, and for horizontal movements a very long vertical pendulum would do. When the equations of motion were worked out, it became clear that the period of free oscillations of the system was the decisive factor, and that quite small oscillating systems could be made to approach the 'ideal' response if only the natural period could be made long enough. The commonest approach was to construct the mass in the form of a rigid boom, hinged so as to rotate about an axis at right angles to the desired degree of freedom, and to adjust the constraints so that the boom was in almost neutral equilibrium for rotations about the hinge. A schematic diagram of one such

Q

system is shown in Fig. 1, and practical variations of this design will be discussed in Section III–5.

As seismographs improved, a point was reached where the continuous, 'microseismic' agitation of the ground appeared in the form of background noise on the records. Further increases in

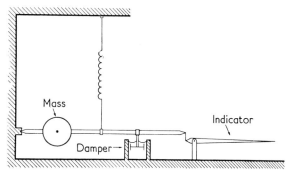

Fig. 1. Elementary schematic diagram of a direct coupled vertical seismograph.

sensitivity could be used only in frequency ranges for which the background amplitude was relatively low. At this point the ideal of the accurate reproduction of earth movement was gradually dropped, and instrumental development turned towards the production of seismographs having enhanced response in selected frequency ranges.

II. REPRESENTATION OF SEISMOGRAPH RESPONSE

Most seismographs produce their final record by moving an indicating point (light spot or stylus) by an amount which is proportional to the ground displacement at any given frequency. The constant of proportionality is called the 'magnification' of the instrument, and a plot of magnification as a function of frequency is called a 'magnification curve'. It is equally possible to consider the ratios between the deflection of the indicating point and the velocity or acceleration of the ground. These quantities are called the velocity and acceleration sensitivities of the seismograph respectively.

As the magnifications of the seismographs in common use cover a range of more than 10^6 to 1 and the frequencies have a range of more than 10^4 to 1, the data are often plotted against logarithmic rather than linear scales. Apart from the mere compression of data, the logarithmic plot has advantages which stem from the fact that a given ratio of magnification or frequency is represented as a corresponding distance between two points on the chart. Thus if we consider two seismographs, identical in design but of different size, the two instruments will have different magnifications and different natural periods. The essential identity of design will be reflected in the fact that logarithmic plots of the two magnification curves will have the same size and shape, one being derived from the other by a simple translation across the chart.

A further advantage of logarithmic plotting is the ease with which certain essential characteristics of the response curve can be recognized. Thus if we consider the response of the seismograph to a sinusoidal ground displacement X, where

$$X = a \cos \omega t$$

then the ground velocity is

$$dX/dt = -a\omega \sin \omega t$$

and the acceleration is

$$d^2X/dt^2 = -a\omega^2 \cos \omega t$$

We therefore see that the velocity of the ground (disregarding phase changes) is obtained by multiplying the displacement by the angular frequency ω, and that the acceleration is obtained by multiplying the displacement by ω^2. Hence the velocity sensitivity of a seismograph may be obtained by dividing the magnification by ω, and the acceleration sensitivity may be obtained by dividing by ω^2. On a logarithmic plot for which lines of constant magnification are shown horizontal, lines of constant velocity sensitivity will slope upwards at 45 degrees in the direction of increasing frequency (or decreasing period). Lines of constant acceleration sensitivity will have a slope of 2, corresponding to an inclination of about 63 degrees.

In the literature one sometimes finds statements to the effect that a certain type of seismograph is 'basically' a displacement meter, a velocity meter or an accelerometer. Such statements are usually made in connection with discussions of the performance of the transducer which detects the relative movement between the suspended mass and the ground, but they confuse the issue when the properties of the transducer are assumed to apply to a complete seismograph. For a sinusoidal ground movement of any given frequency, the displacement, velocity and acceleration are analytically related, and any seismograph which records one parameter will record the others with equal fidelity. The only sense in which the response of a seismograph can be associated with one parameter rather than either of the others is if the corresponding sensitivity curve is horizontal over a significant range of frequencies, but *any* sensitivity curve for a practical seismograph will have at least one maximum, in the vicinity of which the curve will be approximately horizontal. It follows that any given instrument can be assigned to any one of the three classes, according to the range of earth frequencies which we choose to investigate with it.

The use of harmonic sensitivity curves has sometimes been criticized on the grounds that such curves do not describe the response of the seismograph to transient disturbances, or that they do not provide a solution of the inverse problem, which is to determine the ground movement which causes an observed transient response of the instrument. This difficulty does not arise if the application of the sensitivity curves is properly understood. Any disturbance of the ground (subject to certain theoretical limitations which are inapplicable in practice) can be represented as the sum of an infinite number of continuous simple harmonic oscillations, whose amplitude and phase can be calculated. The response of the seismograph to the ground disturbance can be analysed in the same way, and the sensitivity curve determines the ratio of any harmonic component of the seismograph deflection to the corresponding component of ground movement.

When the seismograph response consists of a long train of almost sinusoidal waves it is easy to measure the dominant frequency, and hence to specify the sensitivity of the seismograph at that frequency. As the harmonic content of the record is, in this case, strongly concentrated in a narrow frequency band close to the one which has been measured, the single value of sensitivity enables one to translate most of the content of the record into a corresponding ground movement. This translation will enable one to give a fairly accurate description of that part of the ground motion whose frequency content falls within the pass band of the seismograph.

When the seismograph trace contains sharp transients or irregular motion a wide band of frequencies has been recorded. In this case it is not easy to recognize the frequency components of the record, and it is therefore not easy to determine the true ground movement. Nevertheless, a skilled observer can make a rough estimate of the dominant frequency in the trace, and can sometimes pick out two or three superimposed components. Estimates of the characteristics of the ground movement derived from such data will be very rough if the response curve of the instrument is steeply sloping in the vicinity of the dominant frequencies, but they will be fairly reliable if the response curve is platykurtic. If greater accuracy is required, there is no escaping the task of making a detailed harmonic analysis of the record, or of trying to match an observed transient on the record against a theoretical response to an assumed disturbance of the earth.

III. THEORY OF PENDULUM SEISMOGRAPHS

Pendulum seismographs include all those instruments in which a suspended mass is used to provide the reference point for determining movements of the ground, and at first sight it might appear that these could be divided between the instruments in which the mass is free to move linearly along a fixed axis and those in which the mass is in the form of a hinged boom. It is true that the equation of motion is slightly more complicated to set up in the latter case, but it will be seen that it reduces to a form which includes both cases. In the following sections the argument will be given in the form which applies to hinged seismographs.

1. The Direct-coupled Pendulum Seismograph

Let us assume that the seismograph has the general form shown in Fig. 1. The boom is held in stable equilibrium by means of a spring, the strength of which is such that an angular displacement ϕ generates a restoring force whose moment about the hinge is $U\phi$.*

---

* Horizontal seismographs are often designed so that the boom swings like a gate about an axis which is slightly inclined to the vertical. In such seismographs a gravitational restoring force takes the place of the spring stiffness, but the mathematical treatment is unaltered.

The initial tension of the spring, which is balanced by gravity, and the initial forces at the hinge, may be ignored. There may be a damping device, such that an angular velocity $d\phi/dt$ is resisted by a force of moment $Dd\phi/dt$. In accordance with an elementary theorem of statics, all these forces may be replaced by forces acting at the hinge, together with a couple of moment $U\phi + Dd\phi/dt$. Let the boom have a mass M whose centre of gravity is at a distance L from the hinge, and let the moment of inertia of the boom about the centre of gravity be K_0. Any inertia in the lever system, and any additional stiffness arising from the use of strip hinges, should be included in the constants K_0 and U.

Next, we assume that the ground is given an upward acceleration d^2X/dt^2. In addition to the forces exerted by the damping system and the spring, a reaction may appear at the hinge. Let the resultant of all forces acting at the hinge have a component H perpendicular to the boom. Then, taking moments about the centre of gravity of the boom, we have

$$K_0 \frac{d^2\phi}{dt^2} + \frac{D\, d\phi}{dt} + U\phi = -LH \qquad (1)$$

The negative sign on the RHS of equation 1 takes account of the fact that an upward movement of the ground produces an upward force at the hinge, but deflects the boom downwards. Since H is now the only force to be considered as acting on the boom, we have

$$H = M\, d^2x/dt^2$$

where x is the displacement of the centre of gravity of the mass. Since X is the displacement of the frame, $x - X = L\phi$, so that

$$H = M \left(\frac{d^2X}{dt^2} + L\, \frac{d^2\phi}{dt^2} \right)$$

Substituting for H in equation 1, we obtain

$$K \frac{d^2\phi}{dt^2} + D\, \frac{d\phi}{dt} + U\phi = -ML\, \frac{d^2X}{dt^2} \qquad (2)$$

where $K = (K_0 + ML^2)$ and is the moment of inertia of the boom about the hinge. Equation 2 shows that the seismograph responds to a ground displacement X as though a force of $-M\, d^2X/dt^2$ was applied to the centre of gravity of the boom.

Equation 2 may be simplified by putting $U/K = \Omega_0^2$, $\beta = D/2K\Omega_0$ and $LM/K = 1/l$. These substitutions yield the equation

$$\frac{d^2\phi}{dt^2} + 2\beta\Omega_0 \frac{d\phi}{dt} + \Omega_0^2\phi = \frac{1}{l}\frac{d^2X}{dt^2} \qquad (3)$$

We see now that the angular movements of the boom are the same as those which would be executed by an equivalent pendulum, consisting of a point mass on the end of a weightless boom of length l, where l is called the 'reduced pendulum length'.

For seismographs in which the mass is free to move along a fixed axis we follow a similar argument, replacing the moments of forces by the forces themselves, and rotations of the boom by linear displacements. The moment of inertia of the boom is replaced by an inertial mass M', such that the total kinetic energy of the pendulum, when it is swinging, is equal to $\frac{1}{2}M' (dx/dt)^2$. Instead of equation 2 we write immediately

$$M' \frac{d^2x}{dt^2} + D\frac{dx}{dt} + Ux = \frac{d^2X}{dt^2} \qquad (2 a)$$

which leads to a reduced equation

$$\frac{d^2x}{dt^2} + 2\beta\Omega_0 \frac{dx}{dt} + \Omega_0^2x = M/M' \frac{d^2X}{dt^2} \qquad (3 a)$$

Equation 3a becomes equivalent to equation 3 if one substitutes $1/l$ for M/M'.

Equation 3 is the basic equation for a simple harmonic oscillator, and its solution is too well known to require detailed treatment here. For the case of simple harmonic ground motion, where

$$X = X_0 \cos \omega t$$

the solution is

$$\phi = \frac{-\omega X_0 \cos (\omega t - \xi)}{l\Omega_0[(\Omega_0/\omega - \omega/\Omega_0)^2 + 4\beta^2]^{\frac{1}{2}}} \qquad (4)$$

where

$$\xi = \tan^{-1} \frac{2\Omega_0\omega\beta}{\Omega_0^2 - \omega^2}$$

As ω tends to infinity, the phase angle ξ tends to π, and ϕ tends to the limit X/l. If the lever system is such that the movements of the indicating point are at all times equal to $l'\phi$ it follows that the indicator will faithfully reproduce all displacements of the ground at frequencies high compared with Ω_0. For very slow oscillations of the ground, ω tends to zero, ξ tends to zero and the equation for ϕ approximates to the form

$$l'\phi = \frac{l'}{l\Omega_0{}^2} \frac{d^2X}{dt^2} \tag{5}$$

Hence the displacement of the indicator tends to become proportional to ground acceleration. The form of the magnification curve between these limits depends on the magnitude of the damping constant β.

Magnification curves for various values of β are given in Fig. 2 (a). Curves of velocity sensitivity and acceleration sensitivity are given in Figs. 2 (b) and 2 (c) respectively. The symmetry of the velocity sensitivity curve sets it conspicuously apart from the others, a property which is maintained for several more complicated types of seismograph. As a corollary of this symmetrical character, the maximum velocity sensitivity always occurs when the frequency of earth motion is equal to the natural frequency of the undamped seismometer, whereas, in the other presentations, the effect of damping is to shift the peak towards the side of the curve which tends towards the horizontal asymptote. Further advantages of the velocity sensitivity over the other characteristics are that the curves can be plotted more compactly (the given examples require only two decades for velocity sensitivity, as against three decades for the other curves) and that a measurement of particle velocity in the earth is directly related to the energy of the waves.

A. *Transient motion of the seismometer*

An important property of the seismograph is the way in which the indicator returns to zero after an initial disturbance. To find the form of this decay, we use the general solution to the equation

$$\frac{d^2\phi}{dt^2} + 2\beta\Omega_0 \frac{d\phi}{dt} + \Omega_0{}^2\phi = 0$$

which, for $\beta < 1$, is

$$\phi = [A_1 \cos (1 - \beta^2)^{\frac{1}{2}}\Omega_0 t \\ + A_2 \sin (1 - \beta^2)^{\frac{1}{2}}\Omega_0 t] \exp (-\beta\Omega_0 t) \tag{6}$$

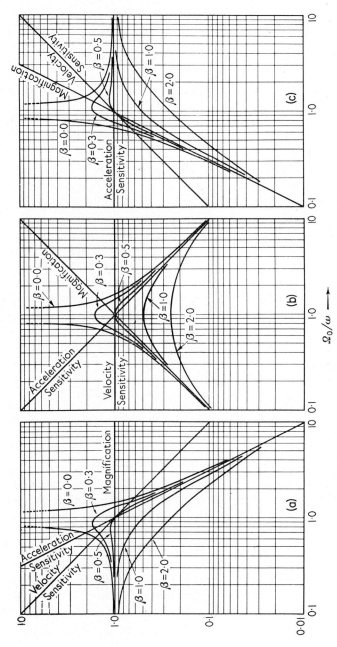

Fig. 2. Normalized response curves for direct-coupled seismographs.

and is

$$\phi = A_1 \exp\left[-\beta + (\beta^2 - 1)^{\frac{1}{2}}\right] \Omega_0 t$$
$$+ A_2 \exp\left[-\beta - (\beta^2 - 1)^{\frac{1}{2}}\right] \Omega_0 t \quad (7)$$

for $\beta \geqslant 1$. The solution for $\beta < 1$ contains an oscillatory term multiplied by a negative exponential factor, which causes the oscillations to decay at a rate which depends on the damping factor β. For $\beta \geqslant 1$ the indicator returns exponentially to zero from its initial displacement.

Since the recovery of the seismograph from a sudden disturbance and the sharpness of the resonant response to sustained oscillations are both dependent on the damping constant, the choice of this factor is of great importance in seismograph design. Underdamping is generally regarded as a serious defect, for this produces slowly decaying transients and a sharp seismometer resonance, so that waves having periods close to that of the seismometer receive undue prominence on the record. Heavily overdamped instruments have usually been avoided in seismology, although gravimeters and tiltmeters are often designed in this way. In consequence, most modern seismographs have values of β between 0·5 and 1, within which range of damping a transient disturbance falls to quite a small fraction of its initial value by the time a half period of the seismometer has elapsed. With this degree of damping, the dynamic magnification remains within a factor of two of the static magnification for earth periods up to and including the natural period of the seismometer.

2. Moving-coil Seismographs

In order to overcome the limitations of mechanical seismographs, Galitzin [6] introduced the principle of attaching a coil to the boom, which would swing between the poles of a magnet when the boom was displaced. The e.m.f.s resulting from such movements were detected by connecting the coil to a sensitive galvanometer. The fact that seismographs of this type are made up of two distinct instruments requires an addition to our terminology, so we shall now refer to the electrical generating component as the 'seismometer'. This will enable us to retain the word 'seismograph' for the complete system.

As the e.m.f. which deflects the galvanometer is proportional to the velocity rather than to the displacement of the seismometer boom, the problem of zero drift is much less severe than for mechanical instruments, and the fact that galvanometer coils can be made much lighter than mechanical lever trains reduces the inertial loading of the seismometer mass and enables high magnifications to be obtained very economically.

Galitzin's theory of his seismograph ignored the fact that the swinging coil of the galvanometer generates an e.m.f. which can profoundly modify the flow of current in the circuit, and it was worked out only for the case in which the seismometer and galvanometer have equal periods and a particular degree of damping. A periodic solution for the complete equation of motion was worked out by Wenner,[17] and put into more convenient form by Coulomb and Grenet.[4, 9, 10] Transient solutions for special cases have been worked out by various authors (see, for example, Eaton [5]), but the mathematics is cumbersome and will be omitted from the present discussion.

A. *The equations of motion*

In setting up the equations of motion we shall assume that the seismometer is essentially similar in design to the mechanical seismograph described in Section II, except that the mechanical-lever system which detects rotations of the boom is replaced by the electromagnetic 'transducer'. Let the flux linkage G between the coil and the magnet be such that an angular velocity $d\phi/dt$ in the boom generates an e.m.f. equal to $G\, d\phi/dt$ in the coil. From the laws of electromagnetic induction, it follows that a current I flowing in the coil will react on the magnetic field with a force whose moment about the hinge is $-GI$. The negative sign is introduced to express the fact that if current is allowed to flow in the same sense as the e.m.f. which is generated by a movement of the coil, then the mechanical reaction of the current will oppose the motion. The equation of motion of the seismometer boom is

$$K \frac{d^2\phi}{dt^2} + D \frac{d\phi}{dt} + U\phi = LM \frac{d^2X}{dt^2} - GI \qquad (8)$$

For the sake of generality, we shall allow the connection between the seismometer and the galvanometer to be made through an attenuating network, so that the current i which flows through the galvanometer may be less than the seismometer current I. The equation of motion of the galvanometer coil will be

$$k \frac{d^2\theta}{dt^2} + d \frac{d\theta}{dt} + u\theta = gi \tag{9}$$

where k, d and u are the moment of inertia of the galvanometer coil, the damping constant and the stiffness of the suspension respectively, θ is the angle of rotation of the coil and g is the flux linkage between the coil and the magnet.

The attenuating network used will have four terminals (two for the seismometer input and two for connection to the galvanometer),

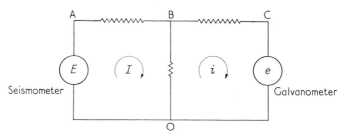

Fig. 3. Attenuating network for electromagnetic seismographs.

and there is a theorem which states that all such networks may be replaced by a set of three resistors in T configuration (Fig. 3). Let the combined resistance of the seismometer coil and the resistor A–B be called R, the combined resistance of the galvanometer and the resistor B–C be called r, and the resistance of the shunt resistor O–B be called S.

Applying Kirchoff's laws to the currents I and i circulating in the network, we have, for the circuit containing the seismometer,

$$IR + (I - i)S = G \, d\phi/dt$$

and for the galvanometer circuit

$$ir + (i - I)S = - g \, d\theta/dt$$

Solving for I and i, we have

$$I = G \frac{(r + S) \, d\phi}{Q^2 \, dt} - g \frac{S \, d\theta}{Q^2 \, dt} \tag{10}$$

and

$$i = g \frac{S}{Q^2} \frac{d\phi}{dt} - G \frac{(R+S)}{Q^2} \frac{d\theta}{dt} \tag{11}$$

where

$$Q^2 = Rr + RS + rS \tag{12}$$

The expressions for I and i respectively will be substituted back into equations 8 and 9. When we make these substitutions it will be possible to regard that part of I which contains $d\phi/dt$ as a contribution to the damping term of the seismometer. Similarly, the part of i which contains $d\theta/dt$ can be included in the damping term of the galvanometer. In order to simplify the equations of motion after this transfer has been made, we put

$$\Delta = D + G^2 (r + S)/Q^2$$

and

$$\delta = d + g^2 (R + S)/Q^2$$

Next, we put

$$\omega_0{}^2 = u/k \quad \Omega_0{}^2 = U/K \quad a = \delta/2k\omega_0$$
$$\beta = \Delta/2K\Omega_0 \quad LM/K = 1/l$$
$$\sigma_s = gGS/\Delta Q^2 \quad \sigma_g = gGS/\delta Q^2$$

so that equations 8 and 9 become

$$\frac{d^2\phi}{dt^2} + 2\beta\Omega_0 \frac{d\phi}{dt} + \Omega_0{}^2\phi = \frac{1}{l}\frac{d^2X}{dt^2} + 2\beta\Omega_0\sigma_s \frac{d\theta}{dt} \tag{13}$$

$$\frac{d^2\theta}{dt^2} + 2a\omega_0 \frac{d\theta}{dt} + \omega_0{}^2\theta = 2a\omega_0\sigma_g \frac{d\phi}{dt} \tag{14}$$

Eliminating ϕ from these equations, we obtain

$$\frac{d^4\theta}{dt^4} + \frac{d^3\theta}{dt^3} (2a\omega_0 + 2\beta\Omega_0)$$

$$+ \frac{d^2\theta}{dt^2} (\omega_0{}^2 + 4a\beta\omega_0\Omega_0 + \Omega_0{}^2 - 4a\beta\omega_0\Omega_0\sigma_g\sigma_s)$$

$$+ \frac{d\theta}{dt} (2\beta\Omega_0\omega_0{}^2 + 2a\omega_0\Omega_0{}^2) + \theta\omega_0{}^2\Omega_0{}^2 = \frac{2a\omega_0\sigma_g}{l}\frac{d^3X}{dt^3} \tag{15}$$

Equation 15 connects the galvanometer deflection θ with the ground displacement X, and in that respect is analogous to the simpler indicator equation (equation 3) which we have already derived for the direct-coupled seismograph. To obtain the solution for harmonic oscillations of the ground, we set X equal to the real part of

$$\mathbf{X} = X_0 \exp{(j\omega t)} \tag{16}$$

and θ equal to the real part of

$$\Theta = \theta_0 \exp{j(\omega t + \gamma)} \tag{17}$$

Equation 15 is regarded as the real part of a complex equation in Θ and $\mathbf{X}$. Differentiating equations 16 and 17, we eliminate the unwanted derivatives of Θ and $\mathbf{X}$, and obtain

$$\frac{\Theta}{d\mathbf{X}/dt} = \frac{-2a\sigma_g}{l\Omega_0\left\{\left[\dfrac{\omega^2}{\omega_0\Omega_0} + \dfrac{\omega_0\Omega_0}{\omega^2} - \dfrac{\omega_0}{\Omega_0} - \dfrac{\Omega_0}{\omega_0} - 4a\beta(1 - \sigma_g\sigma_s)\right] - j\left[2a\left(\dfrac{\omega}{\Omega_0} - \dfrac{\Omega_0}{\omega}\right) + 2\beta\left(\dfrac{\omega}{\omega_0} - \dfrac{\omega_0}{\omega}\right)\right]\right\}} \tag{18}$$

The real part of equation 18 gives the velocity sensitivity of the seismograph for sustained simple harmonic oscillations. On examining the form of the equation, we can draw the following general conclusions:

(a) The constants of the galvanometer and of the seismometer enter symmetrically into all terms which involve the ground frequency ω. It follows that the constants of the galvanometer can be exchanged for those of the seismometer without altering the shape of the response curve.

(b) If $a = \beta$ (equal damping of seismometer and galvanometer) or if $\Omega_0 = \omega_0$ (equal periods) the curve is symmetrical about the line $\omega = (\omega_0\Omega_0)^{\frac{1}{2}}$.

(c) For values of ω much greater than ω_0 or Ω_0 the sensitivity becomes proportional to $1/\omega^2$.

(d) For values of ω much less than ω_0 or Ω_0 the sensitivity is proportional to ω^2.

(e) For the case $a \approx \beta \approx 1$, and $\Omega_0 \gg \omega \gg \omega_0$, the denominator becomes dominated by the term Ω_0/ω_0, and the velocity sensitivity is therefore almost independent of frequency for a wide range of ω. This property of the equation gives a characteristically flat response to seismographs which, like the long-period Benioff combination, are made up of a seismometer and galvanometer having widely different periods and approximately critical damping.

B. *The reaction of the galvanometer*

The reaction of the galvanometer may be defined as the effect of movements of the galvanometer coil on the motion of the seismometer boom. Mathematically, the reaction is described by the appearance of the term in $d\theta/dt$ on the RHS of equation 13. The neglect of this term is equivalent to putting $\sigma_s = 0$. In equation 18, σ_s appears only in the term $4\alpha\beta(1 - \sigma_g\sigma_s)$, so that the effect of the galvanometer reaction depends on the value of $\sigma_g\sigma_s$ in comparison with unity, and on the ratio of $4\alpha\beta(1 - \sigma_g\sigma_s)$ to the other terms in the denominator.

To determine the magnitude of $\sigma_g\sigma_s$, we write

$$\sigma_g\sigma_s = \frac{(\Delta - D)(\delta - d)}{\Delta\delta} \times \frac{S^2}{(r + S)(R + S)} \qquad (19)$$

Evidently, $\sigma_g\sigma_s$ will be small if S is small in relation to R or r, if D is a large fraction of Δ or if d is a large fraction of δ.

When $\sigma_g\sigma_s = 1$ the denominator of equation 18 vanishes when $\omega = \Omega_0 = \omega_0$, so that the seismograph will have infinite magnification on resonance. When $\Omega_0 \neq \omega_0$ the denominator of equation 18 cannot vanish in this way, and the effect of reaction therefore beomes less extreme. To sum up, we may say that the effect of reaction depends on the ratio between the seismometer and the galvanometer period, on the attenuation of the coupling network and on the fraction of the total damping which depends on the current flowing through the coils of both the seismometer and galvanometer.

It is often stated in the literature that the galvanometer reaction depends on the ratio of the mass of the seismometer boom to that of the galvanometer coil, and that the reaction of a very light galvanometer coil can never appreciably disturb the movement of a heavy seismometer mass. The foregoing discussion should have disclosed the fallacy of this belief, for the fact is that the reaction is quite independent of the mass ratio, and depends only on the closeness of coupling. If the galvanometer coil is made lighter under given coupling conditions the magnification will increase, and the more violent movements of the lighter coil will produce the same reaction as the smaller rotations of the heavier one.

C. Determination of instrumental constants for a given response

Having set up the equation of motion for a seismograph with any given set of seismometer and galvanometer constants, we may now ask ourselves whether the instrumental constants are determined if the equation of motion is given. The problem was treated by Grenet and Coulomb,[9] who set up a 'reduced equation of motion' by transforming the time scale of equation 15. Setting $(\Omega_0/\omega_0)^{\frac{1}{2}} = \rho$ and $\omega't = \tau$, where $\omega'^2 = \omega_0\Omega_0$, equation 15 becomes

$$\frac{d^4\theta}{d\tau^4} + A\frac{d^3\theta}{d\tau^3} + B\frac{d^2\theta}{d\tau^2} + C\frac{d\theta}{d\tau} + \theta = F\frac{d^3X}{d\tau^3}$$

where

$$\left.\begin{array}{l} A = 2(\beta\rho + a/\rho) \\ B = \rho^2 + \rho^{-2} + 4\lambda a\beta \\ C = 2(\beta/\rho + a\rho) \\ \lambda = (1 - \sigma_s\sigma_g) \end{array}\right\} \qquad (21)$$

and F is a constant which determines the absolute magnification.

In the general case, for which $A \neq C$, $\omega_0 \neq \Omega_0$, and $a \neq \beta$, we can solve the first and last equations of 21 for a and β, giving

$$\left.\begin{array}{l} 2a(\rho^2 - \rho^{-2}) = C\rho - A/\rho \\ 2\beta(\rho^2 - \rho^{-2}) = A\rho - C/\rho \end{array}\right\} \qquad (22)$$

Substituting for a and β in the second equation of 21 we find

$$f(a) \equiv (a^2 - 4)(a - B) + \lambda AC(a - A/C - C/A) = 0 \qquad (23)$$

where $a = (\rho^2 + \rho^{-2})$.

Equation 23 has at least one root, and it still contains the adjustable parameter λ. Hence if A, B and C are of such magnitude that they can define the properties of any one real seismograph, an infinity of different seismographs can be found to produce the same response curve. Of these new seismographs, at least one will exist for every possible value of λ. As one of these possible solutions covers the case in which $\lambda = 1$, we see that the reaction of the galvanometer can never produce types of response curve which cannot be produced by seismographs in which the reaction is negligible.

The case for which $\lambda = 1$ (galvanometer reaction negligible) leads to some interesting examples. The most direct way of treating this case is to return to equation 18, which, when $\lambda = 1$, can be factorized as follows

$$\frac{\Theta}{d\mathbf{X}/dt} = \frac{2a\sigma_g\omega^2}{l\Omega_0{}^2\omega_0\left[\dfrac{\omega}{\omega_0} - ja + (1 - a^2)^{\frac{1}{2}}\right]\left[\dfrac{\omega}{\omega_0} - ja - (1 - a^2)^{\frac{1}{2}}\right]}$$

$$\left[\dfrac{\omega}{\Omega_0} - j\beta + (1 - \beta^2)^{\frac{1}{2}}\right]\left[\dfrac{\omega}{\Omega_0} - j\beta - (1 - \beta^2)^{\frac{1}{2}}\right] \quad (24)$$

In the denominator of equation 24 the first two factors contain the constants of the galvanometer in the seismograph for which the equation was originally derived, whereas the last two factors contain the constants of the seismometer. A different seismograph having the same response may be derived by combining the first and third factors to represent the galvanometer and the second and fourth for the seismometer. The third variation is obtained by combining the first and fourth factors for the galvanometer, and the second and third for the seismometer.

A typical pair of terms may be multiplied out as follows

$$[\omega/\omega_0 - ja + (1 - a^2)^{\frac{1}{2}}][\omega/\Omega_0 - j\beta + (1 - \beta^2)^{\frac{1}{2}}]$$

$$= pP\left\{\frac{\omega^2}{\omega_0\Omega_0 pP} - \frac{j\omega}{(\omega_0\Omega_0 pP)^{\frac{1}{2}}}\left[\frac{\Omega_0{}^{\frac{1}{2}} P}{\omega_0{}^{\frac{1}{2}} p} + \frac{\omega_0{}^{\frac{1}{2}} p}{\Omega_0{}^{\frac{1}{2}} P}\right] - 1\right\} \quad (25)$$

where $p = a - (a^2 - 1)^{\frac{1}{2}}$ and $P = \beta - (\beta^2 - 1)^{\frac{1}{2}}$.

Equation 25 can be taken to represent a galvanometer having constants ω_0' and a', where

$$\omega_0'^2 = \omega_0\Omega_0 pP$$

and

$$a' = \frac{1}{2}\left[\frac{\Omega_0{}^{\frac{1}{2}} P}{\omega_0{}^{\frac{1}{2}} p} + \frac{\omega_0{}^{\frac{1}{2}} p}{\Omega_0{}^{\frac{1}{2}} P}\right] \quad (26)$$

provided that p and P are real, i.e. provided that a and β are both greater than unity. The products of the other pairs of factors will have the same form as equation 25, except for appropriate changes of sign in the expressions for p and P.

One of the more striking examples which can be worked out is that of the long-period Benioff combination, for which $a = \beta$

R

$= p = P = 1$, and for which Ω_0/ω_0 is about 100. Thus a long-period Benioff combination having seismometer and galvanometer periods of 1 sec and 100 sec respectively has the same response as a combination in which both the seismometer and galvanometer have periods of 10 sec and about 5 times critical damping.

Numerous other cases are worked out by Grenet and Coulomb, including the family of 'false Galitzins' whose response is equivalent to that of the ideal Galitzin seismograph for which $\rho = 1$, $a = \beta = 1$, $A = C = 4$ and $B = 6$. It is shown that 'false Galitzins' can have values of ρ as large as $3 + 2\sqrt{2}$.

3. The Variable-reluctance Seismometer

In moving-coil seismometers the windings have to be placed in a gap in a magnetic circuit, and the power output which can be obtained from a given relative velocity of the transducer elements is proportional to the energy content of the magnetic field. This power output determines not only the magnification of the complete system but also the extent to which the load of the external circuit contributes to the seismometer damping. Before 1939 the energy content of available permanent magnets was much smaller than it is now, so that some or all of the following features had to be incorporated:

(1) Magnets much larger than the suspended mass.

(2) Auxiliary magnets, or fluid dashpots to increase the damping.

(3) Coil mounted on a long lever, to provide a mechanical advantage for the transducer.

In 1930–32 Benioff [1] introduced the variable-reluctance transducer into earthquake seismology. In its modern form the transducer consists of a magnet (Fig. 4), set up between two armatures on which coils are wound. The armatures are fixed to a frame, such that there is a gap of length l_g between each end of the magnet and each armature when the magnet is in the central position. Let the magnetic flux in each gap be ϕ_g and the area of each face A_g.

Let the magnet be displaced a small distance x away from one armature and towards the other. Since the length of one pair of gaps has been increased and the length of the other pair has been decreased by the same amount, the total reluctance of the magnetic circuit has hardly changed, and the effect is therefore to divert an amount of flux $\delta\phi_g$ from one pair of gaps to the other, without appreciably changing the total flux in the magnet. Since the flux will distribute itself between the gaps in inverse ratio to the reluctance of the two halves of the magnetic circuit, we have

$$(\phi_g + \delta\phi_g)/(\phi_g - \delta\phi_g) = (l_g + x)/(l_g - x)$$

or

$$\delta\phi_g = x\phi_g/l_g \tag{27}$$

The net effect of the displacement of the magnet is to cause a flux $\delta\phi_g$ to circulate through the two coils. As l_g is made smaller, an increasingly large flux can be maintained by a given volume of

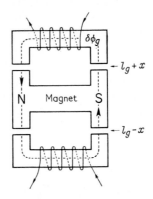

Fig. 4. Schematic diagram of balanced variable-reluctance transducer.

magnetic material, and an increasing proportion of this flux can be diverted by a given movement of the mass. Moreover, there is no obvious limit to the amount of wire which can be wound on to the armatures. In consequence, a very powerful transducer can be constructed with a small magnet. The transducer in the standard Benioff seismograph is capable of handling all the power required to damp a mass of 100 kg, suspended with a natural period of 1 sec.

Further study of the theory of the variable-reluctance transducer shows that it introduces two complicating factors into the equation of motion of the seismometer. These are, first, that the unbalanced flux which results from any displacement of the magnet exerts an attraction which tends to pull the system farther off-centre, and secondly, that the inductance of the coils shifts the phase of the current in relation to the relative velocity of the transducer elements and thereby complicates the mechanical reaction of the current on the seismometer mass.

The theory of a variable-reluctance seismometer working into a resistive load has been given by Washburn [16] and extended by Sparks and Hawley.[15] In accordance with the usual Benioff design, we shall set up the theory on the assumption that the seismometer mass moves along a fixed axis, rather than being in the form of a hinged boom. We shall also assume that the only damping is that which arises from currents flowing in the coils. Let the total number of turns on the coils be n. Let the combined inductance of the coils be considered in two parts, of which L' is the part associated with the flux that passes through the gaps, and L'' is the part associated with leakage flux.

Now suppose that a current i flows through the coils. This generates a flux ϕ_L in each gap, where

$$\phi_L = L'i/n \tag{28}$$

The attraction between the faces of each gap when the armature is in the central position is $\phi_g{}^2/8\pi A_g$. When the armature is displaced and a current i flows through the coils the total unbalanced force F_g is given by

$$F_g = \phi_g(\delta\phi_g + \phi_L)/\pi A_g$$
$$= \phi_g(\phi_g x/l_g + L'i/n)/\pi A_g \tag{29}$$

The term in equation 29 which contains x acts like a negative contribution to the restoring force of the spring. Hence if we call the actual spring stiffness U', and put $U'' = \phi_g{}^2/\pi A_g l_g$, the equation of motion becomes

$$M\frac{d^2x}{dt^2} + (U' - U'')x - \frac{L'\phi_g i}{\pi A_g n} = M\frac{d^2X}{dt^2} \tag{30}$$

where X is the displacement of the ground.

Now, the e.m.f. developed is given by

$$e = iR = -n\left(\frac{\phi_g}{l_g}\frac{dx}{dt} + \frac{L' + L''}{n}\frac{di}{dt}\right) \tag{31}$$

where R is the total resistance of the circuit. Differentiating equation 30, and substituting for dx/dt from equation 31, we find for the output of the seismometer

$$\frac{d^3e}{dt^3} + \frac{d^2e}{dt^2}\frac{R}{(L' + L'')} + \frac{de}{dt}\left[\frac{(U' - U'')(L' + L'') + L'U''}{M(L' + L'')}\right]$$

$$+ \frac{e(U' - U'')}{L' + L''}\frac{R}{M} = \frac{Rn\phi_g}{l_g(L' + L'')}\frac{d^3X}{dt^3} \quad (32)$$

Putting

$$(U' - U'')/M = \Omega_0{}^2$$

and

$$\{(U' - U'')(L' + L'') + L'U''\}/\{M(L' + L'')\} = \Omega_1{}^2$$

and setting $X \equiv 0$, the equation for free oscillations of the seismometer becomes

$$\frac{d^3e}{dt^3} + \frac{R}{L' + L''}\frac{d^2e}{dt^2} + \Omega_1{}^2\frac{de}{dt} + \frac{R}{L' + L''}\Omega_0{}^2e = 0 \quad (33)$$

On examining the form of equation 33 as R tends to zero or infinity, we see that $\Omega_0/2\pi$ is the natural frequency of free oscillations on open-circuit, and that $\Omega_1/2\pi$ is the natural frequency for short-circuit. As there is no damping in either case, it follows that some load resistance between zero and infinity must give maximum damping. Note also that if there is no leakage from the magnetic circuit, $L'' = 0$ and $\Omega_1{}^2 = U'/M$. This means that the short-circuited inductance prevents the flux through the gaps from changing in response to oscillations of the mass, so that the negative stiffness associated with the magnetic field is suppressed.

By solving equation 33, Sparks and Hawley show that when the seismometer mass is displaced and the resistance is adjusted for maximum damping, the e.m.f. generated during its recovery is given by

$$e = E_1 \sin (\beta t - \delta) \exp (at) + E_2 \exp (-\Omega_0 t) \quad (34)$$

where E_1, E_2 and δ depend on the initial conditions. The form of the equation is that of a damped harmonic motion superimposed on a non-oscillatory decay term. The constants of equation 34 are as follows:

$$a/\Omega_0 = -(\Omega_1{}^2 - \Omega_0{}^2)/4\Omega_0{}^2 \quad (35)$$

and

$$\beta/\Omega_0 = [1 + (\Omega_1{}^2 - \Omega_0{}^2)/2\Omega_0{}^2 - (\Omega_1{}^2 - \Omega_0{}^2)^2/16\Omega_0{}^4]^{\frac{1}{2}} \quad (36)$$

The resistance R_m required to produce maximum damping is given by

$$R_m/(L' + L'') = (\Omega_1{}^2 + \Omega_0{}^2)/2\Omega_0 \qquad (37)$$

The concept of 'critical damping' is not strictly applicable to anything other than a damped simple harmonic oscillator, but we may define an analogous quantity for the variable-reluctance seismograph by investigating the condition for the disappearance of the oscillatory term, at which $\beta = 0$.

On solving equation 36 when $\beta = 0$, we find

$$\Omega_1/\Omega_0 = (5 + 4\sqrt{2})^{\frac{1}{2}} \qquad (38)$$

The most efficient damping is obtained when there is no leakage from the magnetic circuit, under which condition we have

$$\Omega_1{}^2/\Omega_0{}^2 = U'/(U' - U'') \qquad (39)$$

On combining equations 37 and 38 we find

$$U''/U' = 0.905$$

It follows that, if a variable-reluctance seismometer is to be critically damped by the currents which it delivers to the load, the equivalent negative stiffness resulting from magnetic forces must exceed 90 per cent of the mechanical spring constant.

Chakrabarty [3] discusses the performance of a variable-reluctance seismograph, including the effect of reaction, but he unfortunately equates the e.m.f. developed to $-n\phi_g dx/dt/l_g$, instead of using the complete form of equation 31. He thereby omits the effects of the coil inductance, and ends up with a set of equations having the same form as those which we have given for the moving-coil instrument. It does not appear that a complete theory, taking into account both the coil inductance and the galvanometer reaction, has yet been published.

4. Calibration of Pendulum Seismographs

In calibrating a seismograph one is seeking to obtain sufficient information to enable one to predict the response of the indicator to any given movement of the ground. This objective may be attained either by determining the overall response curve (e.g. by the use of a shaking table) or by determining the individual constants which enter into the equations of motion. With direct-coupled seismographs, both types of approach will yield the same information. When we consider instruments using galvanometric registration, we see that methods which treat the entire seismograph as an indivisible unit can at most only determine the five constants $(A, B, C, F$ and $\omega')$ which have been used to describe the overall response. The complete description of the seismometer and galvanometer requires seven constants $(\omega_0, \Omega_0, \alpha, \beta, \sigma_s, \sigma_g$ and $l)$, and if we wish to determine all of these we must perform experiments on the seismometer and galvanometer separately.

A. *Impulse methods*

The impulse methods of calibration consist of the application of a known disturbance to the seismometer boom and the observation of the resulting movement of the indicator. In principle, the methods are capable of yielding a frequency response for the entire seismograph without reference to the constants of its component parts, for the impulse (which may be a tap on the boom or a sudden tilting of the support) can be chosen to be equivalent to some hypothetical movement of the ground, and we have already seen that the magnification of the seismograph is simply the ratio of the harmonic component of the indicator displacement to the corresponding component of the simulated earth displacement at any given frequency.

In practice, impulse tests are seldom, if ever, used in this way, and the normal procedure is to observe the response of the seismograph to several different types of disturbance, and hence to deduce the constants which appear in the equation of motion.

With direct-coupled seismographs, the procedure is, first, to remove the damping system and to observe the period, τ, of free oscillations. Dividing τ into 2π yields the constant Ω_0 for the seismograph. It may happen that the oscillations of the mass will still be damped appreciably by air resistance or by losses in the springs even when the damping device is removed. In that case the time interval between successive maxima of the indicator displacement will have a different period τ_1, but τ can be determined from the equation

$$\frac{1}{\tau^2} = \frac{1}{\tau_1{}^2}\left(1 + \frac{\Lambda_1{}^2}{2\pi^2}\right) \tag{40}$$

where Λ_1 is the natural logarithm of the ratio of the amplitudes of two successive swings of the indicator.

When Ω_0 has been determined the damping system is restored and adjusted until the indicator returns to zero from an initial displacement without overshooting (critical damping), or until the ratio between the amplitudes of successive swings agrees with the value determined by setting an acceptable value of the damping constant into equation 6. Finally, a small test mass is applied to the boom, or the seismograph is tilted, so as to simulate the effect of a ground acceleration d^2X/dt^2. The displacement of the indicator is observed and is inserted, along with the known values of d^2X/dt^2 and Ω_0, into equation 5. The equation then yields a value for l'/l, which completes the calibration.

The results obtained by this method may be in error if the forces exerted by the damping system on the boom are not strictly proportional to dx/dt. Thus if the damping is accomplished by means of an oil-filled dashpot the motion of the oil will involve inertia terms which may be equivalent to the addition of mass to the pendulum. A damping vane moving between the poles of a magnet may experience a component of force proportional to its displacement if any ferromagnetic impurities are present. If, however, the instruments are well designed and in good condition the errors arising from the foregoing causes should amount only to a few per cent of the overall sensitivity, and the precision normally required for amplitude measurements is not sufficient for such errors to constitute a very serious difficulty.

In calibrating electromagnetic seismographs, impulse methods are usually applied to the determination of all of the seven constants of the seismometer and of the galvanometer. It has already been pointed out that, to achieve this objective, we shall have to observe movements of the seismometer boom independently of those of the galvanometer, and this requires an auxiliary indicating device (such as a mirror attached to the boom, arranged to reflect a beam of light). A procedure which can in principle be applied to any combination of galvanometer and seismometer is as follows:

(1) Disconnect the galvanometer from the rest of the circuit, set it swinging and observe the decay of free oscillations. Hence determine the constants ω_0 and d/k.

(2) Connect a known shunt, S_1, across the galvanometer terminals. Deflect the coil and observe the movement. This will yield a new damping constant

$$\frac{\delta_1}{k} = \frac{d}{k} + \frac{g^2}{(r + S_1)k} \qquad (41)$$

Knowing δ_1/k and d/k, calculate g^2/k. Hence calculate δ/k for the final operating circuit.

(3) Carry out experiments similar to (1) and (2) on the seismometer, and hence determine Ω_0, D/K and Δ/K. Hence calculate $\sigma_s\sigma_g$ from equation 19.

(4) By tilting the seismometer, determine the reduced pendulum length, l, as for the direct-coupled seismograph.

(5) Connect the seismometer to the galvanometer through a high resistance R_1, and set up a pair of stops on either side of the seismometer boom. Move the boom suddenly from one stop to the other. Note the angle ϕ_1 through which the boom is displaced, and record the resulting oscillations of the galvanometer. Use the known amplitude and frequency of these oscillations to determine the initial angular velocity, $\dot{\theta}_1$, of the galvanometer coil, and hence determine the constant gG/k from the equation

$$\dot{\theta}_1 = gG\phi_1/k(R_1 + r + R) \qquad (42)$$

By combining the value of gG/k with the known value of δ/k, we find σ_g. Setting $a = \delta/2k\omega_0$ and $\beta = \Delta/2K\Omega_0$ completes the calibration.

In certain special cases it is possible to avoid the necessity of recording the deflections of the seismometer in detail. Thus, the classical Galitzin seismograph is defined as one in which the seismometer and galvanometer have equal periods and critical damping, and in which the galvanometer reaction is negligible. The theory of the instrument shows that if the seismometer boom is given a sharp tap the galvanometer will be deflected to one side of the zero line, will overshoot once to the other side and then return to zero without further oscillation. The ratio of the first swing to the overshoot is 2·29. In setting up such a seismograph one adjusts first the seismometer period to match that of the galvanometer, then the shunt to provide critical damping for the galvanometer and, finally, the seismometer damping magnet to provide the proper response to the tapping test.

B. *Shaking-table calibrations*

A much more direct method than the foregoing one is to set up the seismograph on a foundation which can be subjected to horizontal or vertical displacements having the same order of magnitude as the ground movement which will have to be detected in normal service. The equipment consists of a platform on an elastic support, constrained so as to be free to vibrate only in the desired direction. Some method of applying a periodic force to the table is required, and it is also necessary to have a device (usually an electrical transducer) for determining the displacements of the table as a function of time. Given such equipment, the seismometer response curve is determined directly by comparing the observed deflections of the indicator with the known movements of the base.

In practice, shaking tables are by no means easy to design or to construct. The table must be free from unwanted modes of vibration over a substantially wider range of frequencies than the seismograph which is to be tested by it, and it must also be a good deal larger and heavier than the seismograph. If the table is to be used for testing horizontal seismographs the requirement for it to operate without tilting is extremely stringent, especially at long periods. Thus for an earth period of 60 sec, the accelerations arising from sinusoidal movements with an amplitude of 1 mm are only of the order of 1 mgal. If the permissible error in calibration is to be less than 10 per cent of the total sensitivity, the table must be capable of oscillating without tilting by more than 10^{-7} of a radian per millimetre of horizontal displacement!

In use, shaking tables have the disadvantage that the seismograph has to be removed from its ordinary operating position for testing, and there is no guarantee that this can be done, or that the instrument can be put back into service after testing, without altering its calibration.

The foregoing difficulties tend to restrict the use of shaking tables to the testing of robust seismographs of relatively short period, such as those used in geophysical prospecting and in short-period earthquake work.

C. *Calibration by harmonic drive*

This method [13] depends on the application of a periodic force to the boom, thereby simulating the effect of an equivalent acceleration of the ground. The simplest device of this kind is a small magnet mounted on the boom, and free to swing inside a fixed coil of wire. The flux linkage between the coil and the magnet is determined in advance of the main calibration, so that the force exerted on the magnet when a given current flows in the coil is known. When an alternating current is supplied from a suitable oscillator a plot of the indicator deflection as a function of oscillator frequency for constant drive current is the acceleration response curve of the seismograph.

The method can be applied either to mechanical or electromagnetic seismographs. When electromagnetic instruments are used it is possible to obtain more detailed information than that which is contained in the overall calibration curve by attaching a mirror to the seismometer boom and reflecting a beam of light off the mirror on to a scale or recording drum. The deflections of the light beam measure the deflections of the seismometer boom, and if these deflections are observed first with the galvanometer clamped and then with it unclamped the galvanometer reaction can be determined.

D. *The bridge method*

It was pointed out by Willmore [19] that the seismometer coil itself can be used for driving electromagnetic seismometers into forced oscillations if the drive is applied through a balanced bridge circuit.

The method is based on the 'superposition theorem' for networks of linear impedances. The theorem states that each e.m.f. in a network acts independently of all others in causing currents to flow, so that if a new e.m.f. is introduced the change in the current flowing in every branch of the network is equal to the current which would flow if the new e.m.f. acted alone. For mechanical systems there is an analogous theorem which states that every force acts independently of all others in producing movements of the component parts.

The procedure is to set up the seismometer in a Maxwell bridge circuit (which can be balanced for both inductance and resistance, and which holds a given balance at all frequencies), and to connect the galvanometer across the output terminals (Fig. 5). The bridge is designed so that the resistance R_R is much smaller than the resistance R_C of the seismometer coil, and R_B is much larger than R_C. In consequence, the seismograph behaves almost as though the seismometer was directly connected to the galvanometer, and the small effects of the bridge resistors are easily allowed for. A known alternating voltage is applied to the 'main input' terminals A and C.

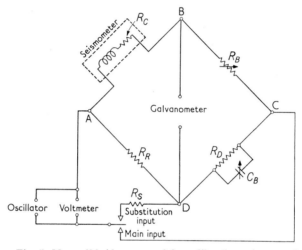

Fig. 5. Maxwell bridge, as used for calibrating seismographs.

The bridge is balanced with the seismometer clamped. In this condition, a known current I_c is passing through the seismometer coil, so that a force of moment GI_c is acting on the boom, and is balanced by the reaction of the clamp. The galvanometer is undeflected during this stage of the experiment. The seismometer is then unclamped, whereupon the boom starts to oscillate under the influence of the force GI_c. These movements generate an e.m.f. which deflects the galvanometer. In accordance with the superposition theorem the force exerted by the coil is equivalent to a ground acceleration of $-GI_c/LM$.

To determine G, we switch the drive to the 'substitution input', and thereby inject a current through the high resistance R_s. This step is equivalent to the introduction of a small known e.m.f. e_s in the arm AD of the bridge.

During the main experiment the velocity of the boom was

$$\frac{d\phi}{dt} = \frac{GI_c}{Z_M + Z_g} \tag{43}$$

where Z_M is the mechanical impedance of the seismometer and Z_g is an additional mechanical impedance which represents the loading effect of the galvanometer circuit. Hence the e.m.f. developed is:

$$e_c = G\frac{d\phi}{dt} = \frac{G^2 I_c}{Z_M + Z_g} \tag{44}$$

If the seismometer is clamped during the substitution experiment the known e.m.f. e_s is substituted for e_c, which can therefore be determined from the equation

$$e_s = e_c\theta_s/\theta \tag{45}$$

where θ and θ_s are the galvanometer deflections in the main experiment and in the substitution experiment respectively. On substituting for e_c in equation 44, we determine G in terms of the mechanical impedance $(Z_M + Z_g)$.

The procedure as outlined is not entirely satisfactory, because Z_g, which involves the galvanometer reaction, is not readily calculated. If the substitution experiment is carried out without clamping the seismometer the algebra becomes rather more complicated, for then the seismometer boom is deflected by the current and an additional e.m.f. is thereby introduced into the circuit. The result, however, is unexpectedly simple, for we now find that

$$e_s'\,\theta/\theta_s' = G^2 I_c/Z_M \tag{46}$$

where e_s' and θ_s' are the substitution e.m.f. and the galvanometer deflection in the new experiment.

The equation for Z_M in terms of the constants of the seismometer is

$$Z_M = jK\omega + D + S/j\omega$$

or

$$|Z_M|^2 = K^2(\omega - \Omega_0^2/\omega)^2 + D^2 \tag{47}$$

If we plot θ_s'/θ as a function of frequency we obtain a curve with a minimum where $\omega = \Omega_0$. Knowing Ω_0, we plot $(\theta_s'/\theta)^2$ against

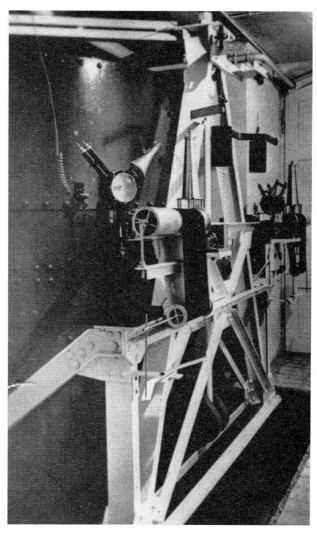

Fig. 6. Large Wiechert seismograph, showing part of the inertial mass (left), the drums carrying the smoked recording paper, and the adjustable air dashpots for providing damping. The drive for the drums comes from the weights, suspended on the wires which pass over the pulleys near the top of the photograph (W. Hiller).

$(\omega - \Omega_0^2/\omega)^2$, which yields a straight line, intercepting the line $(\theta_s'/\theta)^2 = 0$ at $-D^2/K^2$. It follows that the only constants required to render the calibration absolute are the mass M and the moment of inertia K of the boom.

5. Practical Details of some Pendulum Seismographs

In the preceding sections we have discussed the fundamental properties of broad classes of instrument, and it now remains to consider the design features which render a given instrument suitable for a particular purpose. In this section we shall make no attempt to cover all the instruments which have been produced, but we shall try to select examples which illustrate most clearly the potentialities and limitations of each class.

In the direct-coupled group we shall begin by discussing the Wiechert instrument (Fig. 6), which was one of the earliest to be produced and which is still giving good service in many older observatories. The instrument consists of a heavy mass, balanced on a vertical column the lower end of which is supported on a pair of crossed strip hinges. The mass is held in stable equilibrium by means of horizontal springs, and damped by means of air-filled dashpots. Systems of levers magnify the displacement of the mass in two perpendicular horizontal directions, and record these movements on smoked paper.

In consequence of the friction between the stylus and the smoked paper, a very heavy mass is required to obtain high magnification. The largest standard instrument uses a rock-filled cage weighing 17 tons to produce a magnification of about 10^4. Instruments with masses of 1000 lb or so yield magnifications of about 500.

The Milne–Shaw seismograph is another of the older instruments which is still widely used, and which provides magnifications up to 350 for a natural period of 10 or 12 sec. Whilst its magnification is inadequate for the study of P waves or the small rapid movements of local earthquakes, the instrument yields clear records of the transverse waves of teleseisms and is sometimes adapted for use as a tiltmeter. The seismograph consists of a horizontal pendulum with an extended lever, the far end of which is linked to a short, light lever bearing a mirror. A light beam originating from a kerosene or electric lamp is reflected by the mirror and recorded photographically (Fig. 7).

The Wood–Anderson seismograph is an instrument of such extraordinary simplicity that its relatively late introduction (1925) is one of the minor mysteries of seismology. It consists simply of a

Fig. 7. Milne-Shaw seismograph, showing the horizontal boom, inertial mass and support. The mirror is on a separate pivot behind the boom, and is connected to the boom by the small L-shaped link. Needles on the link rest in jewelled cups in the boom and on the mirror mount respectively. The damping magnets are beneath the curved slot in the smaller frame, which can be raised and lowered independently of the main support (Hilger and Watts).

small cylinder, attached eccentrically to a taut suspension fibre, and bearing a mirror to reflect a light beam. A fixed mirror is used to reflect the beam for a second time on to the suspended system, and by means of this double reflection, magnification up to 2 800 for a period of 0·8 sec can be obtained. This magnification is still too low for the detection of the smallest short-period movements, but the simplicity and reliability of the instrument have led to its adoption as the standard for near-earthquake magnitude determinations.

Numerous other types of direct-coupled pendulums are used for strong-motion observations, as tiltmeters and as gravimeters, but until the last few years the shortcomings of this class of instrument

Fig. 8. Columbia vertical seismometer. The coil is mounted on the light aluminium framework which rises vertically from the boom, and moves inside the pot magnet which is mounted between the main frame members. The adjusting screw for the inclined spring, and the rider for balancing the boom can also be seen (Sprengnether Instrument Corpn.).

seemed to be limiting the development of modern variants for use in seismology. Recently, however, the use of displacement transducers in conjunction with electronic amplifiers has resulted in the development of new seismometers, whose response characteristics have the same form as those of the older direct-coupled instruments, but which are free from the limitation on magnification. Furthermore, the electronic systems permit the introduction of long-period feedback devices, which eliminate the undesirable effects of zero drift.

s

On passing to electromagnetic seismometers we must first mention the Galitzin horizontal and vertical seismographs, which are the ancestors of numerous more modern instruments of medium and long period. The most recent introductions in this group are the Columbia seismometers, the excellent zero stability of which renders them particularly suitable for the detection of waves having very long periods (Fig. 8).

The key to the design of long-period vertical seismometers lies in the use of a spring which will support the boom against gravity

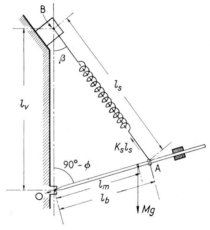

Fig. 9. Schematic diagram of the La Coste spring system. See Fig. 8 for a practical design using the La Coste principle.

without excessively shortening the natural period. The most satisfactory solution to this problem is that due to La Coste,[11] whose system is illustrated in Fig. 9.

The system consists of a pendulum OA, hinged so as to be free to oscillate in a vertical plane, and supported by a spring AB. The spring is so designed that the tension in it is equal to $K_s(AB)$, where K_s is the modulus of the spring. The end B of the spring is attached to a support, vertically above the hinge point O. Let $OB = l_v$, $OA = l_b$ and let the centre of gravity of the boom be a distance l_m from the hinge. Let the boom have a total mass M, let the deflection of the boom from the horizontal $= \phi$, and let $O\hat{B}A = \beta$.

We now have

$$l_s = l_b \cos \phi / \sin \beta$$

Moment of spring tension about hinge $= K_s l_s l_v \sin \beta$
$$= K_s l_b l_v \cos \phi$$

Moment of gravity about hinge $= M g l_m \cos \phi$

where g is the acceleration due to gravity.*

Hence, if $K_s l_b l_v = M g l_m$ the tension in the spring will balance gravity for all positions of the boom.

The practical realization of the principle depends on the possibility of constructing a spring whose tension is proportional to its stretched length. This requires a substantial degree of tension to remain in the spring when the coils are in contact, so that the physical contraction of the spring to zero length at zero tension is prevented only by the interference of the coils. It is not necessary to construct the spring to exactly zero length or to an exactly specified tension, for by mounting the end of the spring on a sliding block which can be adjusted along the line AB the effective zero point of the spring can be set in any desired position. Movable weights on the boom can then be used to adjust the moment of the gravitational forces to provide the desired equilibrium.

Long-period vertical seismometers are very subject to drift arising from changes in the spring or to changes in the buoyancy of the air, and even if the units are sealed, or compensated for these effects, it is difficult to maintain stability at periods exceeding 30 sec. Response to periods much longer than 30 sec is usually obtained by the use of very-long-period galvanometers, although, as we have seen above, it is equally possible, and might prove more convenient, to obtain long-period response by using overdamped seismometers and galvanometers of moderate period.

The use of a hinged boom is essentially an artifice for obtaining a long-period oscillatory system, and for periods of 1 sec or less more compact instruments can be made if the mass is constrained to move along a fixed axis. The Benioff seismometer (Fig. 10) is the most powerful of these instruments in common use. The suspended mass is of the order of 100 kg, and yields sufficient power to drive short-period galvanometers to yield velocity sensitivities

---

* Note that the symbols β and g here have different meanings from those used elsewhere in this chapter.

Fig. 10. Benioff short-period vertical seismograph. In this instrument, the lifting spring is concealed inside the mass. Lateral constraint is provided by the six horizontal tension members (Benioff, Academic Press Inc.).

of the order of 2×10^4, and long-period galvanometers to a velocity sensitivity of about 1 000. If this performance is expressed in terms of magnification we see that short-period galvanometers have maximum magnifications of a few hundred thousand, whereas

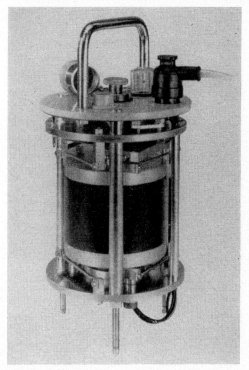

Fig. 11. Willmore short-period vertical seismometer. The lifting spring consists of two pairs of horizontal leaf springs, and vertical adjustment is provided by mounting the upper leaf of each pair on a rocker plate, which can be seen between the top two plates of the frame. The lateral restraining members are stiffened to resist compression as well as tension, so only five such members are needed, as compared with six for the Benioff.

a typical long-period system would have a magnification of about 6 000 at 1 c/s, falling to about 60 at 100 sec period.

In 1950 Willmore [18] discussed the practical limits to the sensitivity of seismographs using direct coupling or galvanometric registration, and concluded that the requirements of a short-period earthquake seismometer could be provided by using a suspended

mass of only a few kilogrammes. Moreover, he noted that the
suspended mass which could be electromagnetically damped by a
given magnet depended on the frequency of the suspension. For a
period of 1 sec, the best available magnets would just about damp
their own weight, so the seismometer was designed by suspending
the magnet, fixing the coil to the case and minimizing the weight
of the rest of the structure (Fig. 11). In consequence, it was found
possible to produce a completely sealed instrument weighing 21 lb

Fig. 12. Interior of S.I.E. portable geophone (Southwestern Industrial Electronics).

with almost half the total weight in the suspended mass. The
instrument can drive a $\frac{1}{4}$ sec galvanometer to yield a maximum
magnification of about 300 000, which is adequate for short-period
recording under all except the most extremely quiet conditions.
The instrument is not large enough to drive a very long-period
galvanometer hard enough to show up the microseismic background, but galvanometers up to 20 sec period can be used, and
give good records of P and S waves from teleseisms.

At the upper end of the frequency range we find the small geo-
phones used in geophysical prospecting, most of which have

natural periods of about 15 c/s. At these frequencies the suspended mass becomes much smaller than the magnet, and usually consists simply of a coil and a supporting structure carried on a pair of flat springs (Fig. 12). The seismometers are normally transformer-coupled into vacuum-tube amplifiers or fed directly into transistors, and, in view of the extremely small amounts of power which can be detected by such amplifiers, the seismometers themselves can be made extremely small.

The McComb–Romberg seismograph,[12] [14] the essential feature of which is a viscous link between the pendulum and the indicator, is illustrated in Fig. 13.

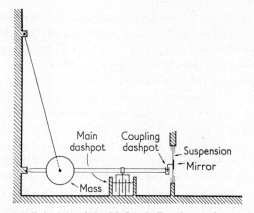

Fig. 13. Principle of the McComb–Romberg seismograph.

To develop the theory of this instrument, we let L_1 be the distance between the coupling unit and the pendulum hinge, and let the corresponding distance for the indicator be l_1. If the rotations of the pendulum and the indicator are ϕ and θ respectively, then the relative velocity between the two sections of the coupling unit is $\{L_1(d\phi/dt) - l_1(d\theta/dt)\}$. The equations of motion for the pendulum and the indicator can then be written in the form

$$K\frac{d^2\phi}{dt^2} + D\frac{d\phi}{dt} + U\phi = L\,M\frac{d^2X}{dt^2} - G\left(L_1\frac{d\phi}{dt} - l_1\frac{d\theta}{dt}\right) \quad (48)$$

and

$$k\frac{d^2\theta}{dt^2} + d\frac{d\theta}{dt} + u\theta = g\left(L_1\frac{d\phi}{dt} - l_1\frac{d\theta}{dt}\right) \quad (49)$$

where G and g are now the moments of the forces acting on the pendulum and the indicator respectively for unit relative velocity between the elements of the viscous link, and the other symbols have the same significance as those used in equations 8 and 9. These equations can be reduced to the same form as those for an electromagnetic instrument with an open shunt, so that the theory requires no further discussion. In practice, the viscous coupling achieves the stability of zero, which is one of the virtues of electro-magnetic instruments, but the principle does not offer any great economy in the inertia of the moving parts. Viscous coupling, therefore, does not enable very high magnifications to be obtained, and is seldom used in modern observatories.

The increasing use of electronic amplifiers in seismology is now making almost unlimited power available for driving the indicator, and has thereby initiated a trend away from photographic record-ing towards systems which write with a stylus or pen. This trend is making seismograph stations more convenient to operate, but the electronic instruments have not yet increased the range of available response characteristics significantly. In terms of the preceding theory most of the electronic instruments can be divided between those which use displacement transducers directly attached to the seismometer boom and those which use photo-electric amplifiers to detect the movements of a galvanometer spot. In either case the response can be reduced to that of a direct-coupled or electromagnetic seismograph, multiplied by the overall response characteristic of the amplifier and the final indicator.

IV. SEISMOGRAPHS MEASURING STRESS OR STRAIN

The ability of pendulum seismographs to provide a wide range of response characteristics from a relatively compact installation has given them a pre-eminent position in earthquake seismology, but there are two other instruments which have established them-selves for special purposes. These are the pressure-sensitive 'hydro-phone' and the strain seismometer respectively.

The use of hydrophones in seismology depends on the fact that any vertical movement of the bottom of a lake or ocean will set up pressure waves in the water, in much the same way as though the water was just another layer of rock. In deep water it may be quite impracticable to place a seismograph on the bottom, so that measurements in the water may provide the only possible method of working.

The pressure, p, at any point in deep water is related to the partical velocity v in a train of plane waves by the relation

$$p = \rho c v \qquad (50)$$

where c is the velocity of sound in water and ρ is the density. In principle, one could consider the use of a seismograph, mounted in a case of neutral buoyancy, to measure the movements of the water directly, but it is not practicable to attach a cable to such an object without shaking it to a prohibitive extent. It is therefore easier to measure pressure changes in the water than to attempt to measure velocity, and, in fact, the detection level of a hydrophone in the ocean is quite comparable to that of a seismograph on the bottom.

The frequency response of a hydrophone to incoming seismic waves is complicated by the interference between waves rising from the bottom and those which are reflected, with reversal of phase, from the free surface. For sinusoidal waves of wavelength λ, approaching the surface at an angle e with the vertical, the interference produces pressure nodes at the surface, and at multiples of the depth of $\frac{1}{2}(\lambda/\cos e)$. The energy in ordinary refracted waves is quite widely distributed over the frequency range, so that a few dips in the response curve of the detecting system can often be tolerated. A fairly satisfactory response will therefore be obtained if the hydrophone is at a depth of at least one-quarter of the longest wavelength which is to be recorded. If the depth of the hydrophone is only a small fraction of a wavelength the pressure which corresponds to a given particle velocity is attenuated in proportion to the wavelength, and a hydrophone of constant pressure sensitivity will approximate to the response of an accelerometer in the water, rather than a velocity meter.

The Benioff strain seismograph [2] consists of a long boom, anchored to the ground at one end, and fitted with a device for detecting movements of the other end relative to the ground (see Fig. 14). For incoming longitudinal waves which are long in

comparison with the boom, the displacement of the free end of
the bar relative to the ground beneath it is

$$Y_L = -\frac{L}{c} \cos^2 a \frac{\partial X}{\partial t} \tag{51}$$

where L is the length of the boom, c is the apparent wave velocity
along the surface, X is the particle displacement in the ground and

Fig. 14. Transducer end of a Benioff strain seismograph. The boom can be
seen leading away to the right (Benioff, Academic Press Inc.).

a is the angle between the boom and the direction of propagation
of the waves. In the case of transverse waves the response is

$$Y_T = \frac{L}{c} \sin a \cos a \frac{\partial X}{\partial t} \tag{52}$$

If two strain seismometers are oriented at right angles the sum
of the response of the two instruments for longitudinal waves is

$$Y_{L1} + Y_{L2} = -\frac{L}{c} \frac{\partial X}{\partial t} \left[\cos^2 a + \cos^2 \left(\frac{\pi}{2} - a \right) \right]$$
$$= -\frac{L}{c} \frac{\partial X}{\partial t} \tag{53}$$

and is therefore independent of the direction of approach. For transverse waves the two instruments respond with equal amplitude and opposite phase, so that the sum of the two outputs vanishes. The significance of this result may be better appreciated if it is realized that the pair of strain detectors responds to changes in the area of an element of the earth's surface, without being affected by changes of shape.

We see from equations 51 and 52 that the displacement of the free end of the boom is proportional to the particle velocity in the ground for all waves which are long in comparison with the boom. If a velocity transducer is fitted to the end of the boom its output is proportional to the particle acceleration in the ground, and a galvanometer coil connected to the transducer will experience a couple proportional to this acceleration. In consequence, the system will behave like a direct-coupled seismograph, having the same period and damping as the galvanometer.

V. THE FURTHER DEVELOPMENT OF SEISMOMETRY

In many fields of seismometry it is clear that the principles are fully understood, and that instruments working up to theoretical limitations are already in existence. Thus, seismographs can be constructed with sufficient sensitivity to reveal the background at all frequencies from some hundreds of cycles per second down to those of long-period tidal forces, and usually the cost of such instruments is not large in relation to the cost of installing them in a suitably quiet environment.

Given that improvements in the detection of earth movements are limited by noise rather than by the availability of detectors, we see that the chief improvements which can arise are in filtering the output of a single detector, or in methods of compounding the outputs from arrays of detectors in such a way that desired signals are added in phase and the noise components at random.

In the field of recording the use of electronic amplifiers is stimulating a return to pen or stylus recording, in preference to the photographic method. Modern communication techniques also permit remote recording, so that the outputs of a number of widely spaced seismographs can be recorded side by side on a single strip, thereby facilitating comparison between records and reducing the difficulty and expense of providing a uniform time scale for all instruments.[8] In the U.S.S.R. strip records are also used to display the outputs of sets of seismographs, mounted with their axes spaced around the surface of a cone. By considering the phase and amplitude relations between the traces it is possible to determine the character of the wave motion and its direction of approach.[7]

In all of the systems which have been discussed the final record is in the form of a line drawn on paper or film. Such records are very convenient for rapid visual inspection, but it is not at all clear that visual inspection will be the chief research technique of future seismologists. Thus, if sharply filtered information is required the alternatives are to record the output of a separate seismograph for each frequency band or to record a wide range of frequencies and to filter out the desired information when the records are interpreted. The latter alternative is much more economical in terms of instrumentation and the storage of records. In compounding traces it is desirable to be able to adjust the phase relations between outputs of the different instruments, and this is not possible if the output has to be recorded immediately in the form of a conventional seismogram. Finally, the detailed interpretation of complex waveforms (such as the dispersion patterns of surface waves) has reached the stage at which the data are best handled by electronic computers, and the task of providing such data by making point-by-point measurements on a conventional seismogram is extremely laborious.

All these potential requirements suggest that conventional seismograms may be supplemented to an increasing extent by analogue or digital records, from which information can be played back and manipulated mechanically. Considerable progress in this direction has been made by the geophysical prospecting industry, where photographic records of both variable-density and variable-area are used, and where magnetic recording methods have been highly developed. In industrial data centres techniques of cross-correlation and auto-correlation are used alongside the ordinary methods of filtering and mixing to enhance desired signals, and ingenious methods of displaying seismic reflection data in the form of geological profiles have been worked out.

Earthquake seismologists have lagged far behind the prospecting industry in their techniques of recording and interpretation, partly through lack of resources and partly because their requirements are much more stringent. Earthquake waves cover a range of period of more than 1000 : 1 (say from a few tenths of a second to a few hundred seconds) and the amplitude range of usable signals is of the order of 1000 : 1 at any one frequency. When the variation of the expected amplitude range with frequency is considered it becomes clear that the frequency characteristics of the detector will have to be carefully chosen if the information is to be stored on a single record, even if the dynamic range of the recording medium is as high as 60 or 70 dB. A further difficulty lies in the requirement for continuous recording, for the information which can be stored in a given volume of recording material is limited, and the high standards required may involve heavy expenditure on material and storage space. Despite the difficulties, a few organizations throughout the world have started to experiment with such recording methods. Probably the early attempts will have to compromise on fidelity or bandwidth, but it seems clear that this is the field in which the next major advances of seismometry will occur.

References

1. Benioff, H. 'A new vertical seismograph.' *Bull. seismol. Soc. Amer.* **22**, 155 (1932).
2. Benioff, H. 'A linear strain seismograph.' *Bull. seismol. Soc. Amer.* **25**, 283 (1935).
3. Chakrabarty, S. K. 'Response characteristics of electromagnetic seismometers and their dependence on instrumental constants.' *Bull. seismol. Soc. Amer.* **39**, 205 (1949).
4. Coulomb, J. 'Séismométrie.' in *Handbuch der Physik*, Vol. **47**, p. 24. Springer, Berlin, 1956.
5. Eaton, J. P. 'Theory of the electromagnetic seismograph.' *Bull. seismol. Soc. Amer.* **47**, 37 (1957).
6. Galitzin, B. *Vorlesungen über Seismometrie*. Deutsche Bearbeitung, Teubner, Leipzig, 1914.
7. Gamburzev, G. A. 'On some new methods of seismological research.' *Trav. sci. Sect. Séism. Un. géod. int.*, ser. A, **19**, 373 (1956).
8. Gane, P. G. Logie, H. J. and Stephen, J. H. 'Triggered teleseismic recording equipment.' *Bull. seismol. Soc. Amer.* **39**, 117 (1949).
9. Grenet, G. and Coulomb, J. 'Nouveaux principes de construction des séismographes électromagnétiques.' *Ann. Phys., Paris*, sér. 11, **3**, 321 (1935).

10. Grenet, G. 'Les characteristiques de séismographes électromagnétiques.' *Ann. Géophys.* **8**, 328 (1952).
11. La Coste, L. 'A simplification in the conditions for the zero-length spring seismograph.' *Bull. seismol. Soc. Amer.* **25**, 176 (1935).
12. McComb, H. E. 'A tilt-compensation seismometer.' *Bull. seismol. Soc. Amer.* **21**, 25 (1931).
13. Murphy, L. M., Wilson, R. M., Burgess, L. R. and Pearce, T. H. 'Response curves of an electromagnetic seismograph by sine-wave simulator method.' *Bull. seismol. Soc. Amer.* **44**, 7 (1954).
14. Romberg, A. 'Theory of a non-tilt seismograph.' *Bull. seismol. Soc. Amer.* **9**, 135 (1919).
15. Sparks, N. R. and Hawley, P. F. 'Maximum electromagnetic damping of a reluctance s eismometer.' *Geophysics.* **4**, 1 (1939).
16. Washburn, H. W. 'Experimental determination of the transient characteristics of seismograph apparatus.' *Geophysics.* **2**, 243 (1937).
17. Wenner, F. 'A new seismometer equipped for electromagnetic damping and electromagnetic and optical magnification.' *Bur. Stand. J. Res., Wash.* **2**, 963 (1929).
18. Willmore, P. L. 'Theory and design of two types of portable seismograph.' *Mon. Not. R. astr. Soc. Geoph. Suppl.* **6**, 129 (1950).
19. Willmore, P. L. 'The application of the Maxwell impedance bridge to the calibration of electromagnetic seismographs.' *Bull. seismol. Soc. Amer.* **49**, 99 (1959).

EARTH CURRENTS

G. D. GARLAND, *University of Alberta, Canada*

CONTENTS

I. INTRODUCTION

Electric currents flow continuously in the earth as the result of a number of causes, both natural and artificial. For example, the oxidation of certain metallic minerals produces chemical differences in potential in the region around the metallic bodies, and this phenomenon has been used as a method of geophysical exploration. However, in this chapter we shall deal only with those currents which are on a sufficient scale to be useful in the study of the earth as a whole, and the source of virtually all of these is electromagnetic induction.

Earth currents were recognized early in the history of telegraphy, when undesired currents were observed in ground-return circuits. The first exposition of them is generally attributed to Barlow.[1] Towards the end of the nineteenth century, measuring systems for earth currents became part of the regular recording equipment of certain magnetic observatories. Since that time, the number of observing stations has varied, but fairly long sequences of observations are available. Earlier works on the subject were concerned chiefly with finding an explanation for the phenomenon, through statistical correlations of the intensity of the currents with other variables. In recent years the aim has been to use the measurements to study the internal conductivity distribution of the earth, or the primary sources of the disturbance, which are now known to be external. As in other fields of geophysics, a good part of the stimulation for the first problem came from the desire for commercial application of the measurements in exploration for mineral-bearing structures.

As much of the instrumentation required for the measurement of earth currents is quite straightforward, the emphasis in the following sections will be on the general instrumental requirements for specific applications, rather than on technical details. Also, since there is still an uncertainty as to the usefulness of earth-current measurements, a discussion will be given of a number of possible uses in the study of the earth, even though these are not yet fully developed. It is hoped, of course, that this will stimulate research along these lines. While a number of the techniques are taken from the work of applied geophysicists, these are included only to the extent of their usefulness in the study of the earth as a whole, or major portions thereof.

II. MEASUREMENT OF EARTH CURRENTS

1. General Principles

The quantity actually measured in earth-current investigations is an electrical potential gradient along the earth's surface, which is equivalent to the tangential electric field intensity in the direction of measurement. It is usual to measure the gradients in two perpendicular directions, north–south and east–west. The gradients involved are normally measured in units of millivolts per kilometre, and an accuracy of one millivolt per kilometre (mV/km) is desirable. It is convenient that 1 mV/km is equivalent to a potential difference of 1 e.m.u./cm. In principle, all that is required therefore is a recording of the difference in potential between electrodes placed in the earth some distance apart, at the ends of the perpendicular lines. There are practical difficulties to measuring the potential differences to a greater precision than 1 mV, so that lines approaching 1 km in length are desirable. Very much longer lines have been used at some permanent establishments, such as the 262-km line at Berlin, but the additional precision in the gradient measurement is obtained at the expense of averaging the intensity of the field over the longer distance.

Difficulties which arise are due chiefly to potentials which are set up at the electrodes themselves, as will be discussed in the next section. It will be assumed that any measurements are made in areas which are completely free from artificial disturbances, such as ground-return electrical systems. Then, apart from the electrodes and recording instrument, the chief requirement is for well-insulated cables connecting the electrodes to the recorder. In theory, the cables should be located close to the ground surface, to avoid induction by time-variations of the magnetic field in the loop formed by cable and earth. However, it is easy to show that this effect is not likely to be serious for lines strung on poles for a distance of 1 km, except for periods much less than 1 sec.

T

2. Electrodes

Whenever a metal stake is driven into the ground, a potential is set up between the metal and the electrolytic solutions in the earth. While this effect would not preclude the measurement of potential differences between two points in the earth's surface if identical conditions existed at each electrode, in fact the conditions may be quite different. There will thus be an apparent potential difference because of differing contact potentials.

The difference in potential between a metal and a solution is given by

$$E = (RT/Fn) \ln (P/p) \qquad (1)$$

where R is the gas constant, T the absolute temperature, F Faraday's constant, n the valency of the metal, P the solution pressure of the metal for the metal for the particular solution and p is the osmotic pressure of the ions in solution. For two identical metal electrodes in solutions of different ion pressures p_1 and p_2 the difference in potential between them depends on $\ln (p_2/p_1)$. Moderate differences in solution pressure can lead to differences in potential of several millivolts, as can be seen by substituting numerical values in equation 1. The dependence of contact potential on temperature is also noteworthy.

With regard to the choice of metal for electrodes, it is desirable that the metal be one for which the electromotive force from the metal to a solution of its salt be small. For common metals in normal solutions typical values are:

Al	+0·22 V	Pb	−0·10 V
Cd	+0·19 V	Cu	−0·60 V
Fe	+0·06 V	Ag	−1·01 V

The table suggests iron and lead as the most suitable metals, and of these lead has been the most widely used.

To overcome the difficulties encountered with metal electrodes in direct contact with the earth, use has been made of 'non-polarizing' or 'reversible' electrodes, especially in temporary installations. In these the cables are connected to a rod, usually copper, immersed in a saturated solution of a salt of the metal, usually copper sulphate, contained in a pot of unglazed porcelain. Electrical contact with the earth is made by the solution diffusing through the pot into the ground. While conditions of concentration at the metal rods are constant with these electrodes, they do not completely solve the problem. Differences in potential between the metal and the earth still vary with temperature and with the rate of diffusion of the solution into the soil. After long periods of use in a fixed location the properties of the soil in the vicinity of the pots change as a result of solution infiltration.

For long-term stability, freedom from temperature effects and ease of maintenance, electrodes of a suitable metal, such as lead, buried several feet below the surface are probably most effective. The character of the soil should be as nearly identical as possible at each electrode site.

The contact resistance between electrode and earth depends on the surface area of the electrode and on the nature of the soil, especially its moisture content. As it is desirable to keep this resistance as low as possible, the form of the electrode should be one that maximizes the area of contact. Grids or networks of wires have been used with success. As the cables joining the electrodes to the recording instrument will generally be copper, some care must be taken with the joint between cable and electrode. The copper should not make contact with the soil, and the joints at each electrode should be protected from temperature changes, to avoid thermoelectric effects.

3. Recording Instruments

Both potentiometers and current-measuring instruments have been used in earth-current observations. Potentiometers have the advantage that no current is drawn from the earth when the system is balanced, so that measurements are independent of electrode resistance. In some of the older installations a single multiple-point potentiometer was used for both components, so that records consisted of a series of intermittent measurements. It is obviously desirable to have a continuously recording instrument available for each component. The chief disadvantage of potentiometers is their appreciable response time, which makes the registration of higher-frequency events difficult. A full-scale travel time of 1 sec for the recorder is about the best that can be done. Current-measuring instruments, such as reflecting galvanometers, can of course be designed to provide more faithful recording of rapid fluctuations. In this case the resistance in the circuit must be high enough to ensure that the current system in the ground is not distorted, and to make changes in electrode resistance negligible. A series resistance of the order of 1 megaohm is usual, and if electrode contact resistances can be kept below 1000 ohms changes in the latter values will be completely negligible. For lines about 1 km long the galvanometer record must be readable to 10^{-9} A if potential gradients of 1 mV/km are to be recorded.

The paper speed of the recorder is chosen to be appropriate for the frequency of events of interest. In permanent observatories speeds of a few centimetres per hour are usual. However, with recent interest in short-period variations, much higher recording speeds are coming into use. It will be shown below that frequency analysis of the records is required for some methods of interpretation, and for this reason, as well as for other advantages, magnetic-tape recording will undoubtedly come to play an important part in earth-current measurements. With potential differences of the order of millivolts it is not difficult to amplify the signals over a wide range of frequencies, and to record these magnetically by amplitude- or frequency-modulation.

4. Earth Resistivities

To convert the measured potential gradient or electric-field intensity E into a current density i, the value of the resistivity ρ of the earth materials in the vicinity of the observing station must be known, for substitution in the relation

$$i = E/\rho \qquad (2)$$

A good deal of early investigations into the measurement of earth resistivities were made for this purpose,[30] but the techniques have since been developed into methods of applied geophysics and are well covered in works on that subject. The basic principle is to apply artificially generated current to the earth at two points, and to measure the potential drop between two other points. An apparent resistivity is obtained from measurements of the potential drop and current, when the geometrical relations of the four electrode positions are known. As the electrode spacing is increased, the effect of material at greater and greater depth becomes significant, and the aim is to deduce true resistivity as a function of depth from the form of the curve of apparent resistivity against spacing. The interpretation leads to fairly definite values if the structure is simple and composed of horizontal layers.[27]

Important as the value of near-surface resistivity is, it will be shown later that the natural earth currents may be affected by changes in electrical properties at greater depths than can be conveniently studied by methods using artificial currents. An analysis using the natural currents themselves, with the associated magnetic variations, is more effective for these depths.

III. GENERAL NATURE OF EARTH-CURRENT RECORDS

1. Long-period Components

While it would be desirable to know if events with periods longer than 24 h occur on earth-current records, the phenomenon of electrode contact potential makes this a very difficult problem. No certain evidence of a long-period or unidirectional current has been presented. For the purpose of studying diurnal variation or shorter-period phenomena, the instantaneous values are stated relative to daily mean potential difference across the lines. Indeed, the steady potential difference due to electrode polarizations may be eliminated by applying a counter-potential in series with the recorder, or by placing a condenser in the circuit in the case of current measurements.

2. Diurnal Variation

Normally two components, north–south and east–west, of the potential gradients are measured. It is convenient to represent the disturbance at any instant as the vector sum of these components and to plot the magnitude and azimuth of this vector for different hours of the day. The disturbance vector is usually found to vary rather irregularly with time, especially in high altitudes, but at most stations one azimuth is characteristic, and the end of the vector may be thought of as describing an elongated ellipse (Fig. 1). If the directions of the vectors at any given time of day are plotted for all stations on a map of the world, an approximation to the world-wide system of currents is obtained. Syntheses of this type were constructed by Gish [10] some years ago, but the number of stations available to him, twelve, was hardly sufficient to provide an accurate picture. The current system suggested by Gish (Fig. 2) consisted of eight current whorls, more or less symmetrical with respect to the equator. These appeared to remain fixed in space, as the earth rotated through them. At the

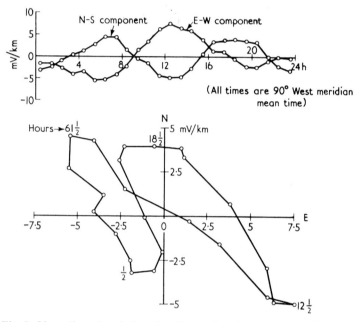

Fig. 1. Mean diurnal variation of north–south and east–west earth-current components, and hodograph of total vector, Chesterfield Inlet, 1932–33, after Currie.[9]

present time there are about 40 earth-current observatories operating and another 20 projected,[13] but the distribution is by no means uniform over the globe. It is still not possible to construct in detail the world-wide system of currents as a function of time of day.

3. Short-period Fluctuations

A correlation between disturbances of short periods (minutes or seconds) on earth-current records and magnetic activity has long been recognized. A statistical treatment of earth-current records shows the well-known 27-day recurrence feature of magnetic dis-

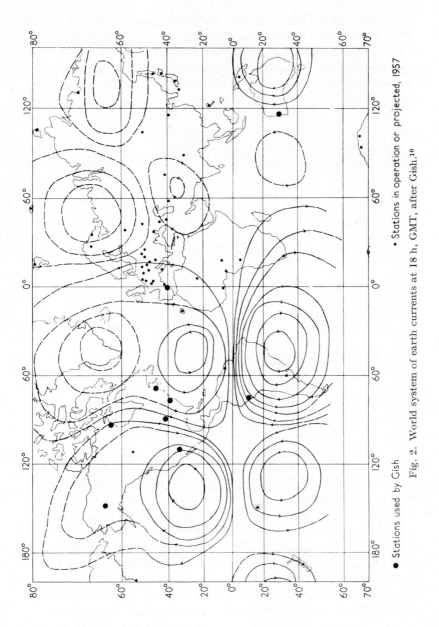

Fig. 2. World system of earth currents at 18 h, GMT, after Gish.[10]

• Stations in operation or projected, 1957

● Stations used by Gish

turbance.[7] What has only recently been appreciated is the great wealth of very-short-period activity, and the remarkable areal uniformity of these high-frequency events. In most of the older installations the low paper speed and the filtering effects of the recording instruments precluded the observing of fluctuations with periods much below 1 min. With modern instruments, variations with periods as low as 0·3 sec are frequently observed. An example of an earth-current record made on a magnetically disturbed day is shown in Fig. 3.

The question of the area over which a short-period disturbance

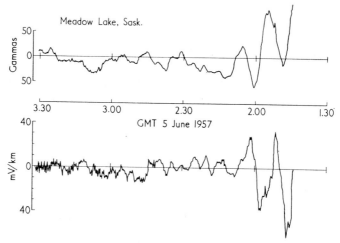

Fig. 3. East–west magnetic (upper) and north–south earth-current records at Meadow Lake, Saskatchewan (Lat. 54° 08′ Long. 108° 26′).

can be observed will not be completely answered until more observatories equipped with suitable instruments are operating. Among the first studies of areal uniformity was that of Schlumberger and Kunetz,[23] who made simultaneous measurements in France and Madagascar while investigating the use of earth currents as a method of geophysical prospecting (see Section V–3–C below). Remarkable similarities were obtained, with events of about 30 sec period, between the two stations. However, a study of the disturbance vector diagrams, in this as in similar cases, shows much less similarity. At times the current may be flowing in similar azimuths at the two stations while at other times the direction of current flow will be quite different. As both the location of the observer relative to the source of the disturbance and the local conductivity in the earth influence the observations, it is perhaps remarkable that any similarity can be obtained over long distances.

4. Classification of Disturbance Types

Magneticians have adopted a classification of types of activity for magnetographs,[13] and the same symbols may be conveniently used to describe the characteristics of earth-current records.

Some of the more important types of events, with their designations, are:

b: an isolated 'bay' type disturbance, with period of about 20 min.
ssc: a sudden impulse followed by increased activity.
si: a sudden impulse during a storm.
pc: pulsations of period from 10 to 40 sec, lasting for several hours.
pt: a series of trains of oscillations, each train of about 10 to 20 min duration.

There are several other special categories. The system is based on the character of the records, rather than on hypotheses of the nature of the sources in each case, and is useful chiefly for reporting this character when it is not convenient to reproduce a complete record.

5. Vertical Earth Currents

In the older literature [20] a number of examples were given of consistent differences in potential between surface electrodes at different elevations. The electrode at the lower elevation was characteristically positive relative to the upper electrode, so that current appeared to flow upward. These apparent vertical currents measured on sloping surfaces did not show variations which correlated with the horizontal components or with magnetic activity, and in all probability the differences in potential were due largely to electrode effects.

More conclusive evidence for a vertical component of earth-current flow comes from an installation made by the University of Alberta in an abandoned oil well at Calmar, near Edmonton, Alberta. Two lead electrodes were placed in the hole at depths of 800 and 3 800 ft, and connected to the surface by insulated cables. Measurements of the potential difference between them, or between one and the surface, have been recorded for about one year. In addition, two components of horizontal currents have been recorded at the site during shorter intervals. There is no question that, during periods of magnetic activity, short-period variations

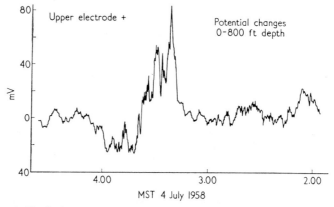

Fig. 4. Vertical component potential gradient variations recorded at Calmar, near Edmonton, Alberta.

in the vertical potential activity occur (Fig. 4). Disturbances with periods from a few seconds to several minutes have been observed. The maximum changes are observed between the surface and the electrode at 800 ft depth, and these have amounted in amplitude to 100 mV across that distance. At the location the dominant direction of horizontal flow is east–west, but the vertical effects appear correlated with the north–south component, as though the current sheet were tilted when flowing in certain azimuths. Such tilting could result from inhomogeneity in conductivity, as will be discussed below, but the variation with depth of the vertical component, especially near the surface, is not yet clear. The normal component of current density across the earth/air boundary must be continuous, and the vertical current density just below the surface must be that given by atmospheric electricity measurements. Typical values for the atmosphere just above the earth's surface are 1 V/cm for the potential gradient, and 6×10^{15} ohm cm for the resistivity. These indicate a downward current density of 2×10^{-16} A/cm². On the other hand, the alternating component current density suggested by the Calmar observations is 2×10^{-10} A/cm². More observations on the three-dimensional distribution of current lines within the earth are seriously needed.

IV. ELECTROMAGNETIC INDUCTION IN THE EARTH

1. The Problems

An evaluation of the place of earth-current measurements in the study of the earth's interior and of the sources of magnetic disturbances is not possible without reference to the theory of electromagnetic induction. The earth-current measurements provide us with the tangential component of the disturbance electric field at the earth's surfaces. Normally, measurements of the variation of the magnetic components will be available at the same location. The purpose of most analyses of these observations is to determine electrical conductivity as a function of position within the earth. At the same time, it is desirable to obtain information on the primary causes of the disturbance, which are known to be external to the earth.

It is convenient to think of the problem in two parts. For the determination of the general variation in conductivity with depth, relatively long-period disturbances (periods of 24 h or more) are studied on a world-wide scale. The problem is then one of electromagnetic induction in a sphere, and this problem has been solved for various regular variations of conductivity with position. In other cases it may be desired to determine in more detail the variations in conductivity within a local area. For these, an analysis of the higher-frequency events is required, and for mathematical convenience in determining the effects of less regular conductivity variations the earth's surface is taken as an infinite horizontal plane.

Both problems have been the subject of a number of investigations, and the developments will only be outlined here.

2. Electromagnetic Induction in a Sphere

The problem of induction of currents in a uniform sphere was studied by Lamb.[15] Extensions to spheres of non-uniform conductivity and to cases of aperiodic inducing fields have been made by Lahiri and Price.[14]

It is usual to start with Maxwell's equations and to work in electromagnetic units. We then have

$$\text{curl } \mathbf{E} = -\dot{\mathbf{B}} \qquad \text{div } \mathbf{B} = 0 \qquad (3)$$
$$\text{curl } \mathbf{H} = 4\pi\mathbf{c} + \dot{\mathbf{D}} \qquad \text{div } \mathbf{D} = 4\pi\rho$$

where $\mathbf{E}$ and $\mathbf{H}$ are electric and magnetic field intensities, $\mathbf{D}$ and $\mathbf{B}$ electric and magnetic inductions, $\mathbf{c}$ is the conduction current density and ρ is the space-charge density.

For an isotropic medium

$$\mathbf{D} = \epsilon\mathbf{E} \qquad \mathbf{B} = \mu\mathbf{H} \qquad \mathbf{c} = \kappa\mathbf{E} \qquad (4)$$

where ϵ, μ and κ are respectively the dielectric constant, magnetic permeability and electrical conductivity.

In many problems it is convenient to introduce a vector potential $\mathbf{A}$ given by

$$\text{curl } \mathbf{A} = \mathbf{B} \qquad (5)$$

The vector $\mathbf{A}$ may have added to it the gradient of a scalar field, and, following Lahiri and Price, we take

$$\mathbf{A}_1 = \mathbf{A} + \text{grad } \psi \qquad (6)$$

where ψ is the time rate of change of the potential of the instantaneous charge distribution. That is

$$\psi = \dot{\phi}, \text{ where } \mathbf{E} = -\text{grad } \phi$$

Then
$$\mathbf{E} = -\dot{\mathbf{A}}_1 \qquad (7)$$

Solutions of the field equations are simplified if the displacement current, $\dot{\mathbf{D}}/4\pi$, can be neglected. This will be so if $\dot{\mathbf{D}}$ is small compared to $4\pi\mathbf{c}$ or to curl $\mathbf{H}$. There is usually no question that $\dot{\mathbf{D}}$ will be negligible relative to $4\pi\mathbf{c}$ in a conductor, but in a dielectric the magnitude of curl $\mathbf{H}$ must be examined. Now curl $\mathbf{H}$ is of order $\mathbf{H}/L$, where L is a typical dimension. The magnetic rate vector $\dot{\mathbf{H}}$ is of order $\mathbf{E}/\mu L$, so that, for oscillatory fields, the condition is satisfied if the period

$$T \gg (\epsilon\mu)^{\frac{1}{2}}L$$

But the electromagnetic wave velocity c is given by

$$c = (\epsilon\mu)^{-\frac{1}{2}}$$

so that T is to be large compared to the time of travel across the medium. For the earth, this is about $0\cdot03$ sec, and we shall therefore neglect the displacement current for periods much longer than this.

In the present problem the aim is to obtain solutions for the current density within, and field intensities on, a spherical earth in which the conductivity is variable. It is usually sufficient, in the spherical problem, to take the conductivity as a function of radius (r) only, and to take ϵ and μ constant. In this case, and with the neglect of displacement currents, the equations for $\mathbf{A}_1$ and c are

$$\text{div } \mathbf{A}_1 = - \nabla^2\psi \tag{8}$$

$$\nabla^2\psi = - \mathbf{c} \cdot \text{grad } (1/\kappa) = -4\pi\rho/\epsilon \tag{9}$$

$$\nabla^2\mathbf{A}_1 + \text{grad } \nabla^2\psi = 4\pi\kappa\mu\dot{\mathbf{A}}_1 \tag{10}$$

The boundary conditions are that the normal component of $\mathbf{B}$, the tangential components of $\mathbf{E}$ and $\mathbf{H}$, and the scalar ϕ are continuous. The normal component of $\mathbf{E}$, and therefore of $\mathbf{A}_1$, must vanish at the boundary.

We consider a sphere of radius a and conductivity $\kappa = \kappa(p)$, where $p = r/a$. A solution of equation 10 is of the form

$$\mathbf{A}_1 = \mathbf{r} \times \text{grad } u$$

where u is a function of position given by

$$\nabla^2 u = 4\pi\kappa\mu\dot{u} \tag{11}$$

The solution of the latter equation is a sum of terms of the form

$$u_n = a_0 f_n(t,p)S_n \tag{12}$$

where S_n is a surface spherical harmonic of degree n, referred to a sphere of radius a_0, and $f_n(t,p)$ satisfies

$$\frac{\partial}{\partial p}\left(p^2 \frac{\partial f_n}{\partial p} \right) = \left\{ n(n+1) + 4\pi\mu a^2 p^2 \kappa(p)\partial/\partial p \right\} f_n \tag{13}$$

Outside the surface of the sphere, curl $\mathbf{H} = 0$, and $\mathbf{H}$ is derivable from a potential Ω, which may be expressed as a sum of terms of the form

$$\Omega_n = a_0\{e_n(t)[qp]^n + i_n(t)[qp]^{n-1}\}S_n \tag{14}$$

where $q = a/a_0$. The functions $e_n(t)$ and $i_n(t)$ represent the contributions to the observed field of external and internal origin.

Terms in A_1 and Ω are related by

$$\text{curl } A_{1n} = -\text{grad } \Omega_n \qquad (15)$$

so that

$$A_{1n} = a_0(r \times \text{grad } S_n)\left\{\frac{(qp)^n}{n+1}\ e_n(t) - \frac{(qp)^{-n-1}}{n}\ i_n(t)\right\} \qquad (16)$$

When $p = 1$, at the spherical surface, the boundary conditions require

$$f_n(t,1) = q^n/(n+1)\ e_n(t) - q^{-n-1}/n\ i_n(t) \qquad (17)$$

and

$$f_n(t,1) + [\partial/\partial p f_n(t,p)]_{p=1} = \mu\{q^n\ e_n(t) + q^{-n-1}\ i_n(t)\} \qquad (18)$$

In general, the inducing field, and therefore $e_n(t)$, will be known, and the functions $i_n(t)$ and $f_n(t,p)$ are to be found from equations 17 and 18.

The current density within the sphere is given by

$$c = \kappa E = -a_0(r \times \text{grad } S_n)\kappa(p)\partial/\partial t f_n(t,p) \qquad (19)$$

The equations for the determination of the functions $i_n(t)$ and $f_n(t,p)$ are relatively simple if the inducing field is periodic, given, say, by $H \exp iat$, and if κ varies as a power of p. Solutions for aperiodic inducing fields have also been given by Lahiri and Price.[14]

From the point of view of earth currents, the importance of equation 19 is that, in theory, measured values of the surface current density, say, $c_{p=1}$, induced by periodic variations in the magnetic field of external origin, should assist in the determination of $\kappa(p)$. In practice, however, local near-surface variations in conductivity distort the current flow to the extent that this approach is not satisfactory. An attempt to compare measured earth currents with values predicted for the diurnal variation was made some years ago by Chapman and Whitehead.[5] A qualitative agreement only was obtained between the calculated and observed values at Berlin and Ebro. The approach does not appear to have been repeated, no doubt because the internal conductivity variation can be obtained more simply and reliably by analysing the magnetic

variations themselves, and separating $e_n(t)$ and $i_n(t)$ as in equation
14. Comparison of the observed values of $i_n(t)$ with those predicted by equations 13, 17 and 18 for different functions $\kappa(p)$ then
allows possible forms of the latter function to be chosen.

3. Relations between the Electric and Magnetic Fields at a Plane Boundary

For the study of the effects of local differences in conductivity
on the earth currents and magnetic variations, the earth's surface
may be taken as an infinite horizontal plane. As the sources of
disturbances are some distance above this plane, the problem is
one involving the incidence on the surface of electromagnetic
waves from above, and in various forms it has been studied by a
number of authors.[24]

Cagniard [4] investigated the surface values of the electric and
magnetic fields, **E** and **H**, for plane waves incident on a stratified
earth. The earth's surface is taken as the x–y plane, with the z
axis vertically downward. The current flow in the earth is to be
entirely in the x direction, so that the only non-zero component
of **E** is E_x. The disturbance is taken as periodic, with time factor
$\exp(-i\omega t)$. Then Maxwell's equations will be satisfied if in each
layer

$$\partial^2 E_x/\partial z^2 + 4\pi\sigma\omega i E_x = 0 \qquad (20)$$

$$H_y = -i/\omega\partial E_x/\partial z \qquad (21)$$

where σ is the conductivity of the layer.

A solution of equation 20 is

$$E_x = A \exp(a\sigma^{\frac{1}{2}}z) + B \exp(-a\sigma^{\frac{1}{2}}z) \qquad (22)$$

where $a = 2\pi/T^{\frac{1}{2}}(1 - i)$ and A and B are arbitrary constants.
The period of the disturbance is $T = 2\pi/\omega$.

If the earth consists of only one layer of conductivity σ extending to great depth, the constant A must vanish, and we find, for
any value of z,

$$H_y = (2\sigma T)^{\frac{1}{2}} \exp(i\pi/4)E_x \qquad (23)$$

This relation holds for the fields measured just above the surface,
as a result of the continuity of tangential **E** and **H** across the
boundary. In this case the magnetic field is retarded in phase by

an angle $\pi/4$ relative to the electric field, and the conductivity of the earth is given by

$$\sigma = \tfrac{1}{2}T(H_y/E_x)^2 \tag{24}$$

If the earth consists of a surface layer of thickness h and conductivity σ_1, underlain by a uniform substratum of conductivity σ_2, we take

$$E_x = A \exp \{a(\sigma_1)^{\frac{1}{2}}z\} + B \exp \{-a(\sigma_1)^{\frac{1}{2}}z\} \tag{25}$$

$$H_y = \exp (i\pi/4)(2\sigma_1 T)^{\frac{1}{2}}[- A \exp \{a(\sigma_1)^{\frac{1}{2}}z\} + B \exp [- a(\sigma_1)z\}] \tag{26}$$

in the surface layer, and

$$E_x = \exp \{- a(\sigma_2)^{\frac{1}{2}}z\} \tag{27}$$

$$H_y = \exp (i\pi/4)(2\sigma_2 T) \exp \{- a(\sigma_2)^{\frac{1}{2}}z\} \tag{28}$$

in the substratum.

The conditions of continuity at the base of the surface layer then require

$$A = (\sigma_1^{\frac{1}{2}} - \sigma_2^{\frac{1}{2}})/2\sigma_1^{\frac{1}{2}} \exp [- ah(\sigma_1^{\frac{1}{2}} + \sigma_2^{\frac{1}{2}})] \tag{29}$$

$$B = (\sigma_1^{\frac{1}{2}} + \sigma_2^{\frac{1}{2}})/2\sigma_1^{\frac{1}{2}} \exp [ah(\sigma_1^{\frac{1}{2}} - \sigma_2^{\frac{1}{2}})] \tag{30}$$

The fields on the earth's surface can then be written as

$$E_x = M \exp (- i\phi) \tag{31}$$

$$H_y = (2\sigma_1 T)^{\frac{1}{2}}N \exp i(\pi/4 - \psi) \tag{32}$$

where

$$\left.\begin{aligned}
M \cos \phi &= (1/p_1 \cosh h/p_1 + 1/p_2 \sinh h/p_1) \cos h/p_1 \\
M \sin \phi &= (1/p_1 \sinh h/p_1 + 1/p_2 \cosh h/p_1) \sin h/p_1 \\
N \cos \psi &= (1/p_1 \sinh h/p_1 + 1/p_2 \cosh h/p_1) \cos h/p_1 \\
N \sin \psi &= (1/p_1 \cosh h/p_1 + 1/p_2 \sinh h/p_1) \sin h/p_1
\end{aligned}\right\} \tag{33}$$

in which

$$p_1 = (1/2\pi)(T/\sigma_1)^{\frac{1}{2}}, \; p_2 = (1/2\pi)(T/\sigma_2)^{\frac{1}{2}}$$

The quantity p has an important physical significance, in that it is the depth in a uniform medium at which an alternating field of period T is reduced to $1/e$ of its surface amplitude. The equations 33 yield values of the quantities M, N, ϕ and ψ, to be determined in terms of period when the conductivities and depth

of the surface layer are given. The amplitude and phase relations
between the surface electric and magnetic fields are therefore
known. Cagniard [4] has given curves showing how the effects vary
with period, and suggests the simultaneous measurement of E_x
and H_y as a method of geophysical prospecting.

All of the above relationships are developed for the case of a
plane electromagnetic wave propagated vertically downward into
the earth, and the effects of departures from this condition should
be examined. We may expect waves arriving at the earth's surface
at various angles of incidence, from sources which may be loops
or lines of current in the ionosphere. However, the angle of incidence is probably of minor importance, for the high-conductivity
contrast between earth and atmosphere will result in essentially
vertical propagation after the wave enters the earth. The effects
of departure from plane wave conditions have been shown by
Wait [28] to consist of additional terms in the expression for E_x/H_y.
These terms depend on the curvature of the wave surface, being
of the form

$$\tfrac{1}{2}H_y\gamma^2(\partial^2/H_y/\partial y^2 - \partial^2 H_y/\partial x^2 + 2\partial^2 H_x/\partial x \partial y)$$

where $\gamma = i\sigma\mu\omega - \epsilon\mu\omega^2$ is the intrinsic propagation constant in
the earth. The quantity $1/\gamma$ has the dimensions of length and is
characteristically of the order of tens of kilometres for periods of
the order of seconds. The importance of the term will therefore
depend on the variation of the field within these differences, a
factor which will be controlled by the distribution of sources. For
example, the field of a dipole situated 100 km above the earth
would certainly vary appreciably within distances of a few tens
of kilometres along the surface, but there are measurements [29]
which suggest greater uniformity. This would be so if the inducing
sources were lines or sheets of ionospheric current.

The importance of Cagniard's equations is that they suggest a
means of determining conductivity as a function of depth beneath
a station where E_x and H_y are measured. Conversely, they show
how we should expect the ratio between **E** and **H** to vary with
period, at a location where the conductivity layers are horizontal.
In other words, in comparing amplitudes of earth currents at
different stations, or in comparing measured with calculated
values, account must be taken, not only of the surface conductivity

U

but also of the structure, both local and regional, at the sites. The longer the periods of interest, the greater the depth at which a conductivity change can affect the surface measurements.

V. PARTICULAR APPLICATIONS OF EARTH-CURRENT MEASUREMENTS

1. The Diurnal Variation

The older earth-current measurements, made for the most part at magnetic observatories, dealt principally with departures from daily average values of the potential gradients. Mention has already been made of the synthesis of these observations, in magnitude and direction, into world-wide patterns [10] of current flow at different hours of the day, and the theory of the induction of these currents in a spherical earth has been given. While it is unlikely that measurements of the current density at a number of stations would improve significantly our knowledge of the average conductivity variation of the outer 1000 km or so of the earth, beyond the values given by analysis of the magnetic variation alone, it would appear desirable to repeat the analysis of Chapman and Whitehead.[5] As a result of the activities of the International Geophysical Year, many more diurnal variation stations are available, as well as a fair number of earth-current stations. The principal results of such an analysis might be twofold. In the first place, comparison of the measured and predicted values of current density for different stations might indicate important departures from a conductivity function that is radially dependent only in the upper few hundred kilometres of the earth. There is a growing volume of evidence that the upper mantle is less uniform than once thought, and that there may be consistent differences between areas under continents and under oceans. Secondly, components of the measured currents of this order of period which are not the result of induction by external fields might appear in the analysis. While there may well be currents in this category, they are probably of longer period, and will be considered in the next section.

In many ways the recording of variations of diurnal period presents fewer difficulties than the measurements of events with very long or very short periods. For example, problems of both electrode potential variation and the response characteristics of the recorder are less serious. On the other hand, the local conductivity conditions at each station used in the world-wide analysis should be known. This should include near-surface values determined by suitable measurements (Section–II–4), and deeper values determined by analysis of the natural fields themselves after the method of Cagniard. Account would have to be taken of the oceans [19] in stations near the margin of continents and on oceanic islands.

2. Unidirectional or Very-long-period Currents

One of the most intriguing problems of earth-current measurements is the possibility of identifying components with periods very much longer than one day. One possible cause would be the existence of currents in the lower mantle, near the mantle/core boundary. In this case the quantity measured at the surface would be simply that portion of the electric field which has not been screened by the mantle conductivity. Runcorn [21] has suggested that thermal electromotive forces between the mantle and core of the order of 1 V could be produced by reasonable temperature differences. If these electromotive forces vary over the surface of the core as a fourth-order harmonic, direct electric fields of the order of 1 mV/km would exist in the lower mantle. Unless there is an intermediate region in the mantle of higher conductivity, unidirectional fields of the same order could exist at the earth's surface. Direct or very-long-period electric fields, due to other sources near the base of the mantle, may also be present at the surface.

Bullard [3] has given the electric fields to be expected in the outer part of the core, if there is relative motion between the outer part and a more rapidly rotating inner part of the core. If the inner part is thought of as a sphere of radius b rotating in an ambient axial magnetic field $\mathbf{H_0}$, the tangential electric field $\mathbf{E}_\theta$ at a radial distance r and colatitude θ in the outer core is given by

$$\mathbf{E}_\theta = -\tfrac{1}{5}\omega\mathbf{H_0}rb^5(1/r^5 + 3/2a^5)\sin 2\theta \qquad (34)$$

where ω is the relative angular velocity between the parts of the core, and a is the outer radius of the entire core.

At the core boundary the maximum tangential field is, for $b = \tfrac{2}{3}a$,

$$[\mathbf{E}_\theta]_{\substack{r=a \\ \theta=\pi/4}} = -0\cdot25\,\omega\mathbf{H_0} \times 10^8 \text{ e.m.u.} \qquad (35)$$

This electric field is related to the system of currents which sustains a toroidal magnetic field within the core. As representative values, Bullard suggests 4 gauss for $\mathbf{H_0}$ and 1×10^{-10} radians/sec for ω, corresponding to a toroidal field of 40 gauss. These lead to

$$[\mathbf{E}_\theta]_{\substack{r=a \\ \theta=\pi/4}} = -1{\cdot}0 \times 10^{-2} \text{ e.m.u. or mV/km} \qquad (36)$$

Thus, the field, even at the core boundary, is one hundred times smaller than those usually considered measurable and the field at the earth's surface would be smaller again. On the other hand, a toroidal magnetic field much larger than that supposed may exist in the core.

It might be supposed that electric fields are induced within the earth as a whole because of its rotation as a magnetized body, or because of its motion relative to a galaxy magnetic field. In calculations of motional electromotive forces of this type account must be taken of the fact that an observer on the earth is moving with the conductor in which inductive effects are sought.[8] For example, Schlomka and Schenkel [22] have shown that an observer outside, but rotating with, a rotating magnetized sphere would observe an electric field. However, the observed field inside the sphere is zero, and the tangential component of the external field therefore approaches zero at the sphere's surface. Similarly, it appears unlikely that earth-current measurements could contribute to the detection of any external field not recognized in magnetic measurements.

It certainly appears desirable to improve the reliability of earth-current measurements for long-period or direct components. There is, in the literature, no authenticated record of a direct or long-period component in the observations of any earth-current station. The limitation at present, of course, is the contact or electrode potential which was discussed earlier. If electrodes could be designed with contact potentials constant to 1 mV over periods of the order of one year, and used with a line 10 km long, our knowledge of the longer-period components would be greatly improved. Possibly research on the use of more stable ion-exchange materials to replace porous pots or metal electrodes would be useful.

3. Short-period Variations

A. *Introduction*

By a short-period variation is meant any cyclic change in the recorded earth potentials with period considerably less than 24 h. Since frequencies of tens or hundreds of cycles per second can be observed, this definition covers a rather wide range of effects. However, over this range there is a difference in the application of the measurements as compared to the much-longer-period changes discussed above.

The theoretical developments in Section IV suggested that the relationship between the surface electric field and magnetic field is determined by both the nature of the source and the conductivity distribution within the earth. Only if the source is such that the disturbance may be treated as a plane wave as it arrives at the earth is the relationship determined by the conductivity alone. While there is this overlapping effect of two influences, it is convenient to discuss separately applications of the measurements to studies in which one or other factor is of chief interest.

B. *Study of sources of disturbance*

It is proposed here to deal only with those problems in which the earth-current systems themselves make a contribution. A great many studies have been made of the ionospheric current systems required to explain magnetic disturbances, in which only the magnetic field intensities are used. On the other hand, some authors [25] have reported cases in which there is apparently a greater correlation between phenomena, such as auroral displays and short-period earth currents, than between auroras and magnetic records. It would appear that much of the difference in these cases may be in the nature of the recording equipment. While it is relatively easy to obtain current-measuring instruments to record signals with frequencies as high as several hundred cycles per second, until recently magnetic observatories were equipped only with instruments which effectively filtered out the higher-frequency components. Provided that instruments of comparable frequency response are available for both types of measurement, the magnetic records should show the same frequency components during times of disturbance.

There is an application in the study of sources in which earth-current measurements are of use. Several investigators (see Heppner [11]) have attempted to estimate the height of equivalent current lines in the upper atmosphere by comparing vertical and horizontal magnetic disturbance components at groups of stations. The ratio of the disturbance in the two components gives a direction towards the equivalent current line, and observations at two stations, in principle, determine the height of the current. Chapman [6] pointed out that this approach gives erroneous results if the effect of the current induced in the earth is neglected. On the other hand, the magnitude of the induced current depends upon the conductivity in the region of the earth beneath the source. It is therefore desirable that still more detailed information on the conductivity in and beneath the crust be obtained, in the vicinity of magnetic observatories as well as at other sites.

C. Studies of internal conductivity variations

(i) Magneto-telluric measurements. Cagniard,[4] whose developments were followed in Section IV–3, intended the simultaneous measurement of the electric and magnetic fields to form the basis of a method of geophysical exploration, which he called the magneto-telluric method. However, there appear to be several problems in pure geophysics as well to which it would be adaptable.

It has been seen that if the earth were of uniform conductivity measurement of the tangential electric and magnetic fields, in perpendicular directions, would determine this conductivity, provided disturbances could be analysed into harmonic components of known period. In an earth where conductivity is not uniform it is possible to speak of an apparent conductivity as that value which, for a uniform earth, would give the same field ratios. If the conductivity varies with depth only, the value of apparent resistivity measured will vary smoothly with the period of the disturbance from which it is calculated, because of the skin effect. Theoretical curves of apparent conductivity against period have been computed by Cagniard for idealized cases, using equations such as 33 of Section IV–3. These show that depths to discontinuities in conductivity should be obtainable from the shape of the apparent conductivity-period curve.

It remains to note some of the instrumental requirements for

magneto-telluric observations. Since the method depends on accurate measurements of the ratio of an electric to magnetic field
over a range of periods, it is essential that the frequency response
characteristics of both types of measuring instruments be known.
The range of periods used depends on the scale of the problem, but
in investigations of major structural features in the earth's crust
measurements at periods from, say, 1 sec to tens of minutes may
be required. For more local studies in geophysical prospecting,
effects with shorter periods would be utilized. The electric field
would therefore most probably be obtained by using a rapid-
response current recorder rather than a potentiometer. In contrast to the very-long-period observations, electrode potentials are
no particular problem, the only requirement being that they remain relatively constant over the time required for a measurement. The magnetic measurements may present more difficulties,
and it is not possible here to describe all of the methods that have
been attempted. For the very short periods it is possible to use
coils with high-permeability cores, provided that the output of
these, which of course depends on the rate of change of field, is
integrated to give a record of field against time. A sensitivity of
1×10^{-7} gauss at 1 c/s can be obtained with suitable amplification,
but as field changes of 1×10^{-5} gauss (or 1 gamma) must be
measured, coils are difficult to apply at periods greater than
100 sec. For these longer periods, a saturation-core, nuclear-
precession or alkali-vapour magnetometer is more suitable.

It is essential to magneto-telluric observations that disturbances
over the required range of periods exist, and also that they may
be isolated into harmonic components. The labour involved in
analysing a record of only a few minutes duration is very great,
especially if the phase as well as amplitude is required for each
component. It would appear that, if the method is to be widely
used, this analysis must be performed instrumentally. Work is in
progress on the magnetic-tape recording of the fields, and on the
electronic analysis of the records.

The type of problem in pure geophysics to which magneto-
telluric measurements are applicable involves broad scale structures with difference in conductivity from their surroundings.
The determination of depth in a basin of relatively conducting
sedimentary rocks is an obvious example. Studies of the depth to

the base of the crust may be possible, although the difference in conductivity between the crust and the top of the mantle is probably not great. Underwater measurements, to determine the thickness of ocean-floor sediments, are another possibility. The method should certainly be applied at all magnetic and earth-current observatories, to give the conductivity–depth relation in their vicinity.

(ii) *Earth-current measurements with portable instruments.* Considerable use has been made in geophysical exploration of simultaneous measurements of earth-current components at pairs of stations, without reference to associated magnetic variations. The principle [16] is that, provided both stations are within the region of influence of the same disturbance source, the ratio of magnitude of the electric field components will vary as some function of the mean earth resistivities at the two stations. The easiest situation to visualize is that of a relatively conducting superficial layer underlain by a poorly conducting igneous basement. Over an uplift of the basement surface the lines of earth-current flow tend to be crowded together, resulting in increased current density. Thus, even if the near-surface resistivity is uniform, a higher electric field will be measured at a station over the uplift than at one at some distance to the side. The fact that the fields vary with time requires the simultaneous measurements at pairs of stations.

The usual method adopted in prospecting is the measurement of two components of potential gradient at both a base station and a portable field location. Recording galvanometers suitable for resolving disturbances with periods of a few seconds are employed. As has been noted earlier, the disturbance vectors, if plotted at a station in direction as well as magnitude, vary widely in azimuth with time. If a series of disturbance vectors for successive intervals of time is plotted for the base station, and normalized so that the ends of the vectors lie on a circle, it is generally found that the ends of the vectors at the field station, when the same normalizing factor is applied, lie on an ellipse. In other words, regardless of the direction of current flow, each component of electric field at the field station is a linear function of both components at the base. The area of the ellipse traced out at the field station is taken as a measure of the relative effective resistivity at the location. Various examples of structural studies by the method have been given [17] and need not be repeated here. The chief interest is that these examples show the influence of concealed inhomogeneities in conductivity on the earth-current measurements, and these must be kept in mind whenever observations at an observatory are being compared with calculated values. Secondly, there is the possibility, as in the case of magneto-telluric observations, of using this method of applied geophysics to study broader features of continental structure. The difficulty here is that there is a maximum distance between the base and field station for meaningful results. If this distance is exceeded, the effect of location relative to the source of the disturbance becomes a factor in determining the nature of the field at each station. Some measurements have been made at stations several hundred miles apart,[29] and while an effect of major structure could be detected, the observations were not conclusive. In general, the method is most suitable for tracing differences in conductivity within a region of the order of 100 miles in diameter.

(iii) *Areas of extreme differences in conductivity.* In recent years, evidence for remarkably large current concentrations beneath Germany [2] and Japan [18, 19] has been found. Both areas were investigated by analyses of the relatively short-period variations of the magnetic field components, known as bays. These disturbances have periods of the order of 20 min, and therefore have associated with them induced currents penetrating to some hundreds of kilometres into the earth. With the German and Japanese observations, a comparison of the magnitude of the disturbance as measured in different components of the magnetic field shows great differences between magnetic observatories. In Japan, for example, the disturbance in the vertical component at some stations ranges up to 100 per cent of the magnitude of the disturbance in the horizontal component, while at other stations there is a disappearingly small vertical component disturbance. As Rikitake and Yokoyama [19] point out, these variations can only be explained on the assumption of large, concentrated currents at depths of about 100 km below the surface. Currents of an intensity of the order of 5000 A are required to explain the anomalous magnetic variations. These of course suggest regions of high conductivity within the upper mantle, but even if these exist, the current strength is too great to result from induction in a local region.

Rather, it appears to result from concentration of currents from some larger region at depth, by conducting channels tapping these depths. It is difficult to visualize the mechanism by which the upper mantle could become so highly conducting locally. Hughes[12] and Runcorn [21] have discussed the dependence of the conductivity of olivine, the dominant mineral in the mantle, on temperature and pressure. Ionic conduction provides much the highest conductivity at high temperatures, but does not become significant until the temperature exceeds 1 100°C. At a depth of 100 km the normal temperature is probably some hundreds of degrees, but local increases in active areas, such as beneath Japan, may account for the higher conductivity.

The relationships between earth currents and magnetic variations in these anomalous areas do not appear to have been investigated. It would appear worthwhile to measure both the electric and magnetic fields, and to apply an analysis after the manner of Cagniard. The ratio E_x/H_y should show a decrease with increasing period, as the disturbing fields penetrate into the region of higher conductivity. Observations of this type might well lead to a better determination of the depth and areal extent of these remarkable regions in the mantle.

VI. CONCLUSIONS

The measurement of earth currents has passed through two or three stages in the last few decades, and may well be entering another. During the first stage a great volume of observational material relating to the diurnal variation was accumulated. When it was found that only limited use could be made of it, interest lagged, and the number of observatories recording earth currents diminished. At the present time interest in specific applications has encouraged the establishment of a greater number of stations than were ever operated before. Many of these are concentrating on specific problems. For example, the network of stations in the U.S.S.R. is equipped for high-speed recording, and important preliminary results on the observations of short-period phenomena have been given by Troitskaya.[26]

The type of information on the earth that my be gained from these measurements has been discussed in the preceding sections.

In the first place, a more detailed knowledge of the variations in conductivity through the crust and upper mantle may be expected. An evaluation of the earth-current and magnetic variations at Meanook, Alberta, has suggested that there is some change in conductivity across the Mohorovicic discontinuity at the base of the crust, and a depth to this discontinuity compatible with seismological observations has been obtained (Dr R. Niblett, Dominion Observatory, personal communication). Apart from the studying of crustal structure, these observations should lead to a better understanding of differences in properties from place to place in the upper mantle.

Secondly, the electrical measurements in conjunction with magnetic observations should assist in determining the nature of the sources of disturbance, for effects of various periods. The difficulty of separating the effects of source distribution from those of conductivity variations, when one is working with regions too local to be treated by spherical harmonic analysis, has been noted. In these cases the measurement of the electrical field as well as the magnetic provides useful additional information.

There is, finally, the possibility of locating components of the measured currents which are not the result of induction by an external varying magnetic field. Such components, if due to internal causes, would almost certainly be of very long period, and would be difficult to isolate with present instrumentation. Improvement in electrode stability is required for this purpose. The results could be extremely important if the currents could be shown to be related to a toroidal magnetic field in the core, or to mantle–core currents, both of which play a prominent role in theories of the origin of the earth's main magnetic field.

In order to illustrate the differences in electrical properties that exist among earth materials, representative values of these properties are summarized in the Appendix following.

APPENDIX

Electrical Properties of Earth Materials

| Material | Typical resistivity, ohm cm | Conductivity, e.m.u. | Current density for $E = 1$ mV/km A/cm² | Depth of penetration * | | | |
				$T = 1$ sec km	$T = 1$ min km	$T = 1$ day km
Sea-water	20	5×10^{-11}	5×10^{-10}	0·22	1·7	64·5
Unconsolidated soils	5 000	2×10^{-13}	2×10^{-12}	3·55	27·5	1 040
Sedimentary rocks	10 000	1×10^{-13}	1×10^{-12}	5·03	38·9	1 480
Igneous rock	1×10^{6}	1×10^{-15}	1×10^{-14}	50·3	389	14 800
Mantle, 1 000 km depth	100	1×10^{-11}	1×10^{-10}	0·50	3·9	147

* The depth of penetration is the depth within the material at which an electric or magnetic field of the period shown would be reduced to $1/e$ of its surface value.

References

1. Barlow, W. H. *Phil. Trans.* **139**, 61–72 (1849).
2. Bartels, J. *Nachr. Akad. Wiss. Göttingen (Phys.-math. Kl.)* Abt. IIa, 95–100 (1954).
3. Bullard, E. C. *Proc. Roy. Soc. A*, **199**, 413–443 (1949).
4. Cagniard, L. *Geophysics*, **18**, 605–635 (1953).
5. Chapman, S., and Whitehead, T. T. *Trans. Camb. phil. Soc.* **22**, 463–482 (1923).
6. Chapman, S. *Terr. Magn. atmos. Elect.* **40**, 349–370 (1935).
7. Chapman, S., and Bartels, J. *Geomagnetism.* Oxford University Press, London, 1940.
8. Cullwick, E. G. *Electromagnetism and Relativity.* Longmans, London, 1957.
9. Currie, B. W. *Canadian Polar Year Expeditions 1932–1933*, Vol. II, 112–130 (1939).
10. Gish, O. H. *J. Wash. Acad. Sci.* **26**, 267–289 (1936).
11. Heppner, J. P. *Thesis*, California Institute of Technology: Pasadena, 1954.
12. Hughes, H. *J. Geophys. Res.* **60**, 187–191 (1955).
13. International Association of Geomagnetism and Aeronomy. *Report* of Special Committee 10, Toronto Meeting, 1957.
14. Lahiri, B. N. and Price, A. T. *Phil. Trans. A*, **237**, 509–540 (1939).
15. Lamb, H. *Proc. Lond. math. Soc.* **13**, 51–66 (1881).
16. Migaux, L. *Ann. Géophys.* **2**, 131–146 (1946).
17. Porstendorfer, G. *Freiberger Forschungshefte* **C 16**, 1–104 (1954).
18. Rikitake, T., Yokoyama, I. and Hishiyama, Y. *Bull. Earthq. Res. Inst. Tokyo*, **30**, 207 (1952); **31**, 19, 89, 101, 119 (1953).
19. Rikitake, T. and Yokoyama, I. *Bull. Earthq. Res. Inst. Tokyo*, **33**, 297–331 (1955).
20. Rooney, W. J. 'Earth currents.' Chapter 6 of *Terrestrial Magnetism and Electricity*, edited by J. A. Fleming, McGraw-Hill, New York, 1939.
21. Runcorn, S. K. 'The magnetism of the earth's body.' Chapter 15 of *Handbuch der Physik*, Vol. **47**, edited by J. Bartels, Springer, Berlin, 1956.
22. Schlomka, T. and Schenkel, G. *Ann. Phys. Lpz.* (Folge 6), **5**, 51–62 (1949).
23. Schlumberger, M. and Kunetz, G. *C.R. Acad. Sci.*, Paris, **223**, 551–553 (1946).
24. Stratton, J. A. *Electromagnetic Theory.* McGraw-Hill, New York, 1941.
25. Sugiura, M. *Geophys. Res. Rep. No. 5.* Geophysical Institute, University of Alaska, College, 1958.
26. Troitskaya, V. A. Abstract in '*Abstracts* of the Reports at the XI General Assembly of the I.U.G.G.', Moscow, 1957.
27. Vozoff, K. *Geophysics*, **23**, 536–556 (1958).
28. Wait, J. R. *Geophysics*, **19**, 281–289 (1954).
29. Webster, T. F. *Thesis*, University of Alberta, Edmonton, 1957.
30. Wenner, F. *Bull. U.S. Bur. Stand.* **12**, 469–478 (1916).

PROPERTIES OF ROCKS UNDER HIGH PRESSURE AND TEMPERATURE

D. S. HUGHES * *Department of Physics, The University of Texas, Austin, Texas*

CONTENTS

I. INTRODUCTION

With the development of modern geology it became obvious that many large bodies of rocks had undergone large plastic deformation without fracture. Deformations of a small fraction of this magnitude would under ordinary conditions have reduced the rocks to a powder. While in some cases high temperature could be postulated as a plasticizing agent, in many cases it was definitely ruled out by the composition of the rocks. The probable importance of confining pressure was soon recognized, and in 1901 experiments on marble were undertaken by Adams and Nicholson.[1] The apparatus by modern standards was somewhat crude, but definite and interesting results were obtained. By placing marble cylinders in tight-fitting steel jackets and putting the assembly in a press it was found possible to compress the marble to 75 per cent of its original length with a corresponding increase in diameter. It not only did not fracture but was actually stronger than the original material. In the period 1910 to 1915 additional work was done by Adams, von Kármán and Boker (ref. 10, pp. 106 to 116). In 1911 Prof. P. W. Bridgman [15] started his work on high-

* Consultant, Los Alamos Scientific Laboratories, University of California, Los Alamos, New Mexico.

pressure physics, and during the next forty years developed apparatus, methods and techniques that have made available to the laboratory worker a tremendous field of investigation.[24, 25] Adams and his associates were the first to utilize this work [2-4] to measure the compressibility of rocks. A complete account and bibliography of their work and indeed all work up to 1942 has been given by Birch and his associates.[10]

One of the most important sources of data on the interior of the earth is seismology. The velocity of dilatational and rotational waves are known with fair precision throughout the earth. Adams and Williamson [4] noted that the seismic velocities could be used to compute the changes of density with pressure. Bullen [28, 29] has extended this idea and made detailed calculations of the density within the earth. Birch [12] and Nishitake [57] have shown how data on rocks at high pressure can be utilized to compute structures for the earth's crust.

A laboratory measurement of elastic wave velocities under temperatures and pressures similar to those in the deep crust may also permit some inference of the types of rocks at various depths.[13] Most rock-forming minerals are quite complex, and it is by no means certain that the forms ordinarily observed are the forms that would be found at depths of 10 to 100 km. Thus a new form of quartz, coesite, has been discovered [32, 56] which has a density of $3 \cdot 01$ g/cm³ and which could be formed at depths of 50 to 80 km depending on the temperature. Polymorphism is being actively investigated at the present and will be discussed in Section IV. The possible importance of high-pressure phenomena in geophysics has been discussed by Bridgman.[23]

II. COMPRESSIBILITY AND ELASTIC PROPERTIES

The pioneer work of Adams and his associates [2-4] on compressibility has been mentioned. The compressibility of a great many rocks and minerals to a pressure of 10 kb (1 kilobar = 987 atmospheres) at 25°C were determined. The importance of excluding the pressure fluid from the rock pores was recognized. Thin metal jackets were designed to stop the fluid and still transmit the pressure. This procedure has become standard practice for nearly all subsequent workers.

Birch and Bancroft [7, 8] in 1938 designed apparatus that permitted the measurement of the velocity of rotational waves in rocks under pressure. This apparatus was so designed that the temperature of the specimen could be varied over the range 30° to 150°C. In later work [9, 11] the upper temperature limit was raised to 600°C at a pressure of 27 kb.

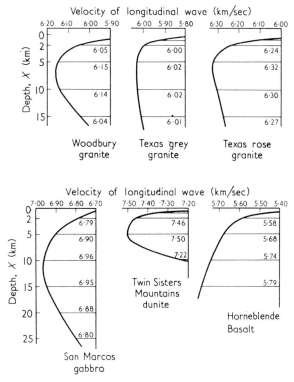

Fig. 1. Variation of V_D with depth for selected igneous rocks.[50]

The method is, briefly, to jacket a cylindrical sample with copper foil. To one end a small bar magnet is secured along a diameter. Four driving coils are arranged so that an axial twist may be applied to the specimen. The frequency of the driving current is varied and the frequencies at which resonances occur noted. From this the velocity of shear waves in the material may be computed. This addition of temperature as a possible parameter in addition to the pressure is extremely important. The physical properties of rocks can now be studied under conditions approximating those existing in the crust to depths of 50 to 60 km.

Hughes and associates developed a method whereby both the dilatational or longitudinal and rotational or shear velocities could be measured under high pressures and temperatures.[46-49] This method uses a quartz crystal on one end of a cylindrical sample as a driver and a second crystal on the opposite end as a detector. Pulses with a rise time of the order of 0·02 μsec and a decay time of 4 to 5 μsec are used. The transmission time through the sample is measured and the velocity computed. In general x-cut crystals are used giving longitudinal waves in the sample. Such a pulse, however, in travelling along a cylindrical rod gives rise to delayed pulses.[54] From this delay time the shear velocity may be computed.[45] With very coarse-grained rocks (crystals 3 to 4 mm) the computed shear velocity may be somewhat low. With fine-grained or homogeneous rocks it appears to be very accurate. Most of the results on shear velocities have been checked using y-cut crystals. A complete review of this work with descriptions of apparatus and experimental procedure has been published.[50]

Fig. 1 shows graphically some of the results of this work. In preparing this graph the following temperature gradients were used.[50]

$$G = (24\cdot8 - 0\cdot9X)°C/km \quad 0 < X < 15 \text{ km}$$
$$G = (13\cdot0 - 0\cdot25X)°C/km \quad 15 < X$$

These values correspond roughly to Birch's case B.[58] Fig. 1 shows that Gutenberg's suggestion of low-velocity channels (ref. 58, p. 19) in the crust is certainly a physical possibility.

It is surprising that seismic velocities measured with effective frequencies of 0·03 to 0·10 c/s, Birch's measurements using frequencies of the order of 10 kc/s, and Hughes's measurements using effective frequencies of 1 to 5 Mc/s should be in apparent agreement. It is highly probable that this result is obtained only because of the confining pressure.

It is the author's opinion that confining pressure is all-important and that few physical properties of rock measured at atmospheric pressure have any geophysical significance. This is probably best illustrated by Figs. 2 and 3. Fig. 2 is typical of most rocks. The

x

initial application of pressure results in a large increase in velocity. With Hughes's method it also gives a large increase in signal strength and high-frequency transmission.[47] This large increase is reversible, i.e. after applying pressure to 10 kb the 50-bar velocity may be a few per cent high, but in general the curve is retraced.

Another fact is brought out by Fig. 3. Frequently the pressure has a tendency to bring the velocities of quite different rocks with very different low-pressure velocities to nearly the same value. Fig. 2 also illustrates two very general tendencies. The change in

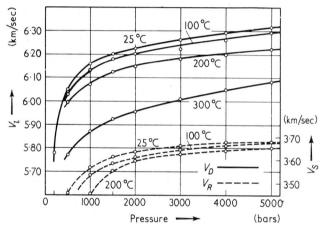

Fig. 2. Variation of V_D and V_R with pressure and temperature in Woodbury granite.[50]

velocity with temperature is generally non-linear and decreases as the pressure is raised. This latter fact, together with the general linearity of the V/P plot at high pressures, may make considerable extrapolation of measurements made to 30 kb possible.

Techniques and methods have now been developed that permit measurement of the shear velocity of rocks to pressures of 30 kb and temperatures of 600°C using Birch's method. Hughes's method for measuring longitudinal velocities can be used to this pressure, but only up to 350° to 400°C because the piezoelectric power of quartz decreases rapidly with temperatures in this range. It is possible that the use of tourmaline crystals would extend this limit.

A considerable body of data on a variety of rocks has now been accumulated. A comparison of this with seismic velocities indicates that the continental crust consists of a few kilometres of sediments and granite, a basic layer extending to the Mohorovicic discontinuity, and an ultra-basic material perhaps dunite, below (ref. 58, p. 19).

The possibility that the Mohorovicic discontinuity is actually a phase boundary has been suggested.[44] Thus the composition above and below could be the same. The discovery that the discontinuity

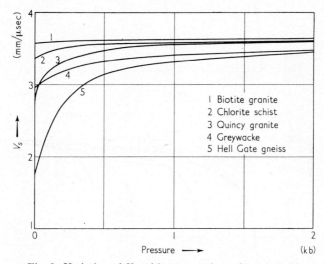

Fig. 3. Variation of V_R with pressure in various rocks.[58]

varies in depth from about 20 km below ocean basins to 30 km under continents and even 40 km beneath mountainous areas would appear to exclude this hypothesis. However, the effect of temperature must be considered, and as this is a low-density to high-density transformation, raising the temperature would probably increase the necessary pressure. Since the change in density is probably of the order of 10 per cent, this could give rise to major tectonic movements which would operate with heating and cooling of the crust. Polymorphism will be discussed more fully in Section IV.

Nishitake [57] has used the Adams method [4, 28, 29] to compute the

densities of granite and dunite at high pressures and temperatures
from laboratory measurements of the elastic wave velocities. In
turn the longitudinal velocity as a function of density is plotted

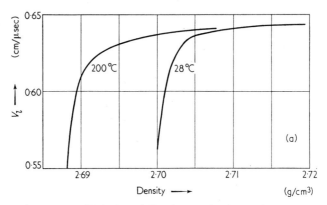

Fig. 4a. Variation of V_D with density in granite.[57]

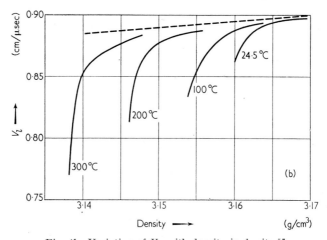

Fig. 4b. Variation of V_D with density in dunite.[57]

for various temperatures. Figs. 4 (a) and 4 (b) show his results.
These curves again demonstrate the large effect of the initial compression. It is generally believed that this rapid change is due to
closure of pores and cracks. This closure is practically complete
at a pressure of 2 kb (about 6 km depth), and above this pressure

the rock is a true solid. Nishitake [57] has discussed this point at some length and finds it quite reasonable. Figs. 4 (a) and 4 (b) show that at high pressures the velocity is a function of density only.

III. PLASTICITY AND FLOW

As was mentioned in the introduction, the geologic observation that many rocks had undergone extensive plastic deformation stimulated early work in this field. Although this early work is interesting and suggestive, it could not give quantitative results. Following Bridgman's development [24, 25] of high-pressure apparatus, Griggs (ref. 10, p. 112, and ref. 34) succeeded in designing apparatus in which rock samples could be subjected to axial compression and hydrostatic pressure simultaneously. Thus two of the principal stresses were equal and the third equal or greater, all being compressive. Bridgman [21] has constructed apparatus in which the third principal stress may be either greater or less than the other two.

Griggs's [34] first work demonstrated clearly the importance of the confining pressure. Solenhofen limestone under 1 kb hydrostatic pressure ruptured under a compressive differential stress of 2·5 kb with a strain of 0·5 per cent. Under 10 kb confining pressure and 10 kb compressive differential stress it shortened 23 per cent without rupture.

It should be noted that although 'plastic' under 10 kb confining stress the rock was not 'weaker', indeed it was much 'stronger' than under low confining stress. It is in general true that confining pressure, if sufficiently high, will introduce the possibility of large plastic deformation without rupture, but it will also raise the elastic limit and greatly increase the strength of the material.[21, 22, 35] An excellent description of apparatus and some results on marble and rock salt are given by Handin.[42]

Griggs and his associates have made a most exhaustive study of marble in extension and compression at room temperature and 10 kb hydrostatic pressure,[35] at 150°C and 10 kb pressure,[37, 62] and at 300°C and 5 kb pressure.[38] In addition to the stress/strain curves ordinarily observed, very complete studies have been made of the petrofabric changes brought about by the deformation.

It was concluded that at room temperatures the marble deformed primarily by twinning and translation on {0112}.[36, 37] At a temperature of 300°C lamellae parallel to {0221} and {1011} also appeared.[26] These were probably present in samples deformed at low temperature, but either not as well developed or as evident. The remarkable deformations obtained without rupture, and the stresses required to produce them, are shown in Fig. 5.

Experiments on dolomite have shown it to be much stronger than marble.[63, 43] At 300°C under 5 kb pressure it deforms by twinning on {0221}. It is not as ductile as marble and in general fails in shear after a deformation of about 4 per cent in tension or

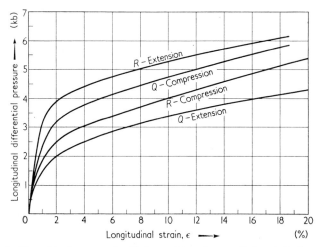

Fig. 5. Stress/strain curve for Yule marble. Q—parallel to foliation, R—perpendicular to foliation.[37]

7 to 10 per cent in compression. With a hydrostatic pressure of 10 kb these limits would doubtless be greatly increased.

This work on deformation or plastic flow, particularly if (as Griggs and Handin [36] have done) careful analyses of the structure before and after deformation are made, is of great importance. With the accumulation of a large volume of data it could conceivably enable one by analysis of a field sample to determine, at least roughly, the direction of application and magnitude of the forces producing the deformation and the depth and temperature at which it took place. It is unfortunate that the time element is so difficult to evaluate. The possibility that stresses required in the laboratory to produce a given plastic deformation over a period of a few minutes to a few hours might be drastically reduced if the deformation took place over a period of a hundred thousand years must be considered. This is a question that cannot be answered by direct experiment. Theoretical consideration of plastic deformation as made by Taylor,[61] and thermodynamic studies such as Goranson's [41] together with a better understanding of the solid state of matter will probably be required.

IV. POLYMORPHISM

The fact that the crystal form of many substances changes with temperature has been known for a long time. During the latter part of the last century several scientists investigated the effect of pressure on some of these transitions. This early work extended to pressures of only 2 to 3 kb. Practically all of this work has been repeated by Bridgman (ref. 24, chap. 8) with a greatly extended pressure range and much greater accuracy, together with work on a large number of new materials. This work has given a vast amount of information on the phase diagram of elements and simple chemical compounds.

The possible complexity of the phase diagram when pressure is introduced as a parameter in addition to temperature is well illustrated by Bridgman's results on water.[24, 19] Seven different forms of ice are now known and the situation is nearly as complex for some other fairly simple compounds. With the complex minerals that compose most of the igneous rocks the situation is very involved at atmospheric pressure [27] and will become correspondingly more involved with pressure as a second parameter.

Although Bridgman [16, 17] had demonstrated the importance of pressure in polymorphic transitions as early as 1914, almost the only material of geological or geophysical interest that had been investigated by 1942 (ref. 10, pp. 175 to 189) was the α–β transition of quartz, and this had only been carried to 2·7 kb. This has since been extended by Yoder to 10 kb.[66]

In 1945 Bridgman [20] pointed out the importance of polymorphic transitions in geology. Since that time a large amount of work has been done, but a tremendous body of data is still needed. Two types of apparatus have been used in this work, both originated by

Bridgman. The closed pressure vessel with nitrogen as the pressure-transmitting fluid [14, 60] can be used to pressures of 27 kb and temperatures of 1400°C. The 'simple squeezer' in which a thin sheet of the material is placed between hardened anvils [40] in a press can be used to 80 kb at 500°C, 50 kb at 800°C and 20 kb at 1000°C. Both systems have relative advantages and disadvantages. The closed system will handle relatively large samples, reach higher temperatures and give a more precise knowledge of the stress system to which the material is subjected. The 'squeezer' will

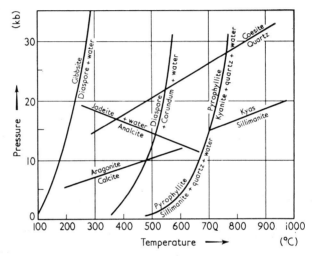

Fig. 6. Phase lines for various materials.[40]

reach higher pressures, but the precise stress system in the sample is not well known. Despite this, however, excellent results have been obtained with it. Jamieson determined the calcite–aragonite phase line with a closed system.[53] McDonald [55] used the 'squeezer' and Clark [31] repeated the work using a closed system. Over the range 4 to 15 kb Clark and Jamieson agree very closely, while McDonald's phase line is parallel to theirs and only about 1 kb low.

Fig. 6 shows the phase lines for several geophysically important materials. The high-pressure form is the high-density modification, but it should be noted that the slope of the phase line in the P/T plane can be either positive or negative. This usually depends upon whether the high-temperature form is the high-density form as in iron or the low density form as in quartz.

The jadeite–analcite transformation has been studied in detail [39, 60, 59] as well as the kyanite–sillimanite transformation.[30] The discovery by Coes of a new high-pressure silica [32] has been mentioned. As work is continued in this field it is certain that a large number of new phases will be discovered. The possible importance of polymorphism in the crust has been discussed by Birch,[12] and by Holser and Schineer.[44]

In addition to the more or less conventional and direct methods described above for reaching high pressure there have been developed, during recent years, methods using high explosives to reach pressures of the order of 1000 kb or about ten times the pressure attainable in laboratory apparatus. This work is made possible by two developments, first, means of generating and maintaining plane detonation waves in blocks of explosives up to 12 in. in diameter [64] and secondly, methods of observation that can take relevant data in periods of the order of a few microseconds.

The transformation in bismuth [33] has been checked by this means and a transformation in iron at 135 kb to, apparently, the gamma phase discovered.[6] Some work has been done on rocks by this method.[51] Dunite shows no transformation up to 750 kb. Two gabbros, however, showed evidence of a transformation with a density change of about 10 per cent between 150 and 300 kb. A specimen of Mount Holyoke diabase on which six shots have been fired shows a similar transformation. Fused quartz also shows evidence of a transformation at about 300 kb or less to a high-density form which is probably coesite. Unfortunately the material cannot in general be recovered for examination after the shot. Some metal samples have been recovered after shooting to 750 kb, but it is highly probable that the minerals and glasses disintegrate completely a few microseconds after the passage of the shock wave. Extensive data on the equation of state of metals [65] have been taken by this method with very interesting results.

V. MISCELLANEOUS

The properties to be considered in this section are quite important, but very little work has been done on them. Thermal

conductivity, thermal capacity, electrical conductivity and magnetic parameters as functions of pressure and temperature would
be of great assistance in formulating and testing hypotheses concerning the structure of the earth.

Bridgman [18] has measured the thermal conductivity of a few
rocks at 30°C and 75°C over the pressure range 0 to 12 kb. He
concludes from this small sample that in general the conductivity
will increase about 0·5 per cent per kilobar of hydrostatic pressure.
Raising the temperature may either increase or decrease the conductivity.

Hughes [52] has measured the electrical conductivity of olivine at
temperatures of 1333°, 1425°, and 1513°C over the pressure range
1·0 to 8·5 kb. The conductivity decreased about 3 per cent per
kilobar pressure increase at all temperatures. This is equivalent to
lowering the temperature about 14°C.

Apparently no measurements of thermal capacity or magnetic
parameters of rocks under pressure have been attempted.

CONCLUSIONS

During the past 35 years a large body of data has been accumulated on the properties of rocks under pressure. Some very important fields, such as elastic constants and velocities, plastic
deformation and polymorphism, are being actively investigated.
The thermal, electrical and magnetic properties have been somewhat neglected. Considerable work has been done on the synthesis
of minerals, effect of water, etc., under high pressures and temperatures. This has been described by Roy and Tuttle (ref. 5,
p. 138).

Acknowledgement

The writer wishes to express his appreciation to the Los Alamos
Scientific Laboratories of the University of California for per-
mission to prepare this material while in residence at the
Laboratories.

References

1. Adams, F. D. and Nicolson, J. L. 'An experimental investigation of the flow of marble.' *Trans. Roy. Soc. A*, **195**, 363–401 (1901).
2. Adams, L. H. and Gibson, R. E. 'The compressibilities of dunite and of basalt glass and their bearing on the composition of the earth.' *Proc. nat. Acad. Sci., Wash.* **12**, 275–283 (1926).
3. Adams, L. H. and Gibson, R. 'The elastic constants of certain basic rocks and their constitutional minerals.' *Proc. nat. Acad. Sci., Wash.* **15**, 713–724 (1929).
4. Adams, L. H. and Williamson, E. D. 'Compressibility rocks and minerals at high pressures.' *J. Franklin Inst.* **195**, 475–527 (1923).
5. Ahrens, T. H., Rankama, K. and Runcorn, S. K. *Physics and Chemistry of the Earth*. McGraw-Hill Co., New York (1956).
6. Bancroft, Dennison, Peterson, E. L. and Minshall, S. F. 'Polymorphism of iron at high pressure.' *J. appl. Phys.* **27**, 291–298 (1955).
7. Birch, Francis and Bancroft, Dennison. 'The effect of pressure on the rigidity of rocks.' *J. Geol.* **46**, 59–87 (1938).
8. Birch, Francis and Bancroft, Dennison. 'New measurements on the rigidity of rocks at high pressure.' *J. Geol.* **48**, 752–766 (1940).
9. Birch, Francis and Bancroft, Dennison. 'The elasticity of glass at high temperature and the vitreous basaltic substratum.' *Amer. J. Sci.* **240**, 457–490 (1942).
10. Birch, Francis. *Handbook of Physical Constants*. Geological Society of America, Special Paper No. 36 (1942).
11. Birch, Francis. 'Elasticity of igneous rocks at high temperatures and pressures.' *Bull. geol. Soc. Amer.* **54**, 263–286 (1943).
12. Birch, Francis. 'Elasticity and constitution of the earth's interior.' *J. geophys. Res.* **57**, 227–289 (1952).
13. Birch, Francis. 'Interpretation of the seismic structure of the crust in the light of experimental studies of wave velocities in rocks.' Ch. 12, Vol. I. *Contributions in Geophysics*. Pergamon Press, New York (1958).
14. Birch, Francis, Robertson, E. C. and Clark, Jr., S. P. 'Apparatus for pressures of 27 000 bars and temperatures of 1400° C.' *Industr. Engng. Chem. (Industr.)*, **49**, 1965–1966 (1957).
15. Bridgman, P. W. 'Mercury solid and liquid under pressure.' *Proc. Amer. Acad. Arts Sci.* **47**, 347–438 (1911).
16. Bridgman, P. W. 'Change of phase under pressure.' *Phys. Rev.* **3**, 126–141 (1914).
17. Bridgman, P. W. 'Change of phase under pressure.' *Phys. Rev.* **3**, 153–203 (1914).
18. Bridgman, P. W. 'The thermal conductivity and compressibility of several rocks under high pressure.' *Amer. J. Sci.* **7**, 81–102 (1924).
19. Bridgman, P. W. 'The phase diagram of water to 45000 kg/cm.' *J. chem. Phys.* **5**, 964–966 (1937).
20. Bridgman, P. W. 'Polymorphic transition and geological phenomena.' *Monthly J. of Geo.* **243** A, 90–97 (1945).

21. Bridgman, P. W. 'The effect of hydrostatic pressure on the fractures of brittle materials.' *J. appl. Phys.* **18**, 246–258 (1947).
22. Bridgman, P. W. 'The rheological properties of matter under high pressure.' *J. Colloid Sci.* **2**, 7–16 (1947).
23. Bridgman, P. W. 'Some implications for geophysics of high pressure phenomena.' *Bull. geol. Soc. Amer.* **62**, 533–536 (1951).
24. Bridgman, P. W. *The Physics of High Pressure.* G. Bell and Sons, London (1952).
25. Bridgman, P. W. *Large Plastic Flow and Fracture.* McGraw–Hill Co., New York (1952).
26. Borg, Iris and Turner, F. J. 'Deformation of Yule marble, Part VI.' *Bull. geol. Soc. Amer.* **64**, 1343–1352 (1953).
27. Bowen, N. L. *The Evolution of the Igneous Rocks.*' Dover Publications, Inc., New York (1956).
28. Bullen, K. E. 'The problem of the earth's density variation.' *Bull. seismol. Soc. Amer.* **30**, 235–250 (1940).
29. Bullen, K. E. *An Introduction to the Theory of Seismology.*' Cambridge University Press, London (1947).
30. Clark, Sydney P. Jr, Robertson, E. C., and Birch, Francis. 'Experimental determination of kyanite–sillimanite equilibrium relation at high temperatures and pressures.' *Amer. J. Sci.* **255**, 628–640 (1957).
31. Clark, Sydney P., Jr. 'A note on calcite–aragonite equilibrium.' *Amer. Min.* **42**, 564–566 (1957).
32. Coes, L. 'A new dense silica.' *Science,* **118**, 131–132 (1953).
33. Duff, R. E. and Minshall, F. S. 'Investigation of a shock induced transition in bismuth.' *Phys. Rev.* **108**, 1207–1212 (1957).
34. Griggs, D. 'Deformation of rocks under high confining pressures.' *J. Geol.* **44**, 541–547 (1936).
35. Griggs, D. and Miller, W. B. 'Deformation of Yule marble, Part I.' *Bull. geol. Soc. Amer.* **62**, 853–862 (1951).
36. Griggs, D. and Handin, John. 'Deformation of Yule marble, Part II.' *Bull. geol. Soc. Amer.* **62**, 863–885 (1951).
37. Griggs, D., Turner, F. J and Borg, I. 'Deformation of Yule marble, Part IV.' *Bull. geol. Soc. Amer.* **62**, 1385–1405 (1951).
38. Griggs, D., Turner, F. J., Borg, I., and Sooska, J. 'Deformation of Yule marble, Part V.' *Bull. geol. Soc. Amer.* **64**, 1327–1342 (1953).
39. Griggs, D. T., Fyfe, W. S. and Kennedy, G. C. 'Jadeite, analcite, and nepheline–albite equilibrium' (abstract). *Bull. geol. Soc. Amer.* **66**, 1569 (1955).
40. Griggs, D. L. and Kennedy, G. C. 'A simple apparatus for high pressures and temperatures.' *Amer. J. Sci.* **254**, 722–735 (1958).
41. Goranson, R. 'Physics of strained solids.' *J. chem. Phys.* **8**, 325–334 (1940).
42. Handin, John. 'An application of high pressures in geophysics: experimental rock deformation.' *Trans. Amer. Soc. mech. Engrs,* **75**, 315–324 (1953).

43. Handin, John and Fairbairn, H. W. 'Experimental deformation of Hasmark dolomite.' *Bull. geol. Soc. Amer.* **66**, 1257–1274 (1955).
44. Holser, W. T., and Schineer, C. J. 'Polymorphism in the earth's mantle.' *Trans. Amer. geophys. Un.* **38**, 569–577 (1957).
45. Hughes, D. S., Pondrom, W. L., and Mims, R. L. 'Transmission of elastic pulses in metal rocks.' *Phys. Rev.* **75**, 1552–1556 (1949).
46. Hughes, D. S. and Jones H. J. 'Variations of elastic moduli of igneous rocks with pressure and temperature.' *Bull. geol. Soc. Amer.* **61**, 843–856 (1950).
47. Hughes, D. S. and Cross, J. H. 'Elastic wave velocities at high pressure and temperature.' *Geophysics*, **16**, 577–593 (1951).
48. Hughes, D. S., and Maurette, C. 'Elastic wave velocities in granite.' *Geophysics*, **21**, 277–284 (1956).
49. Hughes, D. S. and Maurette, C. 'Variation of elastic wave velocities in basic igneous rocks.' *Geophysics*, **22**, 23–31 (1957).
50. Hughes, D. S. and Maurette, C. 'Détermination des vitesses d'onde élastique dans diverses roches en fonction de la pression et de la température.' *Rev. Inst. franç. Pétrole*, 730–752 (1957).
51. Hughes, D. S. and McQueen, R. G. 'Density of basic rocks at very hign pressures.' *Trans. Amer. geophys. Un.* **39**, 959–965 (1958).
52. Hughes, Harry. 'The pressure effect on the electrical conductivity of peridot.' *J. geophys. Res.* **60**, 187–191 (1955).
53. Jamieson, John C. 'Phase equilibrium in the system calcite–aragonite.' *J. chem. Phys.* **21**, 1385–1390 (1953).
54. Mason, W. P., and McSkimin, H. J. 'Attenuation and scattering of high frequency sound waves in metals and glass.' *J. acoust. Soc. Amer.* **19**, 464–473 (1947).
55. McDonald, Gordon J. F. 'Experimental determination of calcite–aragonite equilibrium resolution at elevated temperatures and pressures.' *Amer. Min.* **41**, 744–756 (1956).
56. McDonald, Gordon J. F. 'Quartz–coesite stability at high pressures and temperatures.' *Amer. J. Sci.* **254**, 713–721 (1956).
57. Nishitake, Teruo. 'Elastic properties of rocks with relation to the earth's interior.' *Mem. Coll. Sci. Kyoto, Ser. A*, **28**, No. 1 (1956).
58. Poldervart, Arie. 'Crust of the earth.' *Spec. Pap. geol. Soc. Amer. No. 62*, New York, N.Y. (1952).
59. Robertson, E. C., Birch, Francis and McDonald, Gordon. 'Fields of stability of jadeite, kyanite and pyrope' (abstract). *Bull. geol. Soc. Amer.*, **66**, 1608 (1956).
60. Robertson, E. C., Birch, Francis and McDonald, Gordon. 'Experimental determination of jadeite stability relations to 25000 bars.' *Amer. J. Sci.* **255**, 115–137 (1957).
61. Taylor, G. Z. 'Plastic strain in metals.' *J. Inst. Met.* **62**, 307–324 (1938).
62. Turner, F. J., and Ch'ih, C. S. 'Deformation of Yule marble, Part III.' *Bull. geol. Soc. Amer.* **62**, 887–905 (1951).
63. Turner, F. J., Griggs, D., Heard, A. and Weiss, L. W., 'Plastic deformation of dolomite at 380° C.' *Amer. J. Sci.* **22**, 477–488 (1954).

64. Walsh, J. M. and Christian, R. H. 'Equation of state of metals from shock wave measurements.' *Phys. Rev.* **97**, 1544–1556 (1955).
65. Walsh, John M., Rice, Melvin H., McQueen, Robert G. and Yarger, Frederick L. 'Shock wave compression of twenty-seven metals. Equations of state of metal.' *Phys. Rev.* **108**, 196–216 (1957).
66. Yoder, H. S., Jr. 'High–low quartz inversion up to 10 000 bars.' *Trans. Amer. geophys. Un.* **31**, 827–835 (1950).

LATITUDE AND LONGITUDE, AND THE SECULAR MOTION OF THE POLE

W. MARKOWITZ, *U.S. Naval Observatory,*
Washington 25, D.C.

CONTENTS

I. INTRODUCTION

Astronomical evidence has been used in the study of two questions which concern geophysics and geology. These are the secular motion of the pole and continental drift. Astronomical theory cannot provide information on these matters for the remote past or for the distant future. Astronomical observation, however, can provide determinations of astronomical latitude and longitude of stations for different epochs. An analysis of the results provides indicated changes in latitude and longitude. It does not necessarily follow, however, that if changes in latitude and longitude are found the stations have moved. The changes may be due to errors of observation.

A comparison of the latitudes and longitudes obtained in this century with the values obtained about 1860 and 1870 shows large changes for a number of field stations. The indicated shift of Greenland in about 60 years is $5^s = 75''$ to the west and $3''$ to the south. The large change in longitude can be ascribed to the relatively crude longitude determinations which were necessarily made before the introduction of radio time signals. The change in latitude is explained by the large uncertainty in the method of observation used in Greenland in 1870. The indicated shifts in position were also within the errors of observation in other similar cases studied.[1]

It is known that horizontal and vertical crustal displacements of small magnitude do occur. The best known example of relative horizontal displacement in modern times has occurred in the region of the San Andreas fault in California. Triangulation measurements made from 1880 to 1947 show relative displacements of about 10 ft between the two sides of the fault.[2] Small vertical displacements, notably in Finland, have been measured by levelling operations.[3] The indicated uplift for Finland from 1900 to 1950 is about 1·5 ft.

Triangulation surveys made at different epochs indicate that horizontal displacements for stations not located near faults are very small. Since 1 ft at the surface of the earth equals about $0''\cdot01$ it is evident that the most refined astronomical methods must be employed in the study of such shifts.

In 1899, what is now the International Association of Geodesy established a chain of six latitude stations on the parallel of latitude $+39°$ to determine the motion of the pole. A complete northern chain and a partial chain in the southern hemisphere form the International Latitude Service (I.L.S.). Observations for latitude have also been made at a number of independent stations.

It is the results of the northern I.L.S. stations, however, that are of principal importance in studying the secular motion of the pole. The reason is, the position of the pole derived from results of a chain of three or more stations is independent of errors in positions and proper motions of the stars observed, if the same stars are observed at all stations on each night. The same stars are not always observed at all I.L.S. stations because of weather conditions. The positions of the stars are corrected internally, so that asymmetry of observation has only a small second order effect on the derived position of the pole. For independent stations, on the other hand, these errors enter directly in the results, and a progressive change in latitude cannot be distinguished from a systematic error in proper motion.

Analyses of the polar motion made about 20 years after the I.L.S. began operations indicated that the centre about which the periodic motion took place was moving in the direction of North America at a rate of about $0''\cdot003$ to $0''\cdot006$/yr. This apparent motion could be due to three causes: (*a*) secular motion of the pole, (*b*) horizontal displacements of individual stations, and (*c*) asymmetry of observation.

It was recognized that there were not enough results available to distinguish between the three possibilities. The total drift in the centre of motion from 1900 to 1920 was only about $0''\cdot08$. Hence, various investigators reached different conclusions, depending upon what other considerations, such as geophysical, were taken into account.

It was suggested in 1922 that the apparent secular motion of the pole was due to a horizontal displacement to the south of the I.L.S. station at Mizusawa, Japan. The view that Mizusawa had moved became widely accepted.

The mean position of the instantaneous pole for an interval of about six years, called the *mean pole*, is practically free of the 12- and 14-month variations. It was noticed in 1922 that the motion of the mean pole was not in a straight line, but that seemingly sudden changes in direction occurred. This phenomenon was well marked by 1954.

Although much observational material was available by that time, it was still not possible to decide if there was a real wandering of the pole because of inhomogeneities which had been introduced

Y

into the I.L.S. results. The general view of astronomers, based on the results of the I.L.S. and of independent stations, was that the existence of a secular motion of the pole had not been proved.

In 1959 a publication of the Central Bureau of the I.L.S. appeared which removed one of the principal sources of uncertainty.[4] By this time nearly 60 years of observation were available, as were improved fundamental systems of star positions and proper motions. The total change in position of the centre of motion of the pole since 1900 was then about $0''\cdot2$. It therefore appeared desirable to make a new study of the polar motion.

This study showed that the motion of the mean pole from 1900 to 1959 was not at random, but can be well represented mathematically as the sum of a secular linear motion and a libration of period 24 years. The various I.L.S. stations appear to be fixed relative to each other, and Mizusawa gives the least indication of any of undergoing horizontal displacements. It appears unlikely that asymmetry in the I.L.S. observations can account for the observed motion of the mean pole.

A study of the latitudes and longitudes of independent stations, although of much less weight than that of the I.L.S. results, indicates a secular motion which is in accord with that derived from the I.L.S. observations.

There thus appears to be a strong probability that the secular motion and libration found for 1900 to 1959 are real. However, no physical causes for these motions are known, and there is no assurance that these motions will continue. Future results of the I.L.S. and of independent stations will be awaited with interest.

The discussion of the secular motion of the pole is preceded by a description of astronomical methods of determining latitude and longitude.

II. ASTRONOMICAL TECHNIQUES

1. Rotation of the Earth

The earth rotates about an instantaneous axis, denoted L. Because of the gravitational attraction of the moon and sun on the equatorial bulge of the earth, the orientation of L in space changes. The progressive part of this motion is called *precession* and the periodic parts are collectively called *nutation*. The principal term in nutation has a period of 18·6 years.

The axis of figure of the earth is defined as the principal axis of inertia. Let P and F, respectively, be the points where the axis of rotation and axis of figure intersect the surface of the earth, near the north pole. Then, according to dynamical theory, P can move about F. The observed period varies, but is about 14 months. The motion is roughly circular. The radius varies from about 15 to 35 ft.

The term *motion of the pole*, by common usage, refers to the motion of P with respect to a point fixed on the earth and not to the motion of L in space. The polar motion has two well known periodic components, of periods 12 and 14 months. Unlike precession and nutation, these terms are not due to gravitation.

2. Equatorial System, Astronomical

L pierces the celestial sphere in two points N and N', which are respectively the north and south *celestial poles*. The great circle which is everywhere 90° from these points is the *celestial equator*. *Declination*, δ, is the angular distance of a star from the equator. The north polar distance is $p = 90° - \delta$.

Because of the rotation of the earth, a star appears to move about N, diurnally, in a circle of radius p. Thus, δ may be found in a fundamental manner by measuring the diameter of the diurnal circle. A photograph of circumpolar star trails could, in theory, furnish fundamental declinations.

In practice, fundamental declinations are obtained with a meridan transit circle. This is a telescope which has only one degree of freedom; its optical axis may be directed to any point in the meridian. An essential part of the transit circle is an accurately divided circle which enables arcs along the meridian to be measured. Fundamental declinations of circumpolar stars are obtained by measuring the altitudes at transit above pole and below pole. The fundamental declinations of other stars may be obtained by transfer from circumpolar stars.

The circle reading of the nadir is found by pointing the instrument downward at a basin of mercury so that the micrometer threads are seen to coincide with the reflected image. The altitude of a star may be determined from its circle reading at time of transit and the circle reading of the nadir.

Let A_1 and A_2 be the altitudes of a circumpolar star as observed above pole and below pole, respectively, 12 h apart. Then

$$\delta = 90° - (A_1 - A_2)/2$$

which is independent of the latitude of the station.

The computation of A_1 and A_2 requires that corrections shall be made for refraction, instrumental flexure, and division errors of the circle. For stars near declination 90° the difference in corrections for A_1 and A_2 are small. The position of the equator may be found by observing the sun and minor planets. Hence, fundamental declinations are found with the highest accuracy for stars near 0° or 90° declination.

It may be noted that the motion of the pole, as defined above, does not affect the declination of a star. The motion of L, however, does affect it. The declination will change, also, if the star has proper motion. Hence, the difference in declination of a star at two epochs is due to precession, nutation, and proper motion. The first two may be obtained by calculation, and proper motion may then be derived. The proper motions of stars with declinations from about 20° to 60° are determined with less accuracy than those near the equator or pole.

The sun appears to move in a plane called the *ecliptic*. The *vernal equinox* is the intersection between the ecliptic and the equator, at which the declination of the sun increases.

Right ascension is defined as the angle between the great circles which pass respectively through the vernal equinox and a star, measured eastward.

Observations of the sun provide the position of the equinox and the inclination of the equator to the ecliptic. Having these, further observations of the sun will provide its fundamental declination and right ascension. By observing the sun and stars, and through use of an accurate clock, fundamental right ascensions of stars may be obtained. Fundamental proper motions in right ascension may be determined in a manner analogous to that described for declination.

Observations made over intervals of about five or six years are combined and published in the form of observational catalogues.

From a series of such catalogues, extending over intervals of 50 to 100 years, there may be derived positions for the mean epoch and also proper motions. These constitute a fundamental system, which is published as a fundamental catalogue.

Generally speaking, observations made in the eighteenth and nineteenth centuries are affected by systematic errors which are much larger than those of observations made in the twentieth century. As observations accumulated it became possible to increase the precision of fundamental catalogues by dropping off the oldest series of fundamental observations. The fundamental catalogues known as *FK3* and *G.C.* have mean epochs of about 1900.[5, 6] The catalogue *N30* has a mean epoch of about 1930.[7] It is based on observational catalogues whose mean epochs are from 1917 to 1949. *FK3* will be replaced by an improved catalogue, *FK4*, about 1962.

The gradual increase in accuracy of fundamental catalogues means that secular changes in latitude may be determined with increased precision as time goes on. At present, in 1959, systematic errors in proper motions of the order of several thousandths of a second of arc per year may exist in even the most modern catalogues.

3. Astronomical Latitude and Longitude

Positions on the earth may be designated by giving the astronomical latitude and longitude. These coordinates cannot be used directly to furnish the geometric position of a station with respect to the centre of mass of the earth because of the existence of gravity anomalies. However, they may be determined with high precision and are therefore useful for studying displacements of stations and the motion of the pole.

The *instantaneous astronomical latitude*, ϕ, of a station, S, is the complement of the angle between the vertical at S and a line L_s through S which is parallel to the instantaneous axis of rotation, L.

Let Q_s be the plane which contains the vertical and L_s. Let Q_g be the plane which passes through the vertical and a line parallel to L at the Airy transit circle of Greenwich, at the original site. The angle between Q_s and Q_g is the *instantaneous astronomical longitude* of S.

It may be shown that the latitude is equal to the altitude of the celestial pole at a station.

4. Determination of Latitude

Latitude may be determined by observing the zenith distance, ζ, of a star of known declination. If the observation is made in the meridan we have $\phi = \delta - \zeta$, where ζ is reckoned positive to the north. Zenith distance may be measured with the aid of a graduated circle and a spirit level.

Modern field instruments of the most precise type utilize circles engraved on glass. Despite the small size of the circle, about 3 in. diameter, the readings may be made to about $1''$ in some theodolites.

The accurate determinations of latitude at fixed stations, however, utilize methods which avoid the use of graduated circles entirely.

A. *Horrebow–Talcott Method*

A suitable pair of stars of known declination δ_1 and δ_2, respectively, is observed at nearly the same altitude in the meridian, one to the north and the other to the south. The telescope is reversed about a vertical axis between the observations. The inclination of the optical axis to the vertical is kept the same in the two positions by means of a spirit level. Micrometer settings are made on each star as it trails through the field of view. The latitude is

$$\phi = [\delta_1 + \delta_2 - (r_1 - r_2)]/2$$

where $(r_1 - r_2)$ is the difference in micrometer readings converted into arc.

B. *Photographic Zenith Tube (PZT) Method*

This method is a form of the preceding one. The same star is photographed near the zenith with the lens and plate rotated as a unit, several times, through $180°$. Hence, $\delta_1 = \delta_2$. The measurement of $(r_1 - r_2)$ is made with a measuring engine. The local sidereal time is determined simultaneously.

C. *Danjon Astrolabe Method*

This instrument is operated in conjunction with a clock. The instant is determined by observation when the zenith distance of a star is 30°. By observing a number of stars of known right ascension and declination in various azimuths it is possible to determine the latitude and local sidereal time.

In all of the three methods described the observations, essentially, are made at equal altitudes on opposite sides of the zenith. If the refraction depends only upon altitude and not upon azimuth the results are independent of refraction.

The latitude obtained is directly dependent upon the declinations used. A systematic error in the proper motions will cause a spurious, progressive change in latitude. There are two ways of avoiding this effect. One is to use a chain of stations on the same parallel. The other is to utilize observations of circumpolar stars. It can readily be shown that

$$\phi = (A_1 + A_2)/2$$

which is independent of the declination of the star observed.

It has been frequently suggested that circumpolar transit observations be used to study secular changes in latitude. The transit circles are designed, however, for the determination of declinations and right ascensions. Latitude cannot be accurately determined because it cannot be well separated from other unknowns, such as refraction, flexure, and division errors. For this reason, the latitude determined as a by-product through observations of circumpolars is not considered by astronomers as having high precision.

Concurrent determinations of latitude obtained with the 6 in. and 9 in. transit circles of the U.S. Naval Observatory at Washington illustrate the uncertainty involved. C. B. Watts, F. P. Scott, A. N. Adams, and G. van Herk have provided me with the following determinations of latitude:

Interval	Latitude (6 in.)	Interval	Latitude (9 in.)
1911–18	38° 55′ 13″·73	1903–13	38° 55′ 14″·07
1925–30	13·86	1913–18	13·91
1930–35	13·77	1918–25	14·07
1936–41	13·86	1935–45	13·73
1941–49	13·91		

Least square solutions indicate shifts in latitude of $+0''\cdot006$/yr
for the 6 in. and $-0''\cdot010$/yr for the 9 in. The indicated relative
shift in latitude in 40 years is about $0''\cdot5$, or 50 ft. With the
two instruments located side by side, 164 ft apart, no such displacement occurred. Thus, we cannot rely on circumpolar observations for precise information on latitude changes.

5. Longitude

The difference in longitude between two stations is obtained by
determining the local times and measuring the difference with the
aid of radio time signals.

The most accurate method of monitoring time signals is by use
of the cathode ray oscilloscope. The incoming signal is displayed
on the oscilloscope, along with time markers produced by a local
clock. The leading edge of the signal may be referred to the clock
with a precision of about $0^s\cdot0005$. The comparison between clocks
at distant stations involves a small uncertainty in the travel
time of radio signals. The total probable error of a comparison
between distant clocks when the oscilloscope is used is about
$0^s\cdot001$.

6. Instruments

A. *Zenith Telescope* [8]

The telescopes used by the International Latitude Service are
of 4·3 in. aperture and 50 in. focal length. The tube is mounted at
the end of a counterbalanced horizontal axis, which is supported
by a vertical axis. The tube is free to move in the plane of the
meridian, either east or west of the vertical axis, about which the
telescope may be rotated. A divided circle is used for setting
the telescope, but the latitude derived is dependent only upon the
readings of the level and micrometer. The probable error of the
latitude for one night is about $0''\cdot10$.

A large zenith telescope was developed in the U.S.S.R. for use
during the International Geophysical Year. The aperture is 7·1 in.
and the focal length is 93 in. Micrometer settings are made
visually, but the readings of micrometer and levels are made
photographically.

Fig. 1. Zenith telescope at International Latitude Station, Carloforte.

B. *Photographic Zenith Tube* [9]

The optical axis of the PZT is directed to the zenith. The rays of light from a star pass through the lens to a basin of mercury, are reflected, and come to a focus on a photographic plate which is placed just below the lens. The plate is held by a plate-carriage,

which moves from west to east so as to track the star during
exposures of 20 sec.

Four exposures are made of each star. The upper part of the
PZT, which contains the lens and plate-carriage, is rotated as a
unit through 180° between exposures. The distance between pairs
of images, measured in the north–south direction, is twice the
zenith distance.

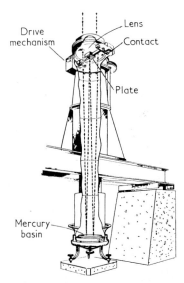

Fig. 2. Schematic view of PZT.

The moving plate-carriage initiates timing pulses during the
exposures, which are recorded by a chronograph or directly compared with a clock. Measurement of the plate enables time to be
determined.

The aperture of the Washington PZT is 8 in. and the focal
length is 180 in. The PZT may be programmed for automatic
operation during the night.

The probable errors for one night are 0″·06 in latitude and 0ˢ·005
in time.

C. Danjon Astrolabe [10]

The essential parts of this instrument are: an objective whose
optical axis is horizontal, a 60° prism placed in front of the objec-

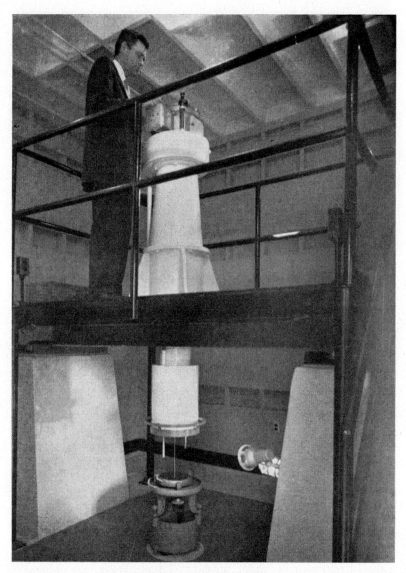

Fig. 3. PZT No. 3, U.S. Naval Observatory
(Official U.S. Navy Photograph).

tive, a basin of mercury, a Wollaston prism, and a viewing eye-piece. Direct and reflected rays from the star enter the 60° prism, forming two images. The diurnal motion of the star causes these images to move. The altitude of the star is 60° when the images coincide.

The moment of coincidence would be difficult to determine, so a Wollaston prism is placed in the optical path. Four images are produced, whose separation depends upon the position of the

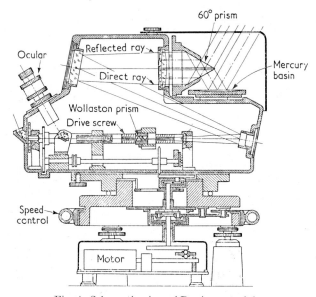

Fig. 4. Schematic view of Danjon astrolabe.

Wollaston prism. Two images are suppressed. The separation of the two that remain depends upon both the position of the Wollaston prism and the altitude of the star. By moving the prism at the proper speed the motion in altitude may be cancelled and the separation remains fixed. In operation, the observer controls the speed of the Wollaston prism so that the images remain parallel to a pair of spider threads. Time markers are generated automatically by the motion of the prism.

The probable errors of the impersonal astrolabe are about the same as for the PZT.

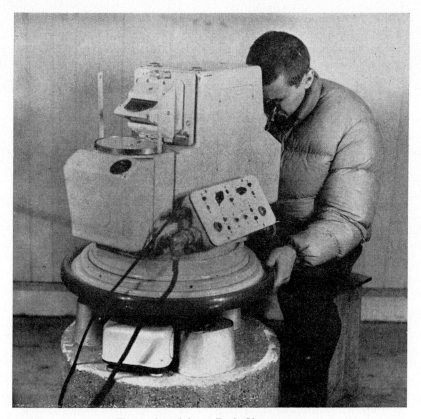

Fig. 5. Astrolabe at Paris Observatory.

7. Corrections to Catalogue Positions

Positions of stars as given in catalogues contain random errors which would seriously affect the results obtained with the I.L.S. zenith telescopes, the PZT's, and the Danjon astrolabe. After observations have been made for a number of years the declinations are corrected internally by prescribing the condition that on any night all stars observed should give the same latitude. Corrections in right ascension are similarly obtained for the instruments which determine time.

The application of internal corrections does not affect any systematic errors in position or proper motion which the catalogue positions contain. Hence, the secular change in latitude derived at an independent station will always be affected by a systematic error in proper motion of the catalogue declinations.

The situation is different for the chain of I.L.S. stations, for it is the position of the pole which they determine. By using declinations which are relatively correct, the latitude derived at a station on any night is influenced but little if some star pairs are not observed. Hence, asymmetry of observation should have little effect on the determination of the position of the pole by the International Latitude Service.

III. THE SECULAR MOTION OF THE POLE

The question of the secular motion of the pole is one that has interested astronomers for more than a century. Many spirited controversies have occurred on this subject because of different interpretations made by various astronomers of nearly the same material. It is not feasible to give a complete history of this subject here, but some of the more important developments will be given.

It was shown by L. Euler in 1765 that the axis of rotation of a rigid earth could have an oscillation about the axis of figure which would be observed as a variation of latitude. Many attempts were made during the nineteenth century to observe this theoretical oscillation of the pole, whose period is 305 days, and also a secular motion, but without success.

In 1872 E. Fergola, Director of the Observatory of Capodimonte, Naples, attempted to show that decreases in latitude of about $1''$ had occurred at several observatories. Fergola proposed in 1883 that a chain of stations be established on the same parallel of latitude in order to study the secular motion of the pole. Several investigations of existing series of latitude determinations were made shortly thereafter as a result. Despite apparent changes in latitude the conclusions generally drawn were that the changes indicated were within the errors of observation.

M. Nyrén, in 1888, listed the following determinations of the meridian circle at Pulkovo

Observer	Mean Epoch	Latitude
C. Peters	1843	$59° 46' 18''\cdot727 \pm 0''\cdot013$
H. Gyldén	1866	$18\cdot654 \pm 0\cdot014$
M. Nyrén	1872	$18\cdot54 \pm 0\cdot014$

Despite the small probable errors, he concluded: [11] 'Altogether, it is yet undecided if our instrument has really changed in latitude since the epoch of Peters.'

Asaph Hall,[12] in 1890, studied determinations of latitude of the U.S. Naval Observatory made at the old site. Some results follow.

Instrument	Mean Epoch	Latitude
Mural Circle	1846	38° 53′ 39″·23
Mural Circle	1863	38·78
Transit Circle	1875	38·38

Observations of Vega made with the prime vertical instrument from 1845 to 1866 had indicated an increase, in the seconds of arc, from 38″·38 to 38″·53. Hall concluded that, taking all the results into account, 'it is evident that there is no proof of a secular change in the latitude.'

S. C. Chandler,[13] who had thoroughly investigated several series of determinations of latitude at various observatories, remarked in 1892, 'if any secular change exists, it must be less than 0″·01 annually'.

About 1890, evidence of changes in latitude appeared, but not of the kind to be expected from the theory of Euler. In a paper published in 1890, F. Küstner [14] gave convincing proof that the latitude of Berlin had decreased by about 0″·4 from June, 1884 to March, 1885. This result was based on observations of the same four pairs of stars during this interval. He also showed that observations made with the vertical circles at Pulkovo in the interval from July 1884 to March 1885 gave nearly the same result.

In 1891 S. Chandler [15] announced that a periodic oscillation of the instantaneous pole about its mean position occurred in the period of about 427 days, instead of the 305 expected. The difference was explained by S. Newcomb as being due to the elastic deformation of the earth. In 1892 Chandler [16] announced that the motion of the pole was the resultant of two components, an annual as well as the 14-month period. Chandler's results were obtained from analyses of long series of observations made at various observatories dating back to about 1840.

To confirm the existence of the variation of latitude, an observing party was sent to Honolulu under the direction of A. Marcuse.

Observations of latitude made there and at Berlin simultaneously from May 1891 to May 1892 established the reality of the variation.

In order to study the phenomenon still further the International Latitude Service (I.L.S.) was established. Observations were begun in September 1899. Although the purpose of the I.L.S. was to study the periodic motion of the pole, it was realized that in the course of time the secular motion might also be determined.

The programmes of the I.L.S. generally extend over intervals of about six or twelve years. Changes in the list of stars observed were made at 1906.0, 1912.0, 1922.7, 1935.0, and 1955.0. Other changes were usually made at these times, namely, in the method of reductions and in the origin to which the instantaneous pole was referred. In addition, changes have been made in the star catalogues used and in the number of observing stations. Because of this inhomogeneity, it has been difficult to judge with confidence whether or not a secular motion of the pole exists.

The first attempt to determine the secular motion of the pole from the I.L.S. results was made by B. Wanach [17] in 1917, who found a motion of $0''{\cdot}003$/yr in the direction of Newfoundland. The material available to Wanach was, of course, scanty, and he noted that the motion found might be due to a variation of long period rather than to a progressive change.

Table 1 gives a list of secular motions found by various investi-

Table 1.   Secular motion of pole from observations of I.L.S.

	Interval	Rate seconds of arc/yr	Longitude W
(1) B. Wanach [17]	1900–1915	$0''{\cdot}003$	55°
(2) W. D. Lambert [18]	1900–1917	0·0048	78
(3) W. D. Lambert [19]	1900–1918	0·0066	81
(4) H. Mahnkopf [20]	1900–1922.7	0·0051	62
(5) H. Kimura [21]	1900–1923	0·0058	57
(6) B. Wanach [22]	1900–1925	0·0047	42
(7) N. Sekiguchi [23]	1922.7–1935.0	0·0103	91
(8) A. I. Orlov [24]	1900–1950	0·0042	69
(9) W. Markowitz	1900–1959	0·0032	60

gators, based on the I.L.S. results. The list is not complete, but is representative of the secular motions obtained for various intervals of observation.

1. Station Displacements

In 1921 A. C. Lawson noted that the latitude of the I.L.S. station at Ukiah, California, was increasing at the rate of $0''{\cdot}0094/$ yr. In consequence, W. D. Lambert [18] made a study of the latitudes of all the I.L.S. stations. He concluded that the apparent motion of Ukiah could be explained by errors in proper motions combined with a secular motion of the pole.

F. Schlesinger,[25] in 1922, utilized improved proper motions to analyse the I.L.S. data. He found that the data could be interpreted as indicating either motion of the mean pole or, if the pole were fixed, an annual displacement to the south of Mizusawa of $0''{\cdot}009$. He favoured the second alternative. Lambert,[19] on geophysical grounds, argued against the possibility of a continuous displacement of nearly 1 ft/yr, and considered it to be more likely that the mean pole was moving.

In 1924 H. Kimura,[21] Director of the Mizusawa station, and at that time in charge of the Central Bureau of the I.L.S., found also that either the pole had moved or that Mizusawa had shifted in position. Later, in 1940, he wrote,[26] 'the most probable explanation is that the station Mizusawa alone has moved considerably under some causes while the remaining three stations remained steady for 35 years since 1900, and that the mean amount of the differences for the three stations is nothing more than the difference of the star systems used in the two volumes. In other words, there would be no displacement of the North Pole during the period 1900–1935.' He adopted $-0''{\cdot}12$ as the change in the latitude of Mizusawa.

T. Hattori [27] attempted to place the results of the various I.L.S. programmes on a somewhat homogeneous system, in 1946, by utilizing the *General Catalogue*. He found that the mean pole moved in the general direction of longitude 90° W from 1900 to 1919, and then along the meridian 30° E for one year. After 1920 it resumed a motion in the general direction of longitude 130° W. Hattori decided that the apparent motion of the pole was due principally to displacements of the stations. He states, 'Secular movement . . . relative to the figure axis of the Earth, if it exists, is considered very small compared with the continental movements. But the rapid change during 1919–1920 is surely the real change of the rotation pole.'

z

G. Cecchini became Director of the Central Bureau of the I.L.S. in 1949. In a paper [28] published in 1950 he decided that there was no secular motion of the pole from 1900 to 1935, and a slight motion thereafter. Also, he decided that the displacement of $0''\cdot12$ of Mizusawa found by Kimura was real. In computing the position of the pole he used an adopted value of the latitude of Mizusawa which differed by $0''\cdot12$ from the value used before 1923. Later, however, in a report [29] issued in August 1958, he stated that it was impossible to decide with certainty whether the position of only Mizusawa (or its vertical) had changed since 1900.

A. I. Orlov,[30] in 1954, decided that there was both a secular motion of the pole and a southward drift of Mizusawa of $0''\cdot006/\mathrm{yr}$. He remarked that this was one of the rare cases of systematic change in latitude not due to polar motion.

2. Random Motion of Mean Pole

Lambert had noted in his early studies that the mean pole moved along one direction and then abruptly changed course. Hattori observed the same phenomenon, but in somewhat more detail.

The apparent random motion was brought out clearly by N.

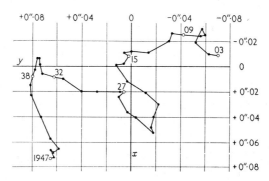

Fig. 6. Motion of Mean Pole, 1903–1947, derived by Sekiguchi.

Sekiguchi [31] in 1954. He formed 6-year running means of x and y, so as to obtain yearly positions of the mean pole. He found that there were changes in direction in the motion of the pole, as shown in Fig. 6. P. Melchior [32] pointed out that the sudden changes in direction of the movement of the mean pole were contemporary with changes in programmes of the I.L.S. Hence, he considered that the changes found by Sekiguchi indicated the effects of discontinuities in the programme, and not a real motion of the pole.

Sekiguchi [23] made a new study so as to eliminate the effects of changes in programme and asymmetry of observation, utilizing the results of a single programme, 1922.7 to 1935.0. He found that the motion of the mean pole was practically the same as previously derived. A study by A. Philippov [33] confirmed the conclusion that programme changes and asymmetry of observation could not account for the erratic motion of the pole. Melchior [34] agreed with this result.

Cecchini [29] derived positions of the pole in 1958 for mean epochs 1903 to 1952. He found that the mean pole moved erratically and that the positions obtained depended upon the combination of stations used.

Various explanations were offered for the apparent motion of the pole. Sekiguchi [31] considered the motion to be real, and suggested that a connection existed with variations in the speed of rotation of the earth. D. Brouwer [35] had suggested that changes in speed of rotation could be due to the cumulative effect of small random variations, and Sekiguchi thought a similar process might account for the motion of the mean pole along segments of straight lines.

Philippov and E. P. Fedorov [33] ascribed the changes to variations in latitude, of obscure origin, and not to motion of the pole.

Cecchini [29] ascribed the erratic motion to individual displacements of the stations, possibly of a periodic nature.

Although the indications are that changes in programme have had little effect on the position of the mean pole, it would be desirable to reduce all the I.L.S. observations made since 1900 with a single catalogue of high accuracy. A project for this purpose was started by the Observatoire Royal de Belgique in 1951. The I.L.S. stars were observed with the transit circle by G. Becq and P. Melchior at Uccle, and a catalogue of declinations with epoch about 1955 was formed.[36] Melchior is combining these declinations with those obtained at various observatories for earlier epochs to obtain the proper motions.

3. New Origin

In June 1959 Cecchini [4] apparently abandoned the hypothesis that Mizusawa had shifted and he returned to the initial value of its adopted mean latitude for determining the position of the pole since 1900. He adopted an origin which he calls the 'new system, 1900–05'. This origin, denoted by P_0, is defined by the latitudes given in Table 2, which we call *initial latitudes*.

Table 2. Initial latitudes, 'New system, 1900–05'

	ϕ_{i0}	λ_i
Mizusawa	39° 8′ 3″·602	−141°
Kitab	1·850	− 67°
Carloforte	8·941	− 8°
Gaithersburg	13·202	+ 77°
Ukiah	12·096	+123°

The latitudes of Table 2, except for Kitab, are the mean latitudes for the initial 6-year programme of the I.L.S., 1899.9 to

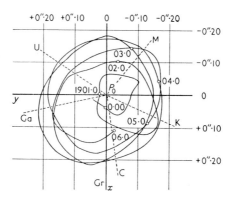

Fig. 7. Motion of the instantaneous pole (Albrecht, Wanach), referred to 'new system, 1900–05' of Cecchini, 1899.9 to 1906.0.

1906.0. Kitab, which replaced one of the original I.L.S. Stations, Tchardjui, was placed in operation in 1930, so that the value 1″·850 was obtained by Cecchini by a process which involves extrapolation.

The polar motion from 1899.9 to 1906.0 and from 1954.4 to 1959.2 with respect to the 'new system' is shown in Figs. 7 and 8, respectively. It is evident that the centre about which the instantaneous pole moves has changed position. This, of itself, does not prove, however, that a real change has occurred.

Cecchini derived the position of the mean pole for epochs from

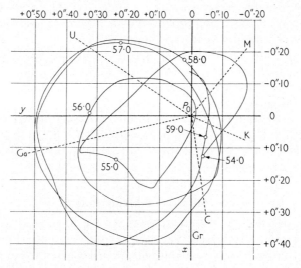

Fig. 8. Motion of instantaneous pole (Cecchini) referred to 'new system, 1900–05', 1954.0 to 1959.20.

1903 to 1952 and of the instantaneous pole from 1949.00 to 1959.20, with respect to the new origin. By referring all the I.L.S. results to the same origin, Cecchini made an important contribution; he removed what was perhaps the major source of uncertainty in studying the polar motion. This led me to undertake a new study of the motion of the mean pole, given below.

4. Definitions

It is desirable, at this point, to define the terms concerning latitude which are used here. The term mean latitude, for example, has been used in different senses by various authors. Latitudes will be defined with respect to the instantaneous pole and a fixed pole.

The *instantaneous latitude*, ϕ_i, of a station, S_i, is the complement of the angle between the vertical and a line parallel to the instantaneous axis of rotation which passes through S_i.

The *station latitude*, Φ_i, is defined as the latitude with respect to a particular axis, fixed in the earth. The axis used here is the one for which the pole is P_0, defined by the 'new system, 1900–05'.

The *programme mean latitude* is defined as the mean value of ϕ_i for a specific observing programme or interval. Means are most often formed for one year or six years.

The observed *variation of latitude* is defined as $\Delta\phi_i = \phi_i - \phi_{i0}$, where ϕ_{i0} is a constant called the initial latitude. The values of ϕ_{i0} used here are equal to the programme mean latitudes for 1900–1905.

Analagous definitions may be formed for longitude. Evidently, the instantaneous latitude and longitude of a fixed station are continually varying quantities, but the station latitude and longitude are constants.

5. Motion of Mean Pole

The programme mean latitudes of the I.L.S. stations are given by Cecchini in Table XII of his 1958 report.[29]

Table 3 reproduces the values for Mizusawa, Kitab, Carloforte,

Table 3.   Observed mean latitudes of I.L.S. stations

Interval	Mean epoch	Mizusawa	Kitab	Carloforte	Gaithersburg	Ukiah
1900–05	1903	3″·602		8″·941	13″·202	12″·096
1906–11	1909	·587		·923	·257	·122
1912–17	1915	·522		·901	(·246)	·131
1923–30	1927	·397	(1″·669)	·855	(·156)	·031
1929–34	1932	·377	(·619)	·837	(·204)	·079
1935–40	1938	·449	·727	·905	·318	·175
1949–54	1952	·389	·690	·928	·294	·114

Gaithersburg, and Ukiah. It should be noted that the quantities given are the mean latitudes obtained by observation. Results not based on the complete interval are marked by parentheses.

The latitude of a station, S_i, when the instantaneous pole of rotation is at a point on the surface of the earth denoted P_0 is ϕ_{i0}. Let the pole move later to a new position, P, whose rectangular coordinates are x and y, measured along the meridians of Greenwich and longitude 90° W, respectively. The variation in latitude which results, as may be seen from Fig. 9, is $x \cos \lambda_i + y \sin \lambda_i$, where λ_i is the longitude of the station.

Let the systematic error in declination of the stars observed when the pole is at P exceed that when at P_0 by the amount z. Then there will be an additional change in the observed latitude,

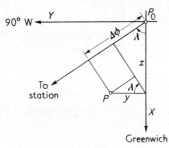

Fig. 9.

equal to z, which is not due to the polar motion. Hence, the observed variation in latitude, $\Delta\phi_i$, is

$$\phi_i - \phi_{i0} = x \cos \lambda_i + y \sin \lambda_i + z \tag{1}$$

where ϕ_i is the observed latitude of the station.

If observations are made at three or more stations it is possible to determine x, y and z. Hence, it is possible to determine the coordinates of the instantaneous pole of rotation, x and y, independently of errors in the positions or proper motions of the stars. In using equation 1 the implicit assumption is made that the positions of the stations with respect to P_0 are fixed, that is, there are no displacements of the stations relative to the crust of the earth.

Cecchini determined mean values of x, y and z for each I.L.S. programme by means of equation 1. The results are given in Table 4.

Table 4. Position of mean pole, P_1

Mean epoch	x_1	y_1	z
1903	0″·000	0″·000	0″·000
1909	−0·007	+0·043	−0·001
1915	+0·001	+0·076	−0·028
1927	+0·039	+0·080	−0·117
1932	+0·027	+0·130	−0·116
1938	+0·031	+0·139	−0·037
1952	+0·074	+0·142	−0·064
1957	+0·071	+0·178	

The values for 1903 to 1915 are based on four stations and those for 1927 to 1952 are based on five. I found that if Kitab is not used the values remain nearly the same. The values of x_1 and y_1 for 1957 were obtained by taking the mean values of these coordinates, as given by Cecchini, for the interval 1954.40 to 1959.20, which contains four Chandler periods. The position of P_1 is plotted in Fig. 10.

An analysis of the data in Table 4 shows that the motion of the mean pole may be represented analytically as the resultant of two

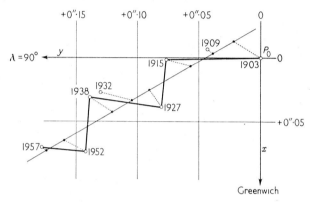

Fig. 10. Position of Mean Pole, P_1, referred to 'new system, 1900–05'. Circles are observed positions. P_p indicated by small dots.

motions, a progressive linear motion, P_p, and a periodic libration, P_l. The equations for the coordinates which I consider to be most probable follow. The progressive, or secular motion is

$$x_p = -0''\cdot018 + 0''\cdot0016\ (t - 1900)$$
$$y_p = +0''\cdot014 + 0''\cdot0028\ (t - 1900) \tag{2}$$

The motion in libration is

$$x_l = +0''\cdot012\ [\cos 15°\ (t - 1902)]$$
$$y_l = -0''\cdot019\ [\cos 15°\ (t - 1902)] \tag{3}$$

The secular motion is $0''\cdot0032$/yr along the meridian 60° W. The libration takes place along the meridian 122° W, or 58° E, in a period of 24 years. Its coefficient is $0''\cdot022$. The angle between the meridians along which the motions occur is 62°.

Let

$$x_2 = x_1 - x_p \qquad y_2 = y_1 - y_p$$
$$x_3 = x_1 - x_l \qquad y_3 = y_1 - y_l$$
$$x_4 = x_1 - (x_p + x_l) \qquad y_4 = y_1 - (y_p + y_l)$$

Let P_2, P_3 and P_4 be points which have coordinates (x_2, y_2),

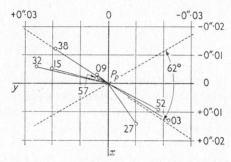

Fig. 11. Libration of Mean Pole.

(x_3, y_3) and (x_4, y_4), respectively. P_2, plotted in Fig. 11, is the position of the mean pole with the secular motion removed. P_3,

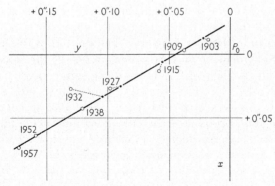

Fig. 12. Secular motion of Mean Pole. Circles represent P_3; dots, P_p.

plotted in Fig. 12, is the position of the mean pole with the libration removed. The coordinates of P_1, P_2, P_3 and P_4 are given in Table 5.

Table 5. Coordinates of P_1, P_p, P_l, P_2, P_3, and P_4. Unit $= 0''\cdot001$

Epoch	x_1	y_1	x_p	y_p	x_l	y_l	x_2	y_2	x_3	y_3	x_4	y_4
1903	0	0	$-13+$	22	$+12-18$		$+13-22$		$-12+$	18	$+1-$	4
1909	$-7+$	43	$-4+$	39	$-3+$	5	$-3+$	4	$-4+$	38	0 $-$	1
1915	$+1+$	76	$+6+$	56	$-12+18$		$-5+20$		$+13+$	58	$+7+$	2
1927	$+39+$	80	$+25+$	90	$+12-18$		$+14-10$		$+27+$	98	$+2+$	8
1932	$+27+130$		$+33+104$		0	0	$-6+26$		$+27+130$		$-6+26$	
1938	$+31+139$		$+43+120$		$-12+19$		$-12+19$		$+43+120$		0	0
1952	$+74+142$		$+65+160$		$+10-17$		$+9-18$		$+64+159$		$-1-$	1
1957	$+71+178$		$+73+174$		$-3+$	5	$-2+$	4	$+74+173$		$+1-$	1

Fig. 11 shows that the position of the mean pole with respect to the uniformly moving pole P_p always lies near the meridian 122° W, or 58° E. If the motion of the mean pole was erratic because of changes in programme the points P_2 should lie at random. Since they do not, the presumption is that the motion of the mean pole shown in Fig. 10 is not due to programme changes, but to a real motion of the pole.

It is apparent from Fig. 11 that the mean pole moves from one side to the other of the uniformly moving point P_p, with one exception, in a period of about 24 years. P_2 for 1932 is anomalous with respect to time along the libration path.

On account of the existence of the secular and libration motions the mean pole moves nearly along the meridian 90° W for 12 years and then almost towards Greenwich for 12 years. This effect is well brought out in Fig. 10. It now becomes clear why the rates and directions of the secular motions listed in Table 1 vary; the results listed are closely in accord with what would be expected from the motion shown in Fig. 10. The motion of the mean pole found by Sekiguchi, it may be noted, is nearly the same as that derived from the data of Cecchini for the same epochs.

The probable error of a coordinate x_4 or y_4 is $0''\cdot007$, as derived from all 16 values, and $0''\cdot004$ when y_4 for 1932 is not used. In computing these probable errors allowance was made for the fact that 8 constants were selected in deriving equations 2 and 3. The value of y_4 for 1932 was not used in deriving the second equation of 2. Had it been used, the constant term would be $+0''\cdot017$.

6. Station Latitudes

The station latitudes for any programme of observation may be obtained from the formula

$$\Phi = \phi_i - (x \cos \lambda_i + y \sin \lambda_i + z)$$

where ϕ_i, x, y and z are given their mean values for the programme concerned. Using the data of Tables 3 and 4, we obtain the station latitudes listed in Table 6. Subtracting the mean value for each station we obtain residuals v, given in Table 7, which represent the deviations in position for each programme.

In obtaining the entries of Table 6, there were selected 18

Table 6.   Station latitudes

Epoch	M	K	C	G	U
1903	3″·602	—	8″·941	13″·202	12″·096
1909	·609	—	·937	·218	·083
1915	·599	—	·939	·200	·096
1927	·595	1″·844	·945	·186	·102
1932	·596	·844	·945	·187	·101
1938	·597	·880	·931	·213	·113
1952	·600	·856	·939	·203	·100
Mean	3·600	1·856	8·940	13·201	12·099

constants, namely, x, y and z for epochs 1903 to 1952. Five more constants were selected in forming Table 7. Taking into account

Table 7.   Residuals, v. Unit = 0″·001

Epoch	M	K	C	G	U
1903	+2		+1	+ 1	− 3
1909	+9		−3	+17	−16
1915	−1		−1	− 1	− 3
1927	−5	−12	+5	−15	+ 3
1932	−4	−12	+5	−14	+ 2
1938	−3	+24	−9	+12	+14
1952	0	0	−1	+ 2	+ 1
Mean $|v|$	3	12	4	9	6

the selection of these 23 constants, it is found that the probable error of a residual v is 0″·011. This small quantity could be due entirely to accidental and systematic errors of observation and to changes in observers. The residuals are so small for several of the stations, notably Mizusawa, that an absolute fixity with respect to the crust of the earth is indicated.

It appears, thus, that the variation in latitude observed at the stations of the International Latitude Service can be accounted for completely by the motion of the pole plus errors of observation.

7. Independent Stations

One of the principal reasons for the reluctance to accept the reality of the secular motion of the pole, cited by many investigators, has been that observations for latitude made at Greenwich, Pulkovo and Washington indicated that their latitudes were constant. We re-examine this question.

The change in latitude of a station due to the progressive motion, P_p, and the libration, P_l, is of the form

$$\Delta\phi = \alpha\ (t - 1900) + \beta\ [\cos 15°\ (t - 1902)]$$

where α and β depend upon the longitude. The coefficients for Washington, Greenwich, and Pulkovo are as follows

	λ	α	β
Washington	$+77°$	$0''{\cdot}0031$	$-0''{\cdot}015$
Greenwich	$0°$	$0''{\cdot}0016$	$+0''{\cdot}013$
Pulkovo	$-30°$	$0''{\cdot}0000$	$+0''{\cdot}020$

If the motion of the mean pole derived from the I.L.S. results is correct there should be observed a progressive change in latitude and an oscillation of period 24 years. We examine the results obtained with PZT No. 1 at Washington from October 1915 to May 1955 for these terms.

The apparent progressive change in latitude of the PZT depends upon the proper motions used. The ones initially used, that of the *Preliminary General Catalogue*, indicated a change of $-0''{\cdot}005$/yr. In 1934 there was introduced a system of proper motions, denoted 1925(1), which was adjusted so as to make the derived latitude nearly constant. The system 1925(1) does not purport, thus, to furnish the secular change in latitude. Fundamental systems of increasing accuracy became available, however, later.

A study of the latitude of the PZT which I made in 1940 indicated that, based on the system of the *General Catalogue*, the latitude was constant within the errors of observation.[37]

A later study,[38, 39] made in 1945, indicated that the PZT stars, which are faint, would be more accurately represented by the system *FK3*. On this system the progressive change in latitude was $+0''{\cdot}005$/yr. I did not, however, regard this as definite proof that the latitude of Washington was increasing because it is not possible to determine what systematic error may exist in the proper motions of *FK3* near declination +39°.

An analysis of the PZT results from 1915 to 1955 shows that on the system 1925(1) the latitude is increasing by 0″·0008/yr. The most recent fundamental catalogue available, which contains 19 PZT stars, is *N30*. This catalogue indicates that the proper motions of 1925(1) require a correction of +0″·0055/yr. Hence, the indicated progressive change in latitude of Washington based on

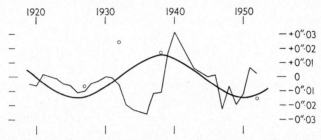

Fig. 13. Six-year running mean latitudes of PZT No. 1, Washington, on system of *N30*, but corrected by −0″·0063/yr. Smooth curve is libration term based on solution for libration of I.L.S. results. Circles are based on observed positions of mean pole of I.L.S.

N30 is +0″·0063/yr. The systematic error in proper motion of *N30* at declination +39° is not known, but it is considered that the rate found is in accordance with that indicated by the I.L.S. results.

To study the periodic term, 6-year running means of the annual mean latitude on *N30* were formed and the term 0″·0063 (t − 1900) and a constant were subtracted. The resulting values are plotted in Fig. 13. There is also plotted the theoretical variation. The agreement, while not strong, is reasonably good. The circles plotted show the variation to be expected on the basis of the observed positions of the pole given in Table 4.

The coefficient α is small for Greenwich and vanishes for Pulkovo. Hence, the fact that progressive changes in latitude have not been observed at these observatories is in accordance with the I.L.S. results.

8. Variations in Longitude

The study of shifts of continents and the motion of the pole from determinations of longitude is more difficult than from determinations of latitude because time is involved. Also, whereas the latitude of a station can be determined independently, only differences in longitude for pairs of stations may be determined.

Formerly, longitudes were determined with much less precision than latitudes. Precise instruments, such as the PZT and the impersonal astrolabe, were not introduced into general use until about 1957, in connection with the International Geophysical Year. About this time, also, the cathode-ray system of monitoring time signals was introduced. Thus, the basis has been laid for obtaining accurate longitude differences which may be compared with other determinations to be made in the future. However, no long series of precise longitude differences exists for the past.

Mme A. Stoyko [40] has utilized such material as is available to study the longitude difference between North America and Europe. From observations for time made from 1924 to 1957 at Washington, Ottawa, and six European observatories she found that the longitude difference of the two continents was decreasing at the rate of $0^s \cdot 0012 = 0'' \cdot 018/\text{yr}$. This corresponds to a decrease in distance of about 1·3 ft/yr.

The material used in the above study was necessarily inhomogeneous, and it seemed desirable to make a new analysis. I selected for study the interval 1934.0–1955.0, during which interval PZT No. 1 was used for the determination of time at Washington. Observations for time were made at the European observatories with visual instruments.

Each year, N. Stoyko publishes in the *Bulletin Horaire* corrections, K, to the adopted longitude of each observatory which determines time. The yearly values of K were taken out for Washington and the six European observatories, corrected for any changes in adopted longitude between 1934 and 1954, and least square solutions were made for K', the indicated yearly change in longitude. The values found are as follows for the European observatories

Observatory	K' sec/yr
Greenwich	$+ 0^s \cdot 0009$
Hamburg	$+ 0 \cdot 0000$
Neuchâtel	$- 0 \cdot 0027$
Paris	$+ 0 \cdot 0009$
Potsdam	$- 0 \cdot 0005$
Uccle	$+ 0 \cdot 0021$
Mean	$+ 0 \cdot 0001$

The value for Washington is $-0^s\!\cdot\!0005$/yr, but this requires a correction for proper motion. The visual observations utilize the stars of a fundamental catalogue, but the PZT stars are too faint to be included therein. Since 1940, for example, *FK3* has been used for time determination. The PZT proper motions were placed on this system, as best as could be, at that time. They can now be related through *N30*, which allows comparison of 17 PZT stars in right ascension. A comparison shows that μ (*N30*) $= \mu$ (PZT) $- 0^s\!\cdot\!0005$, where μ is the annual proper motion in right ascension. A comparison of *N30* and *FK3* for declinations $+ 30°$ to $+45°$ shows that μ (*FK3*) $= \mu$ (*N30*) $- 0^s\!\cdot\!0001$. Hence, a correction of $-0^s\!\cdot\!0006$/yr is required by the PZT proper motions to be on *FK3*.

The value of K' for Washington when corrected by this amount becomes $+0^s\!\cdot\!0001$/yr. The indicated separation between Washington and the European stations is $0^s\!\cdot\!0000$/yr.

It is difficult to calculate a probable error for this determination. The large discordances in the values of K' show that the values are affected by systematic errors. The probable error of a value of K' as derived from the differences from the mean is $0^s\!\cdot\!0010$. Other sources of error may exist, but for want of anything better a probable error of $0^s\!\cdot\!0010 = 0''\!\cdot\!015$/yr is adopted.

The motion of the pole must be considered. The variation in longitude due to the polar motion is

$$\Delta\lambda = \tan \phi \; (x \sin \lambda - y \cos \lambda)/15$$

where $\Delta\lambda$ is in seconds of time when x and y are in seconds of arc. In obtaining K, N. Stoyko has corrected for the polar motion, using the results of the I.L.S. Stoyko gives the values of x and y which he used, and from these I computed annual means. The progressive changes in x and y from 1934 to 1955 are practically the same as indicated in Fig. 10. The values of K obtained by Stoyko have thus been corrected, in effect, for the total motion of the pole. Hence, within the errors of observation the distance between Washington and the European stations is constant.

IV. DISCUSSION

Studies of the polar motion based on the results of the International Latitude Service indicated at an early date an apparent wandering of the pole in addition to the 12- and 14-month periodic variations. This wandering was variously interpreted as being due to horizontal displacements of stations, to changes in the direction of the verticals, to asymmetry of observation, and to a real motion of the pole.

In the interval from 1900 to 1959 the mean pole has moved about $0''\cdot2$. It appears unlikely that a change as great as this could be due to asymmetry of observation.

When a term for secular motion is removed from the position of the mean pole, the latter is found to move to and fro, nearly along a straight line. Such an effect could hardly be due to changes in the I.L.S. programme.

On the assumption that the observed variation in latitude is due to the motion of the pole, the probable error of the mean latitude for a station for a 6-year programme is about $0''\cdot01$, which corresponds to 1 ft. Since this could be due to errors of observation, the implication is that the I.L.S. stations are fixed in position with respect to the crust of the earth.

The secular increase in latitude observed with PZT No. 1 at Washington from 1915 to 1955 tends to confirm the value expected from the I.L.S. results.

Similarly, a study of the progressive variations in longitude between the U.S. Naval Observatory and European observatories for the interval 1934–1955 indicates agreement with the I.L.S. secular motion if it is assumed that the observatories are fixed with respect to each other. The confirmation from longitudes, however, has low weight.

The motion of the mean pole from 1900 to 1959, it has been shown, can be expressed as the sum of two motions, a progressive secular motion and a libration of period 24 years. There is no need to assume that local displacements of stations occur to satisfy the observations. When the catalogue of declinations and proper motions of the I.L.S. stars which is being compiled by Melchior is completed we shall be better able to judge the reality of the secular motion found here. In the meantime, it appears more probable that the secular motion is real than that it is due to systematic errors.

To summarize, the polar motion from 1900 to 1959 appears to have three periodic motions

Period	Coefficient	Nature
(1) 12 mo.	$0''\cdot06$ to $0''\cdot10$	Forced oscillation,
(2) 14 mo.	$0''\cdot08$ to $0''\cdot18$	Free oscillation,
(3) 24 yr	$0''\cdot02$	Libration, cause unknown,

and (4), a secular motion, whose rate is $0''\cdot0032/\text{yr}$. The first term is known to be of meteorological origin. The mechanism which sustains the second term is not known.

The third and fourth terms are unexplained, although the melting of ice has been suggested to account for a progressive motion. These terms might also be due to continental uplift. However, no quantitative data are known which would account for the specific motions found.

It is emphasized that the third and fourth terms were found only for the interval 1900–1959. Since a physical cause for their existence has not been given, these terms cannot safely be extrapolated for great eras of time in the past or the future. The progressive term may itself be a libration whose period is as short as several centuries.

If the secular motion continued at its present rate the movement in 10 000 years would be 3 000 ft, about 1 km. This motion is too small to account directly for the occurrence of ice ages within the last 50 000 years.

Assuming that the secular motion of the pole is real, it is safe to say that its characteristics would not have been determined by now but for the continued operation of the chain of stations of the International Latitude Service. Clearly, further study of the motion requires that the results shall be based on chains of stations which observe the same stars.

The PZT's of the Naval Observatory at Washington and the I.L.S. station at Mizusawa observe 40 stars in common.[41] The establishment of a third PZT near latitude $+39°$ would provide an independent chain for studying the secular motion of the pole. However, until such time as some new chain of stations is established the International Latitude Service will continue to provide the principal data for studying the secular motion of the pole.

I am indebted to Dr. R. Glenn Hall for many helpful discussions while making this study.

A A

References

1. Markowitz, W. *Trans. Amer. geophys. Un.* **26**, 197 (1945).
2. Whitten, C. A. *Trans. Amer. geophys. Un.* **29**, 318 (1948).
3. Kääriäinen, E. On the Recent Uplift of the Earth's Crust in Finland, *Veröff. finn. geod. Inst.* No. 42, (1953).
4. Cecchini, G. *Pubblicazioni dell'Ufficio Centrale delle Latitudini, Pino Torinese*, June, 1959.
5. *Dritter Fundamentalkatalog des Berliner Astronomischen Jahrbuchs*, 1937, 1938.
6. *General Catalogue of* **33342** *Stars*, Carnegie Institution of Washington, No. 468, 1936, 1937.
7. Morgan, H. R. *Astr. Pap., Wash.* **13**, Part 3 (1952).
8. Melchior, P. *Commun. Obs. Belg.* No. 130, 216 (1957); Chap. 7 *Progress in Physics and Chemistry of the Earth* Vol. 2. 1957.
   Fichera, E. 'Theorie et pratique astronomiques dans les stations du S.I.L.' *Monographies 6, Observatoire Royal de Belgique*, (1958).
9. Markowitz, W. *Stars and Stellar Systems*, Vol. 1, Chap. 8. (In press).
10. Danjon, A. *Bull. Astr.* **18**, 251 (1955).
11. Nyrén, M. *Obs. de Pulkowa*, **14**, 49 (1888).
12. Hall, A. *Astr. J.* **10**, 57 (1890).
13. Chandler, C. S. *Astr. J.* **11**, 174 (1892).
14. Küstner, F. *Astr. Nachr.* **125**, 273 (1890).
15. Chandler, C. S. *Astr. J.* **11**, 65 (1891). See also subsequent articles in Vols. 11 and 12.
16. Chandler, C. S. *Astr. J.* **12**, 97 (1892).
17. Wanach, B. *Veröff. Zent-Bur. int. Erdmess.* **5**, 220 (1916).
18. Lambert, W. D. 'An Investigation of the Latitude of Ukiah, California, and of the Motion of the Pole.' *Special Pub. No. 80, U.S. Coast and Geodetic Survey* 35 (1922).
19. Lambert, W. D. *Astr. J.* **34**, 103 (1922).
20. Mahnkopf, H. *Ergebn. int. Breitendienst.* **6**, 232 (1932).
21. Kimura, H. *Jap. J. Astr. Geophys.* **2**, 140 (1924).
22. Wanach, B. *Z. Geophys.* **3**, 103 (1927).
23. Sekiguchi, N. *Publ. astr. Soc. Japan* **8**, 13 (1956).
24. Orlov, A. I. *Sur le But et le Programme d'Observation du Service Internationale de Latitude* p. 86. Moscow, 1954.
25. Schlesinger, F. *Astr. J.* **34**, 42 (1922).
26. Kimura, H. *Results int. Lat. Serv.*, 1922.7 *to* 1935.0 8, 232 (1940).
27. Hattori, T. *Proc. imp. Acad. Japan* **22**, 151, 157 (1946).
28. Cecchini, G. *Bull. géod. int.*, No. 17, 325 (1950).
29. Cecchini, G. *Relazione sull'Attivita del Servizio Internazionale delle Latitudini dal* 1957.0 *al* 1958.3, Pino Torinese, August 1958.
30. Orlov, A. I. *Service des Latitudes* p. 102. Moscow, 1958.
31. Sekiguchi, N. *Pub. astr. Soc. Japan* **5**, 109 (1954).
32. Melchior, P. *Commun. Obs. Belg.* No. 79 (1955).
33. Fedorov, E. P. *Some Remarks on Latitude Observations during the*

International Geophysical Year. (General Assembly I.A.U., Dublin, 1955.)

34. Melchior, P. *Commun. Obs. Belg.* No. **134**, 11 (1958).
35. Brouwer, D. *Astr. J.* **57**, 125 (1952).
36. Becq, G. and Melchior, P. *Ann. Obs. Belg.* 3d series, Vol. 8, part 3, 1959.
37. Markowitz, W. *Astr. J.* **50**, 17 (1942).
38. Sollenberger, P. *Astr. J.* **51**, 147 (1945).
39. Markowitz, W. *Astr. J.* **51**, 153 (1945).
40. Stoyko, A. *C. R.* **248**, 190 (1959).
41. Takagi, S. *Publ. int. Lat. Obs. Mizusawa* **3**, 42 (1959).

AUTHOR INDEX

SUBJECT INDEX